SILVER BURDETT & GINN

GENERAL SCIENCE

BOOK TWO

Series Authors

Peter Alexander, Ph.D.
Professor of Biology and Computer Science
St. Peter's College
Jersey City, New Jersey

Marilyn Fiegel, Ed.D.
Educational Consultant and
Former District Science Coordinator
West Seneca Central Schools
West Seneca, New York

Anne F. Harris
Environmental Scientist
Black and Veatch, Engineers/Architects
Kansas City, Missouri

Joseph G. Krajkovich, Ed.D.
Principal
Martin Luther King School
Edison, New Jersey

Kenneth W. May
Chairperson, Science Department and
Teacher of Chemistry
Camden Central School
Camden, New York

Nicholas D. Tzimopoulos, Ph.D.
Director of Science
Public Schools of the Tarrytowns
North Tarrytown, New York

Rita K. Voltmer, Ph.D.
Assistant Professor of Science Education
Miami University
Oxford, Ohio

SILVER BURDETT & GINN
MORRISTOWN, NJ • NEEDHAM, MA
Atlanta, GA • Cincinnati, OH • Dallas, TX • Menlo Park, CA • Northfield, IL

Content Reviewers

Samuel Bieber, Ph.D.
Professor of Biological Sciences
Old Dominion University
Norfolk, Virginia

Alexei V. Filippenko, Ph.D.
Professor of Astronomy
University of California
Berkeley, California

James E. Platt, Ph.D.
Associate Professor Biological Sciences
University of Denver
Denver, Colorado

Rudolph S. Bottei, Ph.D.
Professor of Chemistry
University of Notre Dame
Notre Dame, Indiana

Carol C. Gilchrist, Ph.D.
Adjunct Professor of Geology
University of New Orleans
New Orleans, Louisiana

Sidney Rudolph, Ph.D.
Research Associate Professor of Physics
University of Utah
Salt Lake City, Utah

Josephine D. Duckett
Associate Director
Center for Mathematics and
 Science Education
University of North Carolina
Chapel Hill, North Carolina

Teacher Reviewers

Otis Autry
Former Science Department Chairperson
B.T. Washington High School
Tulsa, Oklahoma

Yvonne Lewis
Chairperson, Science Department
Douglass Junior High School
Washington, D.C.

Gregg Schell
Science/Mathematics Curriculum
 Coordinator
Southeast Middle Magnet School
Kansas City, Missouri

Linda C. Boone
Science Teacher
District of Columbia Public School System
Washington, D.C.

Gordon L. Mendenhall
Teacher/Consultant
Lawrence Central High School
Indianapolis, Indiana

Marvin D. Selnes
Chemistry/Physical Science
 Teacher
Lincoln High School
Sioux Falls, South Dakota

Ronald James Cisar
Chairperson, Science Department
Lewis and Clark Junior High School
Omaha, Nebraska

Bonnie Moody
Chairperson, Science Department
Ridgeroad Junior High School
North Little Rock, Arkansas

Dennis B. Travis
Teacher/Science Coordinator
Lahser High School
Bloomfield Hills, Michigan

Alfred W. Guenther
Chairperson, Science Department
Stephen M. White Junior High School
Los Angeles, California

Lawrence O'Keefe
Director/Teacher, Paradise Project
Edmunds Middle School
Burlington, Vermont

Lowell G. Herr
Chairperson, Science Department
The Catlin Gabel School
Portland, Oregon

Mary Ethel Parrott, S.N.D.
Science Teacher
Notre Dame Academy
Covington, Kentucky

Robert E. Lewis
Science Teacher
Hanby Junior High School
Wilmington, Delaware

Aguinaldo Rodriguez
Science Instructor
St. Michael's High School
Santa Fe, New Mexico

About the cover
The front and back covers illustrate a group of young and adult Alaskan Brown Bears
feeding on spawning salmon. The Alaskan Brown Bear, closely related to the grizzly
bear, is the largest of the bears. Adults can weigh 1500 pounds (680 kilograms) or
more. When standing erect, this bear may be over 9 feet (2.7 meters) in height. The
prey of these bears is usually salmon, caught when the fish are in the rivers for
spawning. More information about predator-prey relationships can be found in
Chapter 7, Section 7•2 of this book.

Contents

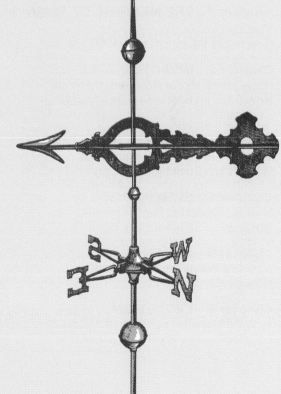

UNIT FOUR INVESTIGATING THE HUMAN BODY ▮▮▮ 530

ACTIVITIES

SPECIAL FEATURES

THE MEANING OF SCIENCE

1·1 How Scientists Think: Investigating Dinosaurs

Look at the paintings on these two pages. You can see that the world changed greatly sometime between 70 million and 60 million years ago. For more than 100 million years before that time, dinosaurs had ruled the earth. That period of the earth's past has come to be known as the Age of Dinosaurs. There were at least 150 different kinds of dinosaurs and they lived on all parts of the earth. But by about 63 million years ago, not a single dinosaur remained on the earth. Furry mammals had become the most important animals on land. There were also many changes in plant life and in the life of the oceans about 63–66 million years ago.

70 MILLION YEARS AGO

CHAPTER 1

60 MILLION YEARS AGO

When a group of organisms ceases to exist on the earth, they are said to be extinct. A time in the earth's history when many kinds of life become extinct is called a mass extinction. There seem to have been several mass extinctions in the distant past. The mass extinction that took place about 65 million years ago was one of the biggest. Along with the dinosaurs, almost half of the other kinds of life on the earth vanished at the same time.

Why did the dinosaurs disappear from the earth? Why did many other life forms vanish at the same time? Did they all become extinct for the same reasons or for many different reasons? How do we know when dinosaurs existed or when they vanished? Did the dinosaurs disappear gradually over a period of several million years? Or did they become extinct suddenly? All of these questions are concerned with things in nature. Finding the answers to such questions is what science is all about.

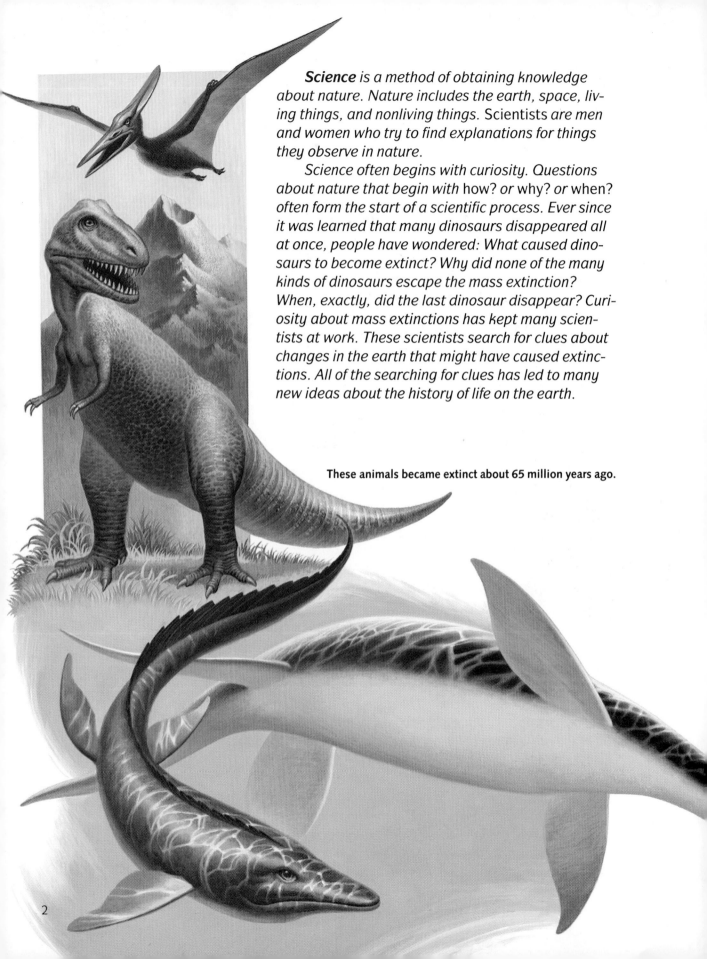

Science is a method of obtaining knowledge about nature. Nature includes the earth, space, living things, and nonliving things. Scientists are men and women who try to find explanations for things they observe in nature.

Science often begins with curiosity. Questions about nature that begin with how? or why? or when? often form the start of a scientific process. Ever since it was learned that many dinosaurs disappeared all at once, people have wondered: What caused dinosaurs to become extinct? Why did none of the many kinds of dinosaurs escape the mass extinction? When, exactly, did the last dinosaur disappear? Curiosity about mass extinctions has kept many scientists at work. These scientists search for clues about changes in the earth that might have caused extinctions. All of the searching for clues has led to many new ideas about the history of life on the earth.

These animals became extinct about 65 million years ago.

These animals survived the mass extinction that took place about 65 million years ago.

After forming a question about some part of nature, a scientist forms a hypothesis. A **hypothesis** is a proposed answer to a question about nature. A hypothesis can be thought of as an educated guess about the answer to a problem. Hypotheses are often based on what is already known about a subject. Consider this question: Why did dinosaurs and many other life forms become extinct at the same time? One hypothesis is that the whole earth grew colder about 65 million years ago. This hypothesis is based on the fact the earth's climate changed many times in the past. Scientists formed this hypothesis soon after it was learned that dinosaurs all became extinct at about 65 million years ago. Recently, several new hypotheses about the extinction of dinosaurs have come about. These new hypotheses are based on new information obtained from rocks formed at the time of the mass extinction.

A hypothesis must be tested to see if it is correct. There are two main ways in which hypotheses can be tested. In some cases, scientists perform experiments to test a hypothesis. In other cases, a hypothesis is tested by seeing if it fits all of the known facts. Since mass extinctions are events of the past, it is not easy to do experiments about them. Hypotheses about extinctions are tested by seeing how well they fit the record of the earth's past that has been left in the rocks.

Any hypotheses about the mass extinction that occurred about 65 million years ago must explain several things. First, it must explain why all dinosaurs vanished from all continents. Second, it must explain why many other land animals and flying animals disappeared at the same time. Third, it must explain why about one fourth of all life forms in the sea disappeared. Fourth, it must explain why more than half the families of life on the earth did survive.

Scientists have known for a long time that the earth's climate changed often in the past. You may have heard about ice ages of the past, during which much of the globe was covered by ice. Although there probably was not an ice age 65 million years ago, there are reasons to believe that the climate changed.

Climate with Distinct Seasons

Temperature — high / low

Fall   Winter   Spring   Summer

Fossils of the plants that lived at the same time as the dinosaurs give some clues about the climate at that time. The plants of the Age of Dinosaurs were plants that grow best in a mild, stable climate. A stable climate is one with only small temperature changes between winter and summer. These plants, along with dinosaurs, lived in places like Canada and Alaska during the Age of Dinosaurs. For this reason it is believed that the climate during the Age of Dinosaurs was mild and stable over much of the earth.

What changed 65 million years ago to cause a mass extinction? Maybe the type of climate we have today, with distinct winters and summers, began to develop at that time. Any animal or plant that needed a stable climate might have become extinct at that time. Animals such as birds and mammals, with their coats of feathers or fur, are better able to survive in a changing climate. But life in the sea is much less affected by climate than is life on land. If climate was the cause, then why was life in the sea also part of the mass extinction?

The Crab Nebula, a supernova that was first seen in 1054.

In February 1987, astronomers in Chile found a new supernova in the night sky. A supernova is a violent explosion of a star. Supernovas give off great force and tremendous amounts of dangerous radiation. A number of supernovas have been observed in the sky, but none have been seen near the earth in modern times. The radiation from a supernova occurring near the earth would surely kill a vast number of living things. Could a supernova have exploded near the earth 65 million years ago? Could the radiation from an exploding star have killed off the dinosaurs as shown below? Some scientists have offered this idea as their hypothesis on the cause of the mass extinction.

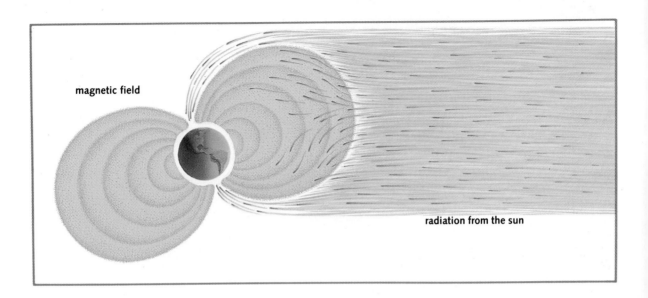

magnetic field

radiation from the sun

A second hypothesis that radiation killed the dinosaurs suggests a different cause. This hypothesis concerns the magnetic field around the earth. You can see in the drawing that a magnetic field exists in space around the earth. The magnetic field protects the earth from some of the radiation that comes from the sun. Notice in the drawing that the magnetic field causes this radiation to hit the earth near the poles. The radiation is kept away from the parts of the earth where most life exists. The sun's radiation striking the earth near the poles causes the display of light called the aurora borealis. The curtains of light in the aurora, shown at right, may be several hundred miles long. This gives an idea of the strength of the radiation from the sun.

Scientists have found that the earth's magnetic field often reversed itself in the past. The magnetic north pole has moved to the south end of the earth. The magnetic south pole has moved to the north. This process may take several thousand years. During that time the magnetic field around the earth might be very weak. Radiation from the sun would not be directed to the poles. The radiation might kill many organisms. A magnetic field reversal may have occurred about 65 million years ago. Could this have been the cause of the mass extinction?

Both the supernova hypothesis and the magnetic field reversal hypothesis involve radiation. But radiation is harmful to all organisms. Why did some organisms survive and others become extinct?

The aurora borealis.

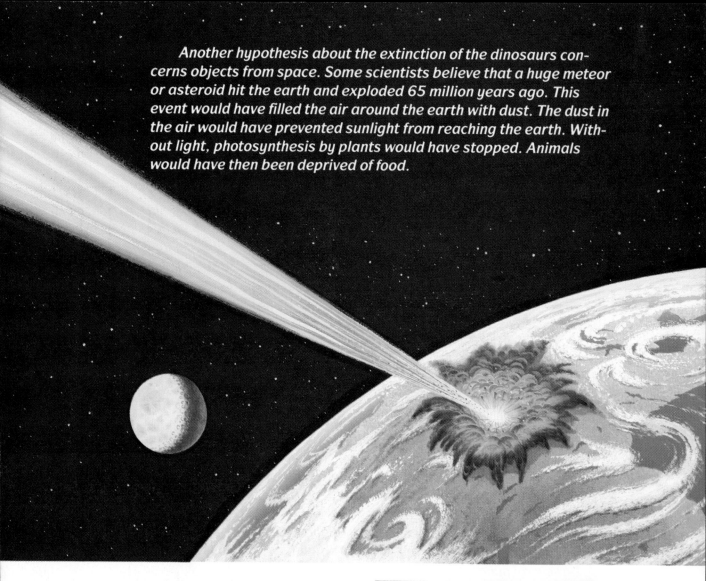

Another hypothesis about the extinction of the dinosaurs concerns objects from space. Some scientists believe that a huge meteor or asteroid hit the earth and exploded 65 million years ago. This event would have filled the air around the earth with dust. The dust in the air would have prevented sunlight from reaching the earth. Without light, photosynthesis by plants would have stopped. Animals would have then been deprived of food.

This hypothesis may seem like science fiction at first. But several kinds of evidence have been found in recent years to support it. Scientists have found that the layer of rock that is 65 million years old is very different from the layers above and below it. The layer of rock that is 65 million years old contains quite a bit of iridium. Iridium is an element that is very rare on the earth. But iridium is much more common in meteors and asteroids. Iridium appears in the layer of the earth that formed about the time when dinosaurs and other life forms vanished. It may be that these two things are connected. It may be that the iridium in this rock layer came from an exploded meteor or asteroid.

A quarter-sized coin marks the 65-million-year-old layer of rock that contains much iridium.

Scientists have calculated that an asteroid 10 km (6 miles) wide would have put enough dust in the air to cause darkness for about 3 months. Many plants and animals would die after 3 months of darkness and lack of food. This fact might explain why many organisms became extinct but some survived.

If an asteroid exploded on hitting the earth, it would have started many fires. What evidence do fires leave behind? Almost always, fires leave soot. Scientists looked again at the layer of rock that is 65 million years old and found large amounts of soot in it. Soot and iridium in this rock show that an asteroid could *have* hit the earth. But did it actually happen? If it did happen, is that what killed the dinosaurs?

*The scientists shown on these pages have formed different hypotheses about why dinosaurs became extinct. No one idea about the extinction of the dinosaurs is accepted by all scientists. No one hypothesis can be accepted yet as a theory. A **theory** is a hypothesis that has been tested many times and that is supported by evidence. A theory can also be thought of as the best available explanation of some part of nature. As new information becomes available, theories may change. For many years the idea that dinosaurs became extinct because of a change in climate was the accepted idea. Because of new information, this idea is no longer accepted by many scientists. The idea that dinosaurs became extinct because of climate changes is only a hypothesis. This hypothesis competes with hypotheses that magnetic field reversals or asteroids or exploding stars caused the extinction of dinosaurs.*

J. John Sepkoski and David Raup are scientists who have studied mass extinctions.

Scientist Robert T. Bakker and one of his drawings. Bakker's hypothesis about the extinction of dinosaurs concerns diseases among dinosaurs and changes in climate.

The future may bring information that will support one of these hypotheses or show others to be false. Or evidence may prove that all of these hypotheses are false, and they may be replaced with new hypotheses. Scientists seek new information to support their hypotheses. This search for new information increases our understanding of nature. In the end the new information is more important than which competing hypothesis becomes the accepted theory.

You will learn many facts as you read the remaining chapters of this book. Those facts are not science. Science is the methods, the activities, and the processes that produced the facts in this book. As you do the activities in the coming chapters, you will be learning to participate in science.

Luis Alvarez and his son Walter are the scientists who proposed the asteroid impact hypothesis to account for the extinction of dinosaurs. The men are looking at a piece of rock from the iridium layer.

1·2 Science for People

Information obtained through science often can be used in practical ways. Knowledge from science is frequently used to make people's lives better or easier. **Technology** is the use of scientific knowledge to improve the quality of human life. As you have learned, science is a way of getting knowledge about nature. Technology is using or applying that knowledge.

Products of technology are all around us. How many items can you identify in your home or your classroom that are made of plastic? Perhaps you are making notes with a pen made of plastic. Scientists who study matter have learned many ways to combine substances to form new materials. This information has been applied in the technology of making plastics. Plastics are used to produce many products that make peoples' lives easier.

Perhaps your grandparents had a radio like the one shown. If so, it may have broken down often, been hard to tune, and made more noise than music. The scientific study of radio waves and electricity has led to better radios that are easier to use and that produce better sound. Along with better radios have come better ways of sending information from place to place. Antennas, like the ones shown below, can send radio waves to satellites which pass the waves on around the world.

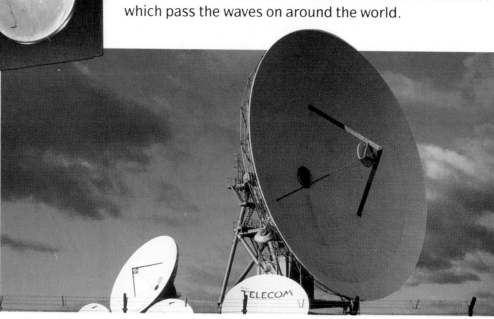

The scientific study of living things often results in new ways of improving people's health. Medical technology uses information that comes from the study of life. Scientists have studied how the hearts of animals and humans work. Knowledge of how hearts work has been applied to the design of artificial hearts, such as the one shown. These devices can pump the blood of a person whose own heart no longer functions.

An artificial heart is an example of technology.

Now try this

Pretend that you are a scientist. You are trying to find a way to help people who have arthritis. This disease can cause people to have great difficulty in using their hands and fingers. Many of the things that you do each day are difficult or impossible for someone whose hands are crippled by arthritis. Such a person might be unable to open a metal screw-top jar. But through technology the design of the jar top could be changed. A plastic lid that lifts off easily might be developed.

Choose one of two common tasks: buttoning clothing or cutting food. Design a device that would help a person with arthritis to perform the task. Describe your device in words and labeled drawings. Tell what materials would be used to make your device and how it would work. If possible, construct a working model of your device.

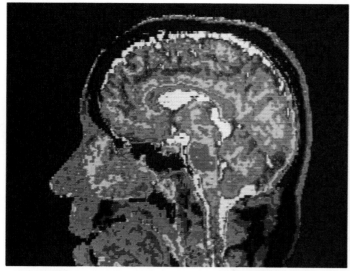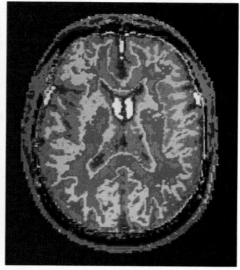

A NMR machine was used to obtain these two views of a human brain. See page 533 to learn more about how this machine functions.

Technology has also produced many kinds of new equipment that allow doctors to find out about a person's health. The photographs above were made by a machine that uses radiation to see inside a person's brain. Such photographs allow doctors to find out about the health of the brain without doing an operation.

A useful technology involves trees that are used for lumber. Lumber is used to build homes, to make paper, and for many other purposes. Fir trees are used for lumber. Some fir trees grow faster and taller than others. There are many factors that affect the way a tree grows. Through much work, scientists have learned what many of these factors are. This knowledge has been put to practical use. Lumber companies now plant specially

The two trees are Douglas firs that are about 6 months old. The taller tree was grown from an improved "super seedling" (*below*). A tree farm of improved fir trees (*right*).

bred fir trees. These trees grow faster and taller than do wild fir trees. As more of these fast-growing fir trees are planted, more lumber becomes available more quickly. Also, fewer natural forests need to be cut down as sources of lumber. The use of scientific knowledge about trees to grow lumber more rapidly is an example of technology that helps people.

You have seen that technology affects many parts of our lives. Technology affects the things we wear, our health, and the things we eat. Technology is intended to improve people's lives. But technology may have unwanted side effects. Aerosol cans are a technology aimed at making household products easier to use. The pressurized gases in spray cans push out the useful products in the cans. But the gases escape into the air. Gases from millions of spray cans are accumulating in the atmosphere. Many scientists believe that these gases are damaging the earth's atmosphere. Damage to the atmosphere by aerosols and other products of technology may have bad effects on people's health.

This satellite photograph shows a hole in the protective ozone layer of the atmosphere. The area of the hole is about 7 million km². This damage to the atmosphere is thought to come from the gases used in aerosol cans.

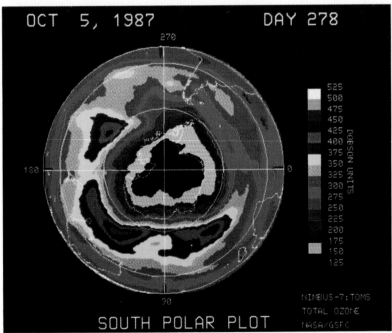

As new technologies arise, people must be aware of problems that might result. Someday you may have to make decisions about balancing the advantages and disadvantages of a new technology. Studying science will help to prepare you to make these decisions.

1·3 Skills of Science

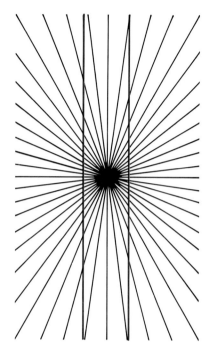

Look at the two vertical lines in the drawing. Is the distance between the lines the same at the middle and the ends? Or are the lines farther apart at the middle? Can you think of a way to find out for sure? Things are not always what they seem. Scientists must make many kinds of accurate measurements to test hypotheses about nature.

Scientists send their results to other scientists around the world. For this reason, measurements must have the same meaning in all countries. When a scientist describes the size of a dinosaur bone, that description should have a clear meaning to any other scientist.

In 1960 a modern system of measurement was adopted by most of the world's countries. It is known as the International System of Units, or *SI*. Four important units used in SI are the meter (m), kilogram (kg), liter (L), and second (s). Each unit can be made larger or smaller by multiplying or dividing by ten. Prefixes are used to show how many times the unit is multiplied or divided. The prefix is added to the name of the unit. Table 1·2 shows some of the prefixes used with SI units. How many meters are there in a kilometer? What part of a liter is a milliliter?

Table 1·1
Units of Measurement

MEASUREMENT	UNIT	SYMBOL
length	meter	m
mass	kilo-gram	kg
volume	liter	L
temperature	degree Celsius	°C
time	second	s

Table 1·2 *Common Prefixes for SI Units*

PREFIX	MEANING	SYMBOL	EXAMPLE
kilo-	one thousand	k	1 km, or 1 kilometer, is 1000 meters.
centi-	one hundredth	c	1 cm, or 1 centimeter, is 1/100 (.01) of 1 meter.
milli-	one thousandth	m	1 mm, or 1 millimeter, is 1/1000 (.001) of 1 meter.
micro-	one millionth	μ	1 μm, or 1 micrometer, is 1/1,000,000 (.000001) of 1 meter.

The **meter** (m) is the SI unit used when measuring length or distance. A meter is slightly longer than a yard. Length can be measured using a meterstick or a metric ruler. Metersticks and metric rulers are marked in centimeters (cm). Look at Table 1•2 to see what part of a meter a centimeter is. The smallest markings on a metric ruler show millimeters (mm). There are 10 mm in 1 cm. How wide is the fossil in the photograph in mm and in cm?

The **kilogram** (kg) is the SI unit used to measure mass. *Mass* is a measure of the amount of matter in an object. Mass is different from weight. Weight is a measure of the force of gravity acting on matter. Gravity is not constant from place to place. The force of gravity is less on the moon than on the earth. Thus an object weighs less on the moon than on the earth. But the object's mass does not change.

An astronaut collect rocks on the moon (*left*). Although its mass is constant, the weight of the moon rock on the earth (*right*) is six times greater than its weight on the moon.

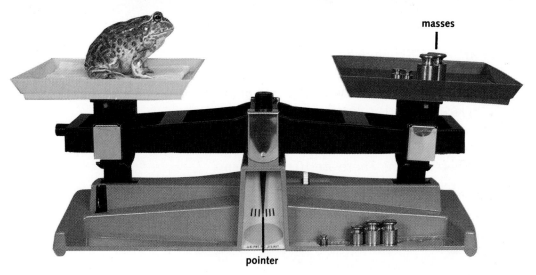

masses

pointer

A double-pan balance is used to measure mass.

Mass is measured with a device called a balance. There are several types of balances. A double-pan balance is shown above. This balance works like a seesaw. The object to be measured is placed on one pan. Objects of known mass are added to the other pan until the pans balance. When the pans balance, the total of the known masses is equal to the mass of the unknown object.

The **liter** (L) is a unit of volume. *Volume* is a measure of how much space something takes up. The volume of liquids can be measured with a graduated cylinder, or graduate. A graduate is marked in milliliters (mL). Notice that the liquid curves upward at the sides of the graduate shown at left. This curved surface is a *meniscus*. To read a graduate, view the liquid's surface at eye level. Read the mark that lines up with the lowest point of the meniscus. What is the volume of the liquid in the graduate shown?

The volume of a solid can be measured in two ways. When a solid has a regular shape, its dimensions can be used. The volume of a box, for example, can be measured by multiplying its three dimensions (Volume = length x width x height). A box that is 8 cm by 6 cm by 4 cm has a volume of 192 cubic centimeters (cm^3), as shown. A volume of 1 cm^3 is equal to 1 mL. What is the volume of a box that is 5 cm by 6 cm by 3 cm?

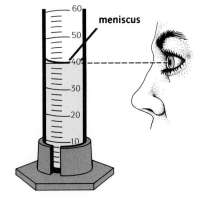

meniscus

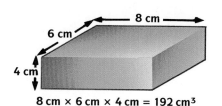

8 cm × 6 cm × 4 cm = 192 cm^3

18

OBJECTIVE

Determine the volume of an irregularly shaped solid by displacement.

MATERIALS

graduate, water, small rock that has an irregular shape

PROCEDURE

A. Make a data table like the one shown.

MEASUREMENT	AMOUNT
Volume of water	
Volume of water and rock	
Volume of rock	

B. Fill a graduate with water to the 20-mL mark. Remember to read the bottom of the meniscus. In your data table, record the volume of the water.

C. Carefully place a rock into the water in the graduate. Record the new volume in your data table. The change in the volume of the water equals the volume of the solid.

RESULTS AND CONCLUSIONS

1. If the rock were shaped like a cube, could you use displacement to determine its volume? Explain.

2. What other method could you use to determine the volume of a cube-shaped rock?

When an object does not have a regular shape, its volume can still be measured. The object is placed in a graduate that is partly filled with water. The amount of water that the object displaces is equal to its volume.

The **degree Celsius** (°C) is a unit for measuring temperature. On the Celsius scale, water freezes at 0° and boils at 100°. Find the normal body temperature of humans on the Celsius thermometer shown.

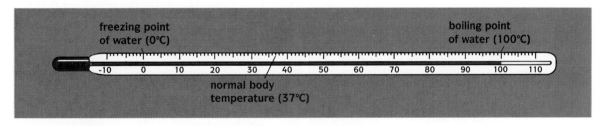

Time is the interval between two events. Measurements of time are needed to study how objects move. The SI unit of time is the *second* (s). In the present system there are 60 seconds in a minute, 60 minutes in an hour, and 24 hours in a day. This system is used everywhere on the earth. Stop watches used in laboratories and at sporting events can measure time in hundredths or thousandths of a second.

One of the most important tools of the scientist is a technique called a controlled experiment. A **controlled experiment** is a method for testing hypotheses. A controlled experiment usually has two parts. One part is called the *control* or the *control setup.* The other part is the *experimental setup.* For some experiments the terms *control group* and *experimental group* are used. The experimental setup differs from the control in only one way. The factor that differs between the experimental setup and the control is called a *variable.*

At the end of the experiment, the two setups are compared with each other. The scientist must then determine if the variable affected the experimental setup. It is best to have only one variable in an experiment. An experiment with more than one variable may give confusing results. It may be hard to decide which one of the variables affected the experimental setup.

Consider the hypothesis that clear glass actually absorbs some of the light that passes through it. A controlled experiment to test this hypothesis might be done in this way: Two identical light beams are each aimed at one of two identical black screens. As light strikes the black screens, they heat up. One light beam is left to shine directly on its screen. This is the control setup. A sheet of clear glass is placed between the second light and its screen. This is the experimental setup. The variable in the experiment is the glass. The two setups are exactly the same in all ways except that the experimental setup has the glass.

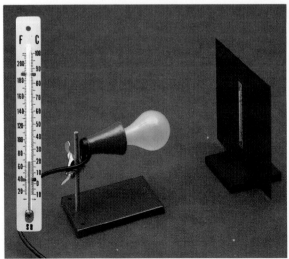

control setup

experimental setup

control setup   experimental setup

During the experiment the temperature of each screen is measured and recorded several times during an hour. Information recorded from an experiment is called *data*. After an hour the data for the two setups are compared. Based on the data, a *conclusion* will be reached on whether glass absorbs light. Any difference in the temperatures must be due to the glass, since all other factors were the same for both setups. Any difference in temperature will show that the glass affected the amount of light reaching the screen. The results of experiments are often used to make *predictions* about answers to other questions. Predict which will absorb more light, a 5-mm or a 10-mm-thick sheet of glass.

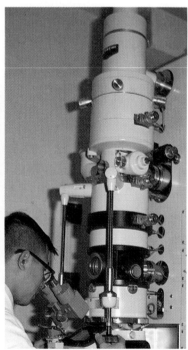

A scanning electron microscope (SEM) is one of the many tools scientists use to help them study nature (*right*).   A microscope allows scientists to study very small things. A record needle in the groove of a record (*left*) and a blood clot (*middle*) as viewed through an SEM.

Chapter Review

CHAPTER SUMMARY

The main ideas in this chapter are listed below. Read these statements before you answer the Chapter Review questions.

- Science is a method of obtaining knowledge about nature. Science begins with questions about nature. Scientists propose hypotheses, or possible answers to these questions.
- A hypothesis can be tested by seeing if it fits observations in nature or by performing controlled experiments. New information may support a hypothesis or prove it false. If the hypothesis is proved false, a new hypothesis may be proposed.
- A hypothesis may become a theory if the hypothesis has been tested many times and is supported by evidence.
- Technology is the use of scientific knowledge in an effort to improve the quality of human life. Technology can sometimes have unwanted side effects.

- SI, the system of measurement used in science, allows scientists worldwide to understand and use each other's data.

- The meter, liter, kilogram, degree Celsius, and second are important units of measurement. Scientists use many different tools to make accurate measurements.

- Controlled experiments are important tools for testing hypotheses. A controlled experiment usually has at least two parts — the control group and the experimental group.

The key terms in this chapter are listed below. Use each term in a sentence that shows the meaning of the term.

controlled experiment
degree Celsius
hypothesis

kilogram
liter
meter

science
technology
theory

VOCABULARY

Answer the following in complete sentences.

1. Distinguish between *science* and *technology*.
2. What is a hypothesis? How does a theory differ from a hypothesis?
3. Distinguish between *mass* and *weight*.
4. Identify the two parts of a typical controlled experiment.
5. Explain what the terms *mass* and *volume* mean.
6. Distinguish between *liters* and *meters*.

CONCEPTS

1. What is a scientist?
2. Why is a hypothesis sometimes described as an educated guess?
3. Describe the four hypotheses about the cause of mass extinction that have been discussed in this chapter.
4. What evidence supports the hypothesis that a body from space caused the extinction of the dinosaurs?
5. What evidence supports the hypothesis that a change in climate caused the extinction of the dinosaurs?

6. Do any of the hypotheses described in this chapter deserve to be called theories? Explain why or why not.
7. List five units of measure that are part of the SI system, and describe what each one measures.
8. Describe a method for measuring the volume of an irregular solid object.
9. What unit would you use to measure fuel being put into a car? Explain why you chose that unit.
10. Describe the Celsius temperature scale.
11. What device is used to measure liquid volume? What is a meniscus, and what part of it is used when measuring liquid volume?
12. What is an experiment?
13. Explain how the two groups used in an experiment differ from each other.
14. Why is it best that there be only one variable in an experiment?

APPLICATION/
CRITICAL
THINKING

1. Trees planted along the sidewalks in a city often grow more slowly than similar trees in a forest. Suggest several hypotheses that might explain this observation.
2. Design an experiment to test the hypothesis that young maple trees or seedlings grow best in shade.
3. Four hypotheses that attempt to explain the extinction of the dinosaurs are given in this chapter. Which of these four hypotheses is the most difficult to test? Explain your answer.
4. The label on a box of cereal shows that the mass of the cereal is 0.5 kg. How many grams and how many milligrams of cereal are there in the box? If there are 454 g in a pound, how many pounds of cereal are there in the box?
5. Is the use of a computer to do math problems an example of science or an example of technology? Explain your answer.

EXTENSION

1. Record the masses or volumes given on the labels of five or more household products. For those masses or volumes that are not expressed in SI units, convert the measurements to SI units.
2. Mass extinctions have occurred a number of times during the history of life on the earth. The extinction that involved the dinosaurs was only one such event. Find out when the other mass extinctions occurred and what life forms disappeared during each event.
3. Only a few of the hypotheses about the cause of mass extinction have been described in this chapter. Find out and report on some of the other hypotheses.

INVESTIGATING
LIFE SCIENCE

*P*eople are familiar with many of the plants and animals in their surroundings. But there are also insects so tiny that they are dwarfed by a honeybee. Colorful sponges populate the ocean. In this unit you will learn about plants and animals and how their traits are passed to their offspring. You will also learn about the interaction of plants and animals in their environment.

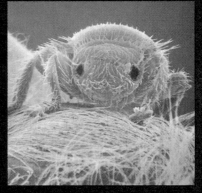

▲ *This tiny bee louse is perched on the back of its host, the honeybee.*

◀ *This flower, Hepatica, is a type of buttercup.*

▲ *Coils of DNA as shown by computer.*

◀ *Detailed etching of a beetle.*

A tiger moth flashing its red hind wings.▼

◀ *Sponges are found in various shapes and colors.*

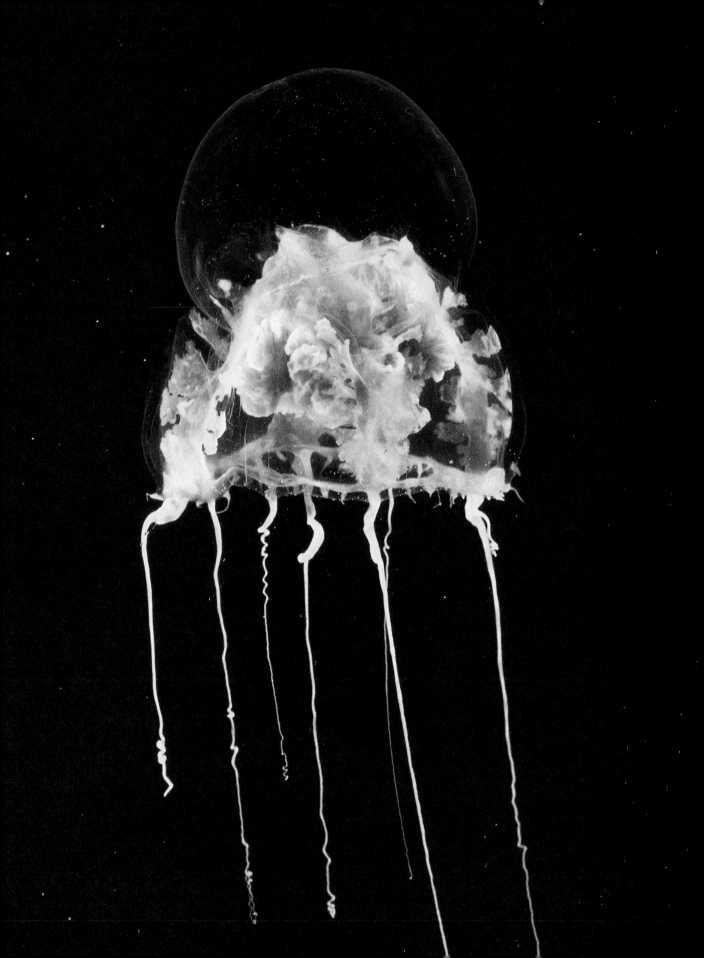

CHAPTER 2

INVERTEBRATES

Do you recognize the animal shown in the photograph? Many people may know this animal not by sight but by its painful sting. A clear, jellylike material within its body gives this simple animal its name. It is a jellyfish.

The delicate streamers hanging from the jellyfish are tentacles. Special cells in the tentacles shoot out and poison small fish and other small animals which are the food of the jellyfish.

Jellyfish living in coastal areas can be a nuisance to humans. Swimmers who brush against the tentacles may receive a painful sting.

- *Why is a jellyfish considered a simple animal?*
- *What are some other types of simple animals?*
- *How do these simple animals eat? How do they move? How do they reproduce?*

2·1 Groups of Invertebrates

-in (not)
vertebratus (jointed)

Figure 2·1
The starfish *(A)*, sponge *(B)*, jellyfish *(C)*, earthworm *(D)*, and butterfly *(E)* are all invertebrates.

CLASSIFYING ORGANISMS

About 1.5 million kinds, or species, of animals have been named by scientists. A *species* is a group of organisms that can mate with each other and whose young can also mate and produce offspring. For example, dogs are one species of animals. All the species of animals put together make up the animal kingdom. Animals differ greatly in size and appearance. But all animals are alike in that they are many-celled organisms that cannot make their own food.

Members of the animal kingdom can be divided into two major groups: invertebrates (ihn VER tuh-brihts) and vertebrates. An **invertebrate** is an animal that does not have a backbone. Invertebrates include the starfish, sponge, jellyfish, earthworm, and butterfly shown in Figure 2·1. A *vertebrate* is an animal that has a backbone. Sharks, frogs, snakes, robins, cats, and humans are examples of vertebrates. Each of these animals has a skeleton with a backbone inside its body.

The animal kingdom is divided into 30 groups called phyla (FĪ luh) (sing., *phylum*). A *phylum* is a large classification grouping of many different species that have major traits in common. Although animals within a phylum may look very different, their basic structure is similar. For example, the lobster and spider, as shown in Figure 2·2 differ greatly. But they belong to the same phylum because they share the traits of a hard body covering and jointed legs. Of the many animal phyla, only one includes vertebrates. All the other phyla are made up of invertebrates.

TRAITS OF INVERTEBRATES

Invertebrates can be grouped according to their body structure. Some simple animals, such as the sponges, have a body that is only two cells thick. More complex animals, such as flatworms, have several cell layers that form tissues. A *tissue* is a group of similar cells that work together to perform a specific function.

Look at Figure 2·3, which shows tissue layers of developing animals. Some simple animals form from only two tissue layers, as shown in part *A*. The outer tissue layer is called the **ectoderm**. The inner tissue layer is the **endoderm**. More complex animals, such as the one shown in part *B*, have a third tissue layer, called the mesoderm. The **mesoderm** is the middle tissue layer. These tissue layers of the developing young, form the tissues and organs of the adult animal.

Figure 2·2

A spider *(A)* and a lobster *(B)*. Why are these animals grouped in the same phylum?

Figure 2·3

Tissue layers in developing animals: animal with two tissue layers *(A)*; animal with three tissue layers *(B)*.

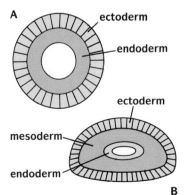

29

Scientists are turning to marine invertebrates for the development of new drugs and other useful chemicals. Sponges, coelenterates, and mollusks are among the animals that are being studied.

Mussels are mollusks that produce a sticky protein that enables them to cling tightly to rocks. Even the battering force of ocean waves does not loosen the mussels. The sticky protein that they produce is an adhesive, or a glue. Scientists are trying to make this adhesive in their laboratories. This adhesive would then be used on materials that are constantly exposed to water or liquids that contain water. For example, scientists hope that this new glue could be used to cement materials together underwater. The substance might be used to repair torn human skin or to patch broken bones. It might also be used as a dental cement.

Many invertebrates can reproduce by both asexual and sexual means. *Asexual reproduction* involves only one parent. In *sexual reproduction* a sperm cell and an egg cell, usually from two parents, join to form a new organism.

CLASSIFYING INVERTEBRATES

There are many invertebrate phyla that only contain a few little-known species. In this book you will learn about the eight largest phyla of invertebrates. Six phyla of simple invertebrates—sponges, coelenterates (sih LEHN tuh rayts), flatworms, roundworms, segmented worms, and mollusks (MAHL uhsks)—will be discussed in this chapter. The other two phyla will be studied in the next chapter. They are the more complex invertebrates—the echinoderms (ih KĪ nuh dermz) and the arthropods (AHR thruh pahdz).

REVIEW

1. What is an invertebrate?
2. Name the three body layers of some invertebrates. Describe the location of each layer.
3. What eight phyla of invertebrates contain the greatest number of species?

CHALLENGE A snail and a clam are in the same invertebrate phylum. What traits common to both animals might be the basis for this grouping?

2·2 Sponges

Sponges make up one phylum of invertebrates. The **sponge** is the simplest invertebrate. Figure 2·4 shows some of the great variety of sponges. Sponges live in both fresh water and salt water. Because adult sponges do not move around as most animals do, people once thought that sponges were plants. Like some plants, sponges grow attached to rocks and other objects at the bottom of a body of water. But sponges are not plants. Unlike plants, sponges cannot make their own food; they must take in food to survive.

After completing this section you will be able to

- **identify** the traits of sponges.
- **describe** how sponges obtain food.
- **describe** reproduction in sponges.

The key terms in this section are

budding	regeneration
central cavity	sponge
pores	

Figure 2·4
Three types of sponges.

TRAITS OF SPONGES

Sponges do not have a skeleton. Support for the body of a sponge comes from other structures. Some kinds of sponges contain *spicules* — hard, pointed structures that support the animal's body. Other kinds of sponges contain *spongin,* a flexible substance that forms a network between cells. Like spicules, spongin helps to support a sponge's body. Some sponges contain both spicules and spongin.

At the top of the sponge is a large opening that connects with a central cavity. The **central cavity**

31

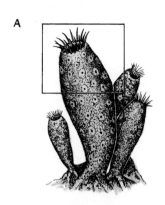

Figure 2·5
A sponge *(A)* and the internal structure of a sponge *(B)*.

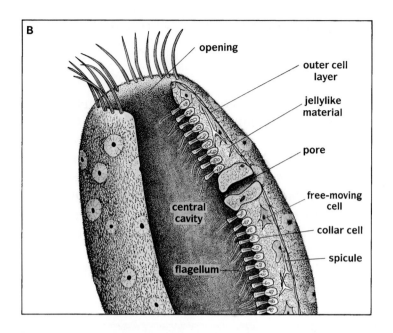

poros (passage)

is the hollow center of the sponge. Locate the central cavity in Figure 2·5. The surface of the sponge is covered with pores. **Pores** are small openings that in the sponge connect with the central cavity. Water flows through these pores and into the central cavity. It is from this water that the sponge filters out its food.

The body of a sponge is formed from two layers of cells. Find the layer of jellylike material between the two cell layers shown in Figure 2·5*B*. This layer contains the spicules. Another type of cell, the free-moving cell, is also found in this layer.

Look at the collar cells that line the central cavity. Notice that each collar cell has a flagellum (fluh JEHL uhm). A *flagellum* (pl., *flagella*) is a whiplike structure on a cell. Each flagellum beats rapidly back and forth, producing a current. The current draws water into the pores.

The action of the flagella causes a steady flow of water through the sponge. The collar cells trap tiny bits of food as water passes over the cells. The collar cells digest some of the food. The rest of the food moves to the free-moving cells. These cells also digest food. Some of the digested food is carried by the free-moving cells to other cells. Water containing wastes passes out the opening at the top.

REPRODUCTION IN SPONGES

Reproduction in sponges is both sexual and asexual. In sexual reproduction an egg cell and a sperm cell join within the jellylike layer. There are two types of asexual reproduction in sponges. **Budding** is a type of asexual reprodution in which a sponge forms a bud that later develops into an adult sponge. The bud grows as it remains attached to the parent. When fully formed, the bud breaks off and may be carried by the water to a new location where it grows into an adult sponge.

Figure 2·6
Sponges that have been harvested and dried *(left)* and close-up of a sponge with buds *(right)*.

The other type of asexual reproduction in sponges is regeneration. **Regeneration** is the re-growth of body parts that have been lost or damaged. It is also the growth of an entire organism from a single part of the body. A sponge can regenerate a whole new sponge from just a few cells. If a sponge is cut into pieces, each piece can grow into a new sponge.

re- (again)
-generare (to produce)

REVIEW

1. What are the traits of sponges?
2. How does a sponge obtain food?
3. What are two ways in which sponges reproduce asexually?

CHALLENGE Suggest a reason why the sponge-growing industry has become much smaller over the last 40 years.

2·3 Coelenterates

coelus (hollow)

TRAITS OF COELENTERATES

Most members of another phylum of simple invertebrates, the coelenterates, live in the ocean. A **coelenterate** is an invertebrate that has a central body cavity with a single opening. The body form is a hollow sac. Figure 2·7 shows three animals in this phylum—the hydra, the jellyfish, and the sea anemone. How do these animals differ? What features do they have in common?

Although coelenterates are simple animals, they are more complex than sponges. Recall that sponges have two layers of cells and these cells do not form true tissues. But coelenterates are made up of two layers that form true tissues.

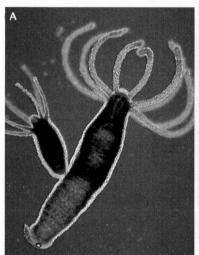

Figure 2·7
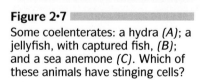
Some coelenterates: a hydra *(A)*; a jellyfish, with captured fish, *(B)*; and a sea anemone *(C)*. Which of these animals have stinging cells?

Coelenterates have a single body opening called a mouth. The mouth is usually surrounded by tentacles (TEHN tuh kuhlz). **Tentacles** are armlike extensions used to catch food and bring it into the body cavity. Stinging cells are located on the tentacles. A **stinging cell** is a cell that has pointed, threadlike parts used in getting food. When an animal brushes against the tentacles, the stinging cells react. The pointed, threadlike parts shoot out and

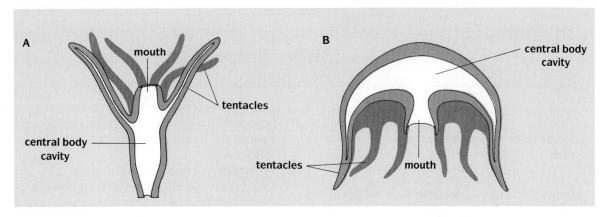

Figure 2·8

Two body forms of coelenterates: tubelike form *(A)* and umbrella-shaped form *(B)*.

pierce the animal. A poison in the threadlike part paralyzes or kills the animal. The stinging cells can wrap around the animal and help to hold it. The tentacles then carry the animal, which is food, into the mouth of the coelenterate.

Most coelenterates have one of two body forms during their life cycle. Find the central cavity in each body form shown in Figure 2·8. One body form is a tubelike structure with the mouth at the top. The mouth is surrounded by tentacles. The other body form is shaped like an umbrella and has the mouth on the underside. In this body form the tentacles hang down. Some coelenterates change from one body form to the other during their life cycle.

Like sponges, coelenterates reproduce both asexually and sexually. When coelenterates reproduce asexually, it is most often by budding. Look back at Figure 2·7. Which of the three animals is forming a bud?

TYPES OF COELENTERATES

There are three major groups of coelenterates —the hydras, the jellyfish, and a third group containing the corals and sea anemones. The hydra is one of the few freshwater coelenterates. Most hydras are only a few millimeters long. The tubelike body form of the hydra can be seen in Figure 2·9. The body cavity of the hydra is a simple hollow sac. The single mouth opening, surrounded by tentacles, leads to this central body cavity. Around the central cavity are two true tissue layers. These tissues are divided by a jellylike layer.

Figure 2·9

Hydra, showing tentacles and tissue layers *(A)*; enlargement of two tissue layers *(B)*.

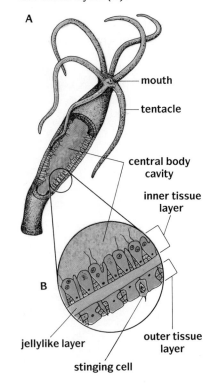

35

Figure 2·10
Red sponges attached to a coral reef.

The second group of coelenterates are the jellyfish. The adult has the umbrella-shaped body form. Most of the animal's body is made up of the jellylike substance found between the two tissue layers.

The third group of coelenterates are animals that have a more complex body structure than hydras or jellyfish. Sea anemones and coral belong to this group. Sea anemones have only a tubelike stage in their life cycle. Corals live in colonies and have a tubelike body that produces a hard outer covering made of limestone. When a coral dies, the limestone covering remains. Coral reefs, such as the one in Figure 2·10, are formed by the buildup of countless limestone coverings.

REVIEW

1. Describe and compare the two body forms of a coelenterate.
2. What is the function of stinging cells?
3. Briefly describe an animal from each of the three groups of coelenterates.

CHALLENGE While swimming in the ocean, people are sometimes injured by large jellyfish. Which trait of coelenterates causes this injury?

2·4 Flatworms

TRAITS OF FLATWORMS

Animals in the flatworm phylum have a more complex body structure than do sponges or coelenterates. A **flatworm** is an invertebrate with a flattened body. It is the simplest of all the worms. Flatworms form from three tissue layers. Unlike sponges and coelenterates, flatworms have true *organs*. An organ is two or more different tissues that work together to perform a function. Flatworms also have *organ systems*, which are groups of organs that work together to perform one or more functions. Flatworms also have a distinct head and tail. They are the simplest animals to have these traits.

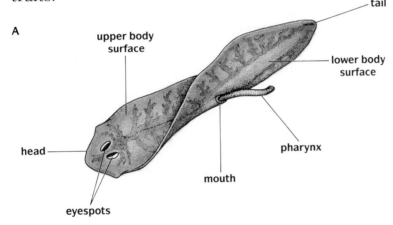

A

- tail
- upper body surface
- lower body surface
- head
- pharynx
- mouth
- eyespots

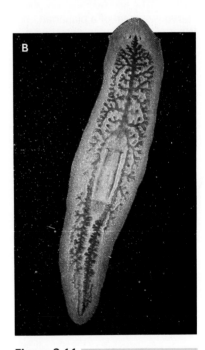

B

Figure 2·11

A planarian is a flatworm. Note the flattened body, pharynx, and eyespots.

Flatworms can be divided into two main groups. They are either parasites (PAR uh sīts) or free-living worms. A *parasite* is an organism that lives on or in another organism and harms it. The organism that is harmed is called the host. A parasite takes food from its host. Most flatworms are parasites. A free-living worm is one that moves about and gets food from its surroundings.

PLANARIANS

Planarians are free-living flatworms. Planarians live in water or in moist soil. In Figure 2·11A you can see how flat the animal's body is. The organ

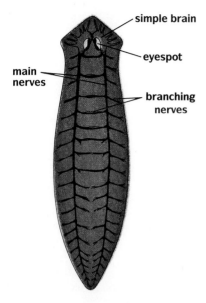

simple brain

eyespot

main nerves

branching nerves

Figure 2·12

Nervous system of a planarian. What can a planarian detect with its eyespots?

Figure 2·13

Regeneration in a planarian. A whole new animal can grow from a small part of the body.

systems of planarians include the digestive system, nervous system, and the reproductive system. Planarians lack circulatory and respiratory systems. Gas exchange occurs through the surface of the animal's body.

The digestive system of planarians consists of a mouth, a pharynx (FAR ihngks), and an intestine. A **pharynx** is a tube that joins the mouth with the rest of the digestive tract. The digestive tract then branches out to all parts of the body. At times the pharynx can extend out of the mouth, as shown in Figure 2·11A. In this way, food is taken into the body. Planarians eat small animals such as insects and other worms. Planarians also feed on the remains of dead organisms. Undigested food passes out of the body through the pharynx.

Figure 2·12 shows the nervous system of a planarian. The nervous system consists of two eyespots, two main nerves, and smaller, branching nerves. Two masses of nerve cells function as a simple brain. The eyespots can sense whether light is strong or dim, but planarians cannot see images.

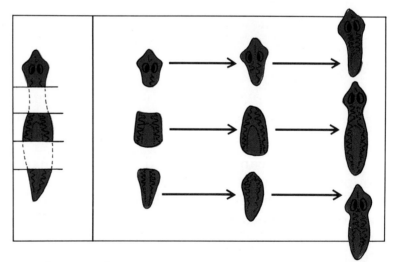

Planarians have a complex reproductive system. They can also reproduce asexually by regeneration. Recall that regeneration is the regrowth of lost body parts or the growth of a new organism from a small part. As shown in Figure 2·13, a planarian that is cut into three parts can grow into three new worms.

FLUKES AND TAPEWORMS

Flukes are flatworms that live as parasites in the liver or blood of certain animals. Humans get liver fluke disease by eating raw or undercooked fish having this parasite. Proper cooking of fish prevents the disease. Keeping human wastes, which may contain liver fluke eggs, out of water supplies also breaks the cycle. In this way the fluke can no longer infect the snail and fish hosts.

Like flukes, tapeworms are flatworms that are parasites. Tapeworms are found in the intestines of vertebrates such as cattle and humans. A tapeworm has a long ribbonlike body and a rounded head. A closeup of the head is shown in Figure 2·14. The head has suckers and hooks with which the worm attaches itself to the intestine of the host. The tapeworm then feeds on the digested food of its host.

Figure 2·14
A tapeworm *(left)*; close-up of the head *(right)*.

Notice in Figure 2·14 that the body of the tapeworm is made up of many sections. As the worm grows, new sections form behind the head. The older end sections break off and pass out of the host's body. Each section produces thousands of eggs that can develop into new tapeworms. Animals become infected when they eat food that contains the eggs. Humans can become infected with tapeworms by eating undercooked meat. Proper cooking and inspection of meat help to control this parasite.

REVIEW

1. What are the traits of flatworms?
2. What are three organ systems of a planarian?
3. How can people avoid infection by parasites?

CHALLENGE How does a mature tapeworm survive despite the fact that it lacks a digestive system?

2·5 Roundworms

anus (ring)

A **roundworm** is a smooth, cylinder-shaped worm with pointed ends and a tubelike digestive system. You can see the tubelike digestive system in Figure 2·15A. There is a mouth at one end and an anus at the other end. An **anus** is an opening at the end of the digestive tract, through which undigested food leaves the body. Roundworms are the simplest animals to have a digestive system with both a mouth and an anus.

Roundworms are among the most plentiful animals and can be found almost everywhere on the earth. Most roundworms are free-living. Roundworms in the soil feed on the remains of dead plants and animals. A roundworm known as the vinegar eel can be seen in Figure 2·15B. This roundworm feeds on bacteria and tiny pieces of fruit in vinegar that has not been pasteurized. Some free-living roundworms live in mud at the bottom of oceans, lakes, and streams.

Many roundworms are parasites. Some do little harm to their hosts. Others are very harmful. The hookworm is one type of roundworm parasite that

Figure 2·15

The digestive system of a roundworm *(A)*; a common roundworm known as a vinegar eel *(B)*.

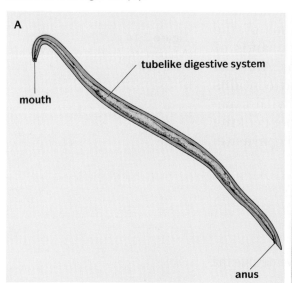

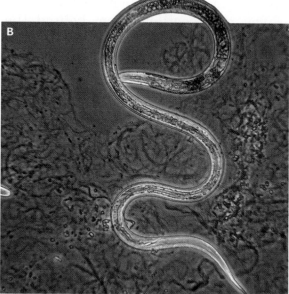

is very harmful. It lives in soil, often in warm places. The hookworm enters the host's body through the soles of the feet. A hookworm, shown in Figure 2·16A, has toothlike parts in its mouth that attach to the intestine of its host. It feeds on blood from the damaged wall of the intestine.

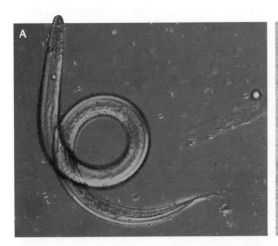

Figure 2·16
Hookworm *(A)*. Muscle infected with parasitic trichina worms *(B)*.

Trichina (trih KĪ nuh) worms, shown in Figure 2·16B, are parasites found in the muscles of pigs. These roundworms cause in humans a disease called trichinosis (trihk uh NOH sihs). This disease causes severe pain in the muscles of the host. Trichinosis can be caused by eating undercooked or raw pork. This disease can be prevented by thoroughly cooking pork.

Some types of roundworms can damage crops. For example, some roundworms damage plants by feeding on the sap of the roots and stems. But other roundworms are helpful. They live in soil and break down the remains of dead organisms. The chemicals produced by this breakdown enrich the soil.

REVIEW

1. Describe the body structure of a roundworm.
2. Name two roundworms that cause disease in humans.
3. How do hookworms and trichina worms harm their hosts? Explain how the diseases they cause can be prevented.

CHALLENGE It has been said that if the earth were to disappear and only the roundworms were left, the shape of the earth would be outlined by these worms. What does this statement mean?

2·6 Segmented Worms

After completing this section, you will be able to

- **describe** the traits of segmented worms.
- **describe** the body systems of an earthworm.
- **recognize** the importance of earthworms to nature.

The key terms in this section are

crop	segmented worm
gizzard	setae

TRAITS OF SEGMENTED WORMS

A **segmented worm** is a worm whose body is made up of ringlike sections, or segments. Segmented worms have three tissue layers. All segmented worms have a complete digestive system with a mouth and an anus.

Scientists have identified more than 9000 species of segmented worms. Most of these worms, such as the clamworm shown in Figure 2·17*A*, are free-living and are found in salt water. Others live in fresh water. But the best-known segmented worm, the earthworm, lives on land.

 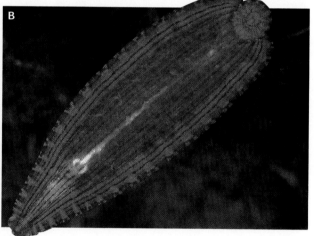

Figure 2·17
A clamworm *(A)* and a freshwater leech *(B)* are segmented.

Some segmented worms are parasites. The leech shown in Figure 2·17*B* is a segmented worm that is a parasite. Some leeches feed on blood. This type of leech attaches itself to its host by means of two suckers. The leech then draws blood from its host.

EARTHWORMS

An earthworm has about 100 segments in its body. Most of the segments have four pairs of setae (SEE tee) on the underside. **Setae** are short bristles that help an earthworm move. Locate the mouth

saeta (bristle)

42

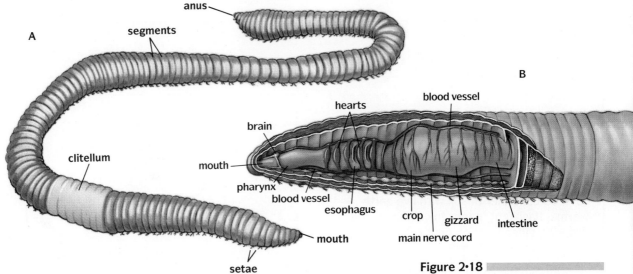

Labels in figure:

A

anus

segments

clitellum

mouth

setae

B

blood vessel

hearts

brain

mouth

pharynx

blood vessel

esophagus

crop

gizzard

intestine

main nerve cord

Figure 2·18

Earthworm: external view *(A)*; internal view showing the digestive, circulatory, and nervous systems *(B)*.

and the anus in Figure 2·18*A*. Find the swollen band called the clitellum (klih TEHL uhm). The *clitellum* functions in reproduction. An earthworm contains both male and female reproductive organs. However, a single earthworm cannot fertilize its own eggs. Earthworms reproduce sexually by exchanging sperm.

Earthworms have a complete digestive system. Look at Figure 2·18*B*, and follow the path of food through the digestive tract. Food enters through the mouth. A muscular pharynx carries the food into a tube called the *esophagus.* This tube joins the pharynx and the crop. The **crop** is a chamber that stores food. From the crop, food enters the gizzard. The **gizzard** is a chamber in which food is ground into small particles by the action of muscles. From the gizzard the food enters the *intestine*, where digestion is completed. Undigested food passes out through the anus.

Earthworms have a *closed circulatory system.* A closed circulatory system is one in which blood travels through a system of joined tubes. In a closed system, blood travels throughout the body at all times. The earthworm has two large blood-carrying tubes, or blood vessels. These two blood vessels extend the full length of the body. The large blood vessels are joined by five short, muscular tubes that act as hearts. These "hearts" help to pump blood

ACTIVITY How Does an Earthworm Respond to Stimuli?

RESULTS AND CONCLUSIONS
1. How did the earthworms react to light? How might this response help an earthworm survive?
2. About how many segments does the earthworm that you observed have?
3. How did the earthworm react to touch?
4. Describe how the earthworms responded to vinegar. How might this response help an earthworm survive?

throughout the body. Look back at Figure 2·18*B* and locate this type of heart.

Earthworms lack a respiratory system. Gas exchange occurs through the skin which is coated with mucus. Oxygen in the air dissolves in the mucous coating. The gas then passes into the worm's body by diffusion. Carbon dioxide diffuses out of the earthworm through the skin.

The nervous system of an earthworm is made up of a simple brain and a main nerve cord. Find these structures in Figure 2·18B. Each segment of the earthworm has smaller nerves that join with the nerve cord. Segments near the brain have nerves that can detect light.

Earthworms serve as a source of food for many animals. However, earthworms are even more important for their role in changing the soil. There are two ways in which they improve the soil. First, as it moves through the soil, an earthworm takes in soil particles through its mouth. It digests bits of food in the soil. Matter that the worm cannot digest is passed out of the body producing waste materials that enrich the soil. Second, earthworms improve soil by leaving tubelike holes as they move through the soil. These holes provide a passage for the air and water needed by plants. Plants usually grow well in soil in which earthworms live.

Figure 2·19
The earthworm enriches the soil.

REVIEW

1. What is a segmented worm? How many body layers does this type of worm have?
2. Trace the path of food through the digestive system of an earthworm.
3. Describe the circulatory system of an earthworm.
4. Describe the two ways in which earthworms improve soil.

CHALLENGE Besides its role in gas exchange, what other function might the coating of mucus on an earthworm serve?

2·7 Mollusks

After completing this section,
you will be able to

- **describe** the traits of mollusks.
- **compare** three types of mollusks on the basis of structure.
- **compare** bivalves and univalves.

The key terms in this section are
bivalve	**mollusk**
foot	**univalve**
mantle	

molluscus (soft bodied)

Figure 2·20

Types of common bivalves: oyster *(A)*, mussels *(B)*, scallop *(C)*, and clams *(D)*. All of these bivalves serve as a food source for humans.

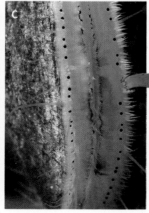

TRAITS OF MOLLUSKS

Scientists believe that there are over 100,000 species of mollusks. A **mollusk** is an animal that has a soft body usually covered by a hard shell. The bodies of all mollusks have a foot and a mantle. Some mollusks also have a head. The head holds the mouth and sense organs. The **foot** is a muscular structure that is used in movement. The **mantle** is a fleshy tissue that covers and protects the organs of a mollusk.

In most mollusks the mantle produces a shell that protects the body. In some mollusks, such as the squid, the shell is inside the body. In others, such as the octopus, there is no shell. Clams and snails are mollusks with an outer shell.

TYPES OF MOLLUSKS

Mollusks are mainly grouped according to the shape of their muscular foot. Mollusks are also grouped according to whether or not they have a shell and according to the form of the shell.

Clams, oysters, mussels, and scallops are mollusks with a wedge-shaped foot. They are known as bivalves (BĪ valvz). A **bivalve** is a mollusk having two shells that are hinged together. Figure 2·20 shows several common bivalves. Unlike other mol-

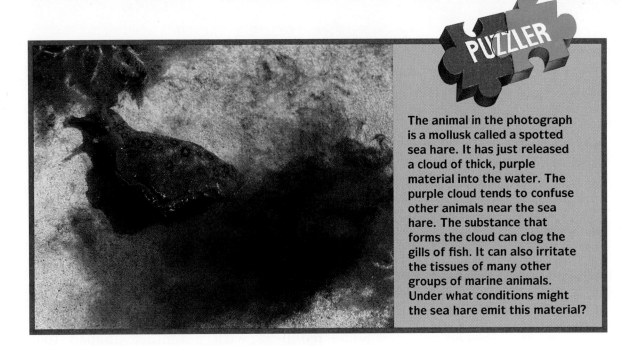

PUZZLER

The animal in the photograph is a mollusk called a spotted sea hare. It has just released a cloud of thick, purple material into the water. The purple cloud tends to confuse other animals near the sea hare. The substance that forms the cloud can clog the gills of fish. It can also irritate the tissues of many other groups of marine animals. Under what conditions might the sea hare emit this material?

lusks, bivalves do not have a head. Notice the two hinged shells from which the group gets its name. Look closely at the scallop shown in Figure 2-20*C*. Note the row of dark spots at the edge of each shell. These structures are simple eyes. Most bivalves get food by filtering particles from water.

Snails, whelks, and slugs are mollusks with a flat foot. They are called univalves (YOO nuh valvz). A **univalve** is a mollusk that is usually covered by a single shell. Although they have no shell, slugs are grouped with the univalves because slugs are snails without shells. All univalves have a distinct head. The head often has two stalks that are sense organs. Many univalves have eyes at the end of the stalks. Figure 2·21 shows a snail and a slug. How do these two univalves differ? Land-dwelling snails and slugs are garden pests in some areas.

Squids, octopuses, nautiluses, and cuttlefish form a third group of mollusks. The foot of these mollusks is divided into long arms, or tentacles. The tentacles of these mollusks have sucking discs along their length. These discs allow the mollusk to cling to surfaces, and to catch and hold animals that are used as food. All members of this group live in water. They are the largest and most complex mollusks. The giant squid may reach a length of 16 m.

uni- (one)
valva (door)

Figure 2·21
A snail *(top)* and a slug *(bottom)* are univalves.

Figure 2·22

Mollusks with a tentacle-shaped foot: nautilus *(A)*, cuttlefish *(B)*, squid *(C)*, and octopus *(D)*. Which of these mollusks lack an external shell?

Some mollusks with a tentacle-shaped foot have an external shell, and others do not. You can see the external shell on the nautilus in Figure 2·22. How can you tell that the nautilus is different from a snail? Both the squid and the cuttlefish have an internal shell. The octopus has no shell.

Mollusks with a tentacle-shaped foot, such as the squid and octopus, have a special type of fast movement. These animals can force water through a tube that leads out of their body. Jets of water are forced out of the body in one direction. As a result, the body is propelled in the opposite direction.

Chitons (KĪ tuhnz) form a fourth group of mollusks. As you can see in Figure 2·23, the shell of a chiton is made up of several plates. Chitons live in the sea and feed by scraping algae off rocks along the shore.

Figure 2·23

Chitons on a rock. How many plates does a chiton have?

REVIEW

1. Describe the three body parts a mollusk may have.
2. Name three types of mollusks. Describe the traits of each. Give an example of a mollusk from each group.
3. How do univalves differ from bivalves?

CHALLENGE More fossils of mollusks than fossils of worms have been found. Explain why this is so.

CHAPTER SUMMARY

The main ideas in this chapter are listed below. Read these statements before you answer the Chapter Review questions.

- An invertebrate is an animal that does not have a backbone. Some invertebrates have a body made up of three cell layers that form from tissues — the ectoderm, the mesoderm, and the endoderm. (2•1)

- Sponges, the simplest invertebrates, have a body that is two cells thick. Sponges have many pores through which water enters the body. A sponge gets particles of food and oxygen from the water that passes through its body. (2•2)

- Coelenterates have a large central body cavity. Tentacles with stinging cells are used in getting food. (2•3)

- Coelenterates have two body forms — a tubelike form and an umbrella-shaped form. The body contains true tissues. Coelenterates include hydras, jellyfish, and corals and sea anemones. (2•3)

- Flatworms are the simplest worms. They have three cell layers and have organs and organ systems. Flatworms may be parasites or be free-living. (2•4)

- Roundworms are smooth, cylinder-shaped worms with a tubelike digestive system. They are the simplest animals to have both a mouth and an anus. (2•5)

- Most roundworms are free-living. Hookworms and trichina worms are examples of parasites that cause disease in humans. (2•5)

- Segmented worms have a body made up of ringlike sections. Earthworms have a complete digestive system and a closed circulatory system. Earthworms improve the quality of soil. (2•6)

- Mollusks have a soft body and a muscular foot that is used in movement. Most have a hard shell. Mollusks are divided into four groups: bivalves, univalves, tentacle-footed mollusks, and chitons. (2•7)

The key terms in this chapter are listed below. Use each term in a sentence that shows the meaning of the term.

anus	foot	roundworm
bivalve	gizzard	segmented worm
budding	invertebrate	setae
central cavity	mantle	sponge
coelenterate	mesoderm	stinging cell
crop	mollusk	tentacles
ectoderm	pharynx	univalve
endoderm	pores	
flatworm	regeneration	

VOCABULARY

Write the letter of the term that best matches the definition. Not all the terms will be used.

1. A chamber in which food is broken down into small parts by muscular action in an earthworm
2. Process of asexual reproduction in which a new individual develops from an outgrowth of the parent
3. Any animal that does not have a backbone
4. A smooth, cylinder-shaped worm that is pointed at both ends and has a tubelike digestive tract
5. A mollusk that is usually covered with a single shell
6. A fleshy tissue that covers and protects the organs of a mollusk
7. A chamber in which food is stored in an earthworm
8. A worm whose body is made of ringlike sections
9. The outer tissue layer in a developing animal
10. Regrowth of body parts that have been lost or damaged

a. bivalve
b. budding
c. crop
d. ectoderm
e. endoderm
f. flatworm
g. gizzard
h. invertebrate
i. mantle
j. mesoderm
k. regeneration
l. roundworm
m. segmented worm
n. univalve

CONCEPTS

Write the correct term for each structure shown in the diagram.

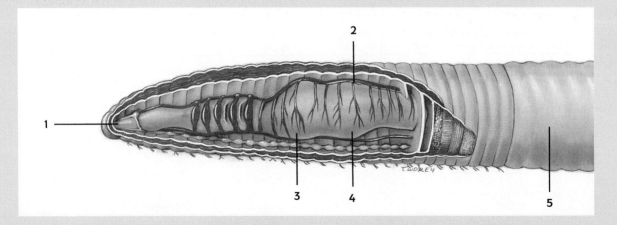

Complete the following sentences.

6. An invertebrate is an animal that does not have a _____ .
7. Two types of asexual reproduction in sponges and coelenterates are _____ and _____ .
8. Coelenterates are the simplest animals to have true _____ .
9. Flatworms are the simplest animals to have _____ and _____ .
10. Blood flow in an earthworm is through a _____ circulatory system.
11. In most mollusks the _____ produces a hard shell that protects the soft body.

Answer the following in complete sentences.

12. Name the eight largest invertebrate phyla.
13. Name and describe the three tissue layers that form the body of some adult animals.
14. How does a sponge obtain food?
15. Identify three groups of coelenterates.
16. Explain how a disease caused by liver flukes can be avoided.
17. What are the traits of a roundworm?
18. How are earthworms important to nature?
19. How does a univalve differ from a bivalve?

APPLICATION/ CRITICAL THINKING

1. You are asked to classify an animal in the correct phylum. The animal has a soft body and armlike tentacles with sucking disks. There is a shell inside the animal. Which is the animal, a coelenterate or a mollusk? Explain your answer.
2. Someone with a tapeworm disease eats a great deal but feels hungry and tired and loses weight. Explain why.
3. Look back through this chapter to see in what order the phyla of invertebrates are presented. What pattern is there in this order?
4. Authorities sometimes close beaches to swimmers because there are a large number of jellyfish in the water. Explain why it is not wise to allow people to swim in these waters.

EXTENSION

1. Do research to find out how oysters produce pearls. Write a report on your findings.
2. Ask a veterinarian for information about the kinds of roundworm and flatworm parasites that can affect pets. Find out how infection by these worms can be prevented. Report your findings to the class.
3. Find out how leeches were used for medical purposes from the Middle Ages to the nineteenth century. Write a brief report.

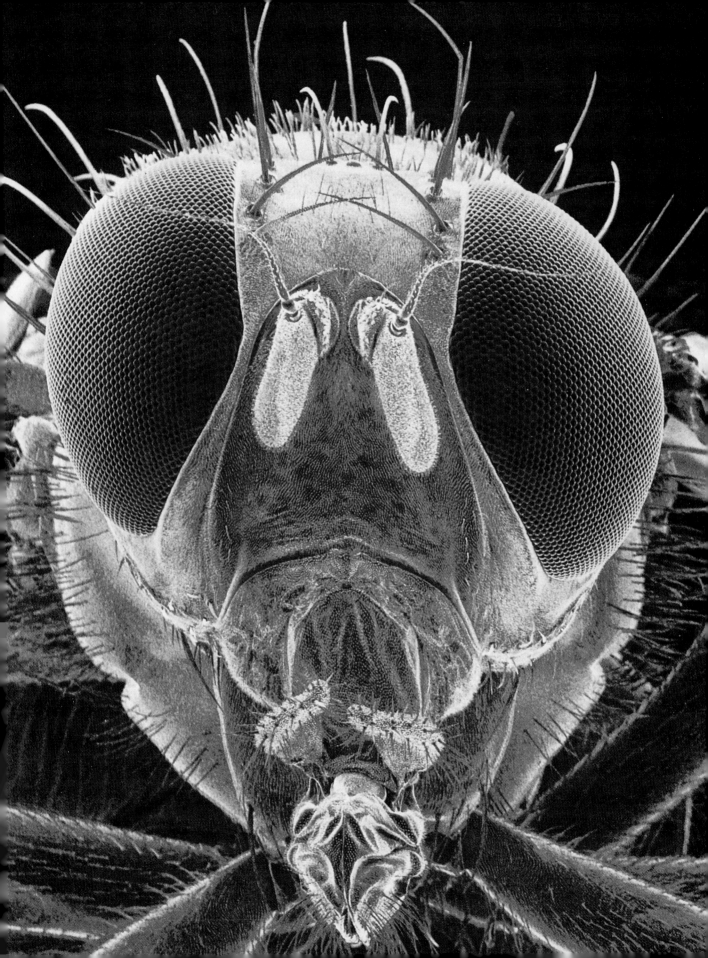

CHAPTER 3

COMPLEX INVERTEBRATES

Do you recognize the armored invader in the photograph? It is actually a Mediterranean fruit fly, an insect much smaller than the common housefly. The Mediterranean fruit fly is a major pest, affecting more than 100 different kinds of fruits. The female fruit fly lays her eggs under the skin of a fruit, where the young flies hatch, live, and eat, thereby spoiling the fruit.

But did you know that another type of fruit fly has been an important part of many scientific experiments? Scientists have studied this fly's wing shape, its body color, and even its eye color.

- *Why does a fruit fly look like it is armored?*
- *What are common traits of all insects?*
- *What is an arthropod, and why is it so successful?*

3·1 Traits of Arthropods

arthron (joint)
podus (foot)

What type of animals can be found on the ocean floor, in deserts and swamps, flying through the air, and crawling on a dog's back? Arthropods can be found in all of these places. An **arthropod** is an animal that has a body made up of segments, a hard outer covering, and jointed legs. There are more species in the arthropod phylum than in all the other animal phyla combined.

Arthropods are considered to be a very successful group. The term *successful* has a special meaning to biologists. A group of animals is called successful if its members either are found in many habitats or exist in great numbers. Since both these conditions describe arthropods, they are a very successful group. The adaptations of the many species of arthropods are a major factor in the success of this group. An *adaptation* is a trait that makes an organism better able to survive in its environment.

BODY PARTS

Although arthropods have many different adaptations, these animals all share certain traits. The body of most arthropods is divided into three main parts. Identify these parts in Figure 3·1. The **head** is the first part of the body and contains the

Figure 3·1

What are the three main parts of the dragonfly *(A)*? A dragonfly at rest *(B)*.

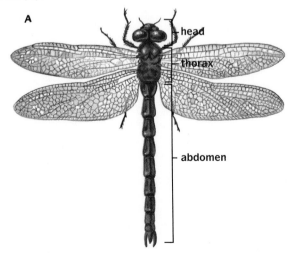

sense organs. The **thorax** is the middle body part that joins the head and abdomen. Walking legs are attached to the thorax. The **abdomen** is the last part of the body and contains reproductive and digestive organs.

thorax (chest)

EXOSKELETON

The hard body covering of an arthropod is called an exoskeleton (ehk soh SKEHL uh tuhn). An **exoskeleton** is a skeleton that covers the outside of an animal's body. This skeleton is like a suit of armor—a hard covering that protects the body. The exoskeleton helps to keep an arthropod from being eaten by other animals and from drying out. The protection given by the exoskeleton is one reason that arthropods are so successful.

exo- (outside of)

Figure 3·2
Arthropods molt at regular intervals as they grow. This is an arthropod one minute after molting.

The exoskeleton is made up of many parts that meet at *joints* and can bend. Joints allow freedom of movement. The exoskeleton also functions as a stiff support to which the muscles are attached. To cause movement, muscles must pull against something. The attachment of muscles to the hard skeleton allows movement.

The exoskeleton is made of a nonliving material. Therefore, it cannot grow. In order for an arthropod to grow, it must shed this covering by a process called *molting*. In Figure 3·2 you can see an arthropod that has just molted. Before an animal molts, a new, soft exoskeleton forms beneath the

By studying dragonflies, engineers hope to learn how to make better and safer airplanes. A dragonfly can move straight up, like a helicopter. A dragonfly can stop in midflight and turn around. It can fly sideways and can even fly backward.

To design better airplanes, engineers are studying how these insects use their wings. Most insects, birds, and airplanes rely on the shape of their wings to lift them in the air. But the dragonfly beats its wings in a way that creates tiny whirl-winds around the wings. These powerful whirlwinds can lift the dragonfly in the air and propel the insect in any direction.

Engineers believe that airplanes could improve their performance by using a technique based on the way the dragonfly flies. The engineers are trying to design airplanes that could create and use the same kind of whirlwinds produced by the dragonfly's wings. Compared with airplanes in use today, these airplanes would have more powerful lift, fly more safely, use less fuel, and provide a smoother ride.

---

old one. The new exoskeleton is larger but somewhat folded, so it fits under the old one. Most arthropods hide while the new coat hardens.

All arthropods have pairs of jointed legs. The joints allow the legs to bend and move in many ways. The legs may be used for walking, swimming, hopping, or food getting.

CLASSES OF ARTHROPODS

The arthropod phylum is broken down into many classes. A *class* is a group of related species. Members of each class of arthropods have a specific number of legs. Therefore the number of legs can be used to classify an arthropod. Most arthropods belong to one of five major classes: *insects, crustaceans* (kruhs TAY shuhnz), *arachnids* (uh RAK-nihdz), *centipedes,* and *millipedes.*

REVIEW

1. What are the traits of arthropods?
2. Why are arthropods considered to be a successful group?
3. What are the five major classes of arthropods?

CHALLENGE After molting but before its new exoskeleton hardens, an arthropod takes in extra water or air. What might be the useful result of this action?

3·2 Insects

Flies, ants, grasshoppers, bees, and butterflies are all insects. An **insect** is an arthropod that has three pairs of jointed legs. Insects make up the largest class of arthropods. There are more species of insects than there are species of all other animals combined.

TRAITS OF INSECTS

Insects are the most successful class of arthropods. To understand the reasons for this success, it is helpful to learn about the traits of insects. Like the body of other arthropods, the body of an insect has three main parts. In Figure 3·3A, locate the three body parts of the grasshopper—the head, thorax, and abdomen.

Look closely at the head shown in Figure 3·3B and locate the mandibles (MAN duh buhlz). The *mandibles* are a pair of jaws that are used for chewing. Grasshoppers cut and chew plants. As the grasshopper bites, these jaws move sideways. Other insects have different mouth parts that are specialized for the kind of food the insect eats.

Insects also have feelers, or antennae (an TEHN-ee) (sing., *antenna*), on their head. An *antenna* is a sense organ found in many arthropods. The antennae of most insects function in the senses of touch and smell. Some also function in taste and hearing.

After completing this section, you will be able to
- **describe** the traits of insects.
- **list** the steps in the life cycle of an insect.
- **compare** incomplete metamorphosis and complete metamorphosis.

The key terms in this section are
adult	metamorphosis
insect	nymph
larva	pupa

insectum (divided)

Figure 3·3

The head, thorax, and abdomen of a grasshopper (A). Close-up of the head of a grasshopper (B).

A

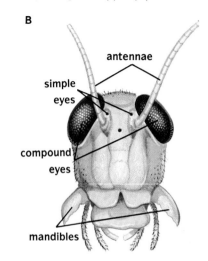

abdomen   thorax   head

wings

spiracles

B

antennae

simple eyes

compound eyes

mandibles

Like most insects, the grasshopper has two types of eyes. *Simple eyes* can sense changes in the amount of light but cannot form clear images.

Locate the compound eyes in Figure 3·3*B*. Unlike a human eye, which has only one lens, a *compound eye* may have several thousand lenses. A *lens* is a structure that focuses light from an object. Within the eye the focused light forms an image of the object. A compound eye forms many images. Each image shows a small part of the surroundings. When the images are combined by the brain, they show the complete surroundings. Figure 3·4*A* shows a flower as it might appear through the compound eye of an insect. Figure 3·4*B* shows the same flower as seen through a human eye. The compound eye is very good at sensing movement. When an object in the surroundings moves, its image moves from one lens to the next. Why is sensing movement very important for an insect?

Figure 3·4

A flower as seen by an insect *(A)*. The same flower as seen by a human *(B)*. How do these images compare?

Look back at Figure 3·3*A*. Like all insects, a grasshopper has three pairs of legs. Notice that all three pairs are attached to the thorax. The first two pairs of legs are used for walking. What do you think is the function of the large hind legs?

Also attached to the thorax in the grasshopper are two pairs of wings. The narrow wings protect the wider, more fragile wings used for flying. When

ACTIVITY — What Is the Structure of an Insect?

OBJECTIVES

Compare the body structure of three types of insects.

Formulate a definition of the term *insect*.

MATERIALS

hand lens; preserved grasshopper, housefly, and butterfly; probe.

PROCEDURE

A. Make a data table with headings like those shown below.

B. Use a hand lens to observe the external structure of three preserved insects—a grasshopper, housefly, and butterfly. Count the main body parts of each insect. Record your observations in your data table. Make a drawing of each insect, and label the body parts.

C. Use the hand lens to examine the legs of each insect. Look for the joints on each leg. Count how many pairs of legs each insect has. Use a probe to gently lift the wings of each insect. Count how many pairs of wings each insect has. Record your observations in your data table.

RESULTS AND CONCLUSIONS

1. How many main body parts does each insect have?
2. How many pairs of legs does each insect have?
3. Using your answers to questions **1** and **2**, define the term *insect*.

INSECT	NUMBER OF BODY PARTS	NUMBER OF PAIRS OF LEGS	NUMBER OF PAIRS OF WINGS

an insect is not in flight, the flying wings are folded under the narrow wings. Although not all insects fly, insects are the only invertebrates that can fly.

The movement of the wings and abdomen pumps air into and out of the spiracles. Locate the spiracles on the abdomen of the grasshopper in Figure 3·3A. A *spiracle* is a small opening through which air enters the body of some arthropods. The spiracles lead to a system of air tubes within the body. Oxygen enters the body and carbon dioxide is released through this system.

INCOMPLETE METAMORPHOSIS

Reproduction in insects is sexual. The female lays a large number of fertilized eggs as often as several times in one season. Although many eggs will never become adults, the large number of eggs makes possible a large number of offspring.

meta- (change)
morphe (form)

All insects undergo metamorphosis (meht uh-MAWR fuh sihs). **Metamorphosis** is a series of distinct changes of form through which an animal passes as it grows from egg to adult. Grasshoppers have *incomplete metamorphosis*. When these insects hatch from the egg, they resemble the adult insect. They have three stages in their life cycle: *egg, nymph,* and *adult.*

Refer to Figure 3·5 as you read about the stages in the life cycle of a grasshopper.

1. A female grasshopper lays fertilized eggs in a hole she has dug.

2. The young that hatch from the eggs are called nymphs. A **nymph** is a young insect that looks

Figure 3·5

The life cycle of a grasshopper. What is the name given to this series of changes?

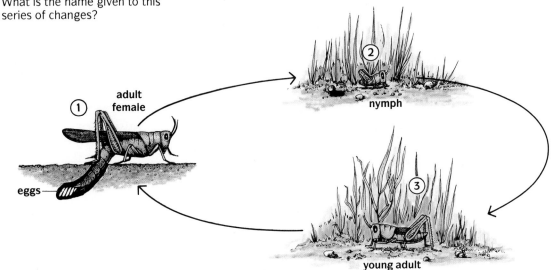

like a small adult. Notice that the nymph lacks wings. As the nymph grows, it molts several times before becoming an adult.

3. Each time the nymph molts, it looks more like the adult. An **adult** is an animal that has grown and developed enough to reproduce.

COMPLETE METAMORPHOSIS

Most insects grow from egg to adult by *complete metamorphosis*. When these insects hatch from the egg, they do not look like the adult. There are four stages of complete metamorphosis: *egg, larva* (LAHR vuh), *pupa* (PYOO puh), and *adult*.

Refer to Figure 3·6 as you read about complete metamorphosis in a moth.

1. The egg hatches into a caterpillar. The caterpillar looks like a worm, not like the adult insect.

2. The caterpillar is the larva of a moth or butterfly. A **larva** (pl., *larvae*) is an insect in its worm-like phase. The larva eats a great deal and grows rapidly. It molts several times as it grows.

3. The caterpillar makes a cocoon, an outer covering, that protects the insect during the next stage in its life cycle. The **pupa** is the stage of insect development between the larva and the adult. Within the cocoon, the tissues of the pupa reorganize to form the adult insect.

4. The adult insect comes out.

Figure 3·6
The life cycle of a moth. What is the name given to this series of changes?

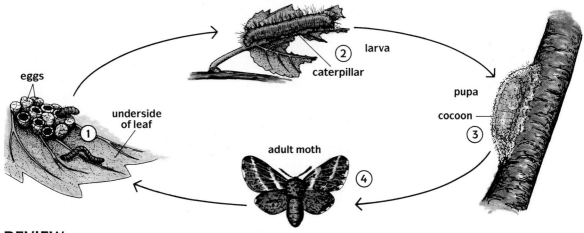

REVIEW

1. What are the traits of insects?
2. What are the steps in the life cycle of an insect having incomplete metamorphosis? Complete metamorphosis?
3. How does incomplete metamorphosis differ from complete metamorphosis?

CHALLENGE A butterfly larva and an adult butterfly use different foods. How does this difference help these insects survive?

3·3 Success of Insects

ADAPTATIONS OF INSECTS

The large size of the grasshopper makes it a good insect to study. But there is no typical insect. Insects vary in their size and form. They also vary in the kinds of structures they have. As a result, different insects are adapted to various food sources and to many kinds of habitats. These adaptations are one reason for the success of insects.

The small size of most insects is another reason for their success. A small insect needs less food than does a larger animal. Small size also means that insects can easily hide from enemies.

How are insects adapted to a variety of food sources? Some insects eat other insects. These meat-eating insects have mouth parts adapted for their food source. Recall that a grasshopper cuts and chews plants with its mandibles. Figure 3·7 shows the mouth parts of three different insects. Compare the mouth part of the butterfly with the mandibles of the grasshopper shown in Figure 3·5. The mouth part of the butterfly is a long tube used in sucking nectar from flowers. When the tube is not

Figure 3·7

The mouth parts of a butterfly *(A)*, housefly *(B)*, and mosquito *(C)*.

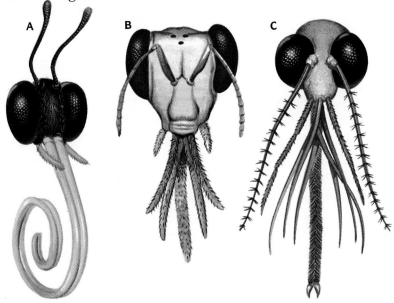

in use, it curls up. The mouth parts of the housefly are spongy and are used in lapping food. Look at the mouth parts of the mosquito in Figure 3·7C. Mosquitoes feed on blood. The mosquito uses its mouth parts to pierce the skin of an animal and to inject a substance that stops blood from clotting. How does this action help a mosquito get food?

Figure 3·8
Insects often are adapted to blend in with their surroundings. Look for the walking stick *(A)*, moth larva *(B)*, and thorn mimic *(C)*.

Flight is an important trait of many insects. It allows an insect to travel great distances in search of food, a home, or a mate. Flight also allows an insect to escape danger. Insects vary in the number of wings they have. Flies and mosquitoes have only one pair. Most other insects, including grasshoppers, bees, and butterflies, have two pairs of wings. Some adult insects have no wings and cannot fly. Look back at Figure 3·1. How many pairs of wings does a dragonfly have?

Many insects are adapted to look like their surroundings. Some insects, such as the moth larva in Figure 3·8B, are the color of the plants on which they live. Other insects actually look like parts of a plant. Try to find the thorn mimic in Figure 3·8C. How is the appearance of each insect shown an adaptation for survival?

PUZZLER

The photograph shows a ladybug beetle along with smaller insects on a leaf. The mouth parts of the ladybug are adapted for biting.

Gardeners and farmers are told that they can get a "ladybug bargain" if they buy 72,000 ladybugs in one order. Why would a farmer or gardener want to buy large quantities of ladybugs?

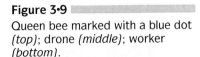

Figure 3·9

Queen bee marked with a blue dot *(top)*; drone *(middle)*; worker *(bottom)*.

SOCIAL INSECTS

Most insects live by themselves. Young insects are usually not cared for by their parents. But some insects live together in colonies. A **colony** of animals is a group of animals that live together and share work and food. An insect that lives in a colony is called a **social insect**. Insects that live in a colony depend on each other for survival. Honeybees, ants, wasps, and termites are social insects.

Living in a colony has some benefits over living alone. An insect that lives alone must protect itself and find its own food and shelter. In a colony these tasks are divided — each insect has one or more special jobs.

A honeybee colony provides a good example of how tasks are divided among members. This colony is made up of one queen, a few hundred drones, and thousands of worker bees. You can see each type of honeybee in Figure 3·9. *Drones* are males. The only function of a drone is to mate with the queen. The *queen* lays eggs for the colony. She is fed and protected by the workers. A *worker* is a female bee that feeds and protects all the other bees in the hive.

The worker bees have different jobs, depending on age. When they are young, workers make food called royal jelly. The workers only feed the royal jelly to the queen and to very young larvae (LAHR vee). Workers also produce wax, which they use to build and repair the hive. The older workers leave the hive to gather nectar and pollen from flowers. The nectar and pollen are used to make food that the young workers feed to the larvae, drones, and queen.

When a worker bee finds a good source of nectar, the bee brings some of the nectar back to the hive. The bee also lets the other workers know where the nectar is located. To do this, the returning bee releases a drop of nectar and begins a dance. There are two types of bee dances. If the nectar source is nearby, the bee dances in circles. If the nectar is farther away, the bee dances in a figure eight. The direction of the figure eight shows the location of the nectar.

Figure 3·10
Workers in a hive, tending the honeybee larvae.

REVIEW

1. What traits make the insect class so successful?
2. Using three different insects as examples, explain how mouth parts adapt insects to different food sources.
3. How is living in a colony helpful to insects?
4. Briefly describes the jobs of each type of bee in a honeybee colony.

CHALLENGE As they feed, flies spit up a drop of their last meal. How might this process result in the spread of disease among humans?

3·4 Crustaceans

After completing this section, you will be able to

- **describe** the traits of crustaceans.
- **give examples** of crustaceans.
- **describe** respiration in a crayfish.

The key term in this section is **crustacean**

crusta (shell)

Shrimp, lobsters, crabs, and crayfish are all crustaceans. A **crustacean** is an arthropod that has five pairs of jointed legs. Crustaceans are found both in water and on land. But most crustaceans live in the oceans. The water flea is a crustacean that is found in fresh water. The pill bug is a crustacean that lives on land.

Crustaceans have a very hard exoskeleton that contains calcium. They also have grinding mouth parts called mandibles. Look at the crayfish in Figure 3·11. Like all crustaceans, the crayfish has two main body parts. The head and thorax are joined, or fused, into a single body part. The abdomen is the second body part.

Like all crustaceans, the crayfish has two pairs of antennae. The shorter pair are used in touch, taste, and balance. The longer pair function in touch, taste, and smell. The crayfish has compound eyes. Each eye is at the end of a short stalk. The stalks can move, allowing the eyes to see in different directions.

Look again at Figure 3·11. Notice that all five pairs of legs are attached to the fused head and thorax. The first pair of legs are claws. How do you think these claws are used? The other four pairs of

Figure 3·11

A crayfish is an animal that has two main body parts.

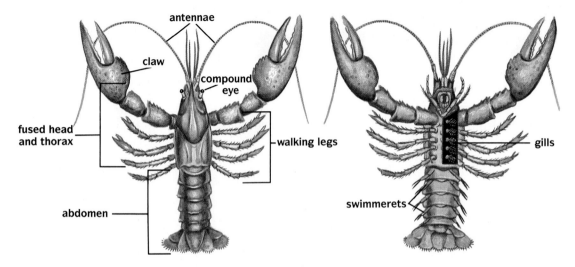

OBJECTIVES

Observe the external structure of a crayfish.
Describe how the structure of a crayfish adapts it to its environment.

MATERIALS

preserved crayfish, hand lens

PROCEDURE

A. Examine a preserved crayfish. Note how the exoskeleton feels, and gently tap it with your finger. Count the main body parts. Record your observations.
B. Locate and count the pairs of antennae.
C. Locate the compound eyes near the antennae. Notice that each eye is at the top of a short stalk. Gently try to bend the stalks with your finger.
D. Examine the large claws, which are the first pair of legs. Open and close the claws. Note that the next four pairs of legs are walking legs.
E. Turn the crayfish over, and examine the structures around the mouth. Hypothesize about the function of these structures.
F. Locate the swimmerets on the underside of the abdomen. Observe their structure.
G. Make a drawing of the crayfish. Label the body parts, antennae, eyes, claws, walking legs, and swimmerets.

RESULTS AND CONCLUSIONS

1. Describe the exoskeleton of a crayfish. How does the structure of the exoskeleton aid its function?
2. How might the location of the eyes at the end of stalks aid their function?
3. How does the structure of the claws aid their functions?
4. What traits does a crayfish have in common with other crustaceans?

legs are walking legs. Small leglike structures called swimmerets are attached to the abdomen. *Swimmerets* are used in reproduction.

As a crayfish swims, water moves over its gills. *Gills* are structures used for respiration. As water passes over them, oxygen moves from the water into the gills. The oxygen is absorbed by blood passing through the gills. Carbon dioxide from the blood moves out through the gills to the water. Land-dwelling crustaceans, such as pill bugs, also need moisture for their gills to function. Pill bugs live in damp places, such as under rocks.

Figure 3·12
Pill bugs are crustaceans.

REVIEW

1. What are the traits of crustaceans?
2. List four examples of crustaceans.
3. How does a crayfish breathe?

CHALLENGE Pill bugs are often seen curled up into tight little balls. How does this behavior help a pill bug survive?

3·5 Other Arthropods

arachne (spider)

ARACHNIDS

Many people think that spiders are insects. But spiders are not in the insect class. Spiders are the largest group in the arachnid class. An **arachnid** is an arthropod that has four pairs of jointed legs. Unlike crustaceans, most of which live in the oceans, arachnids live on land. Like crustaceans, arachnids have a fused head and thorax. The four pairs of legs are attached to this body part.

Most spiders have four pairs of simple eyes located on the fused head and thorax. Spiders and other arachnids lack compound eyes and antennae. Look at the spider in Figure 3·13. Locate the spiracle on the abdomen. Air enters a spider's body through the spiracles and passes to the book lungs. A *book lung* is a series of flat, air-filled plates that function in respiration. Within the book lungs, oxygen from the air diffuses into the blood. And carbon dioxide in the blood is released into the air. How does the structure of the book lung, as shown in Figure 3·13B, relate to its name?

Some people fear spiders, but most spiders are helpful. Many types of spiders eat insects that are harmful to humans or to crops. Most spiders build

Figure 3·13
Structure of a spider *(A)*. Enlargement of a book lung *(B)*. What takes place in the book lungs?

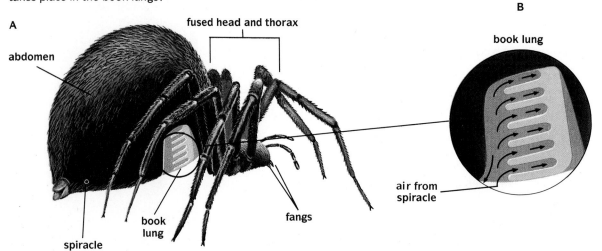

silk webs in which they trap insects. A spider has poison fangs near its mouth. These fangs pierce the insect's body and then release a poison that paralyzes or kills the insect. The spider then sucks out liquids from the insect's body.

A daddy longlegs has poor vision. It uses its longest pair of legs to explore its environment. A daddy longlegs does not build a web. This arachnid feeds on mites and small insects.

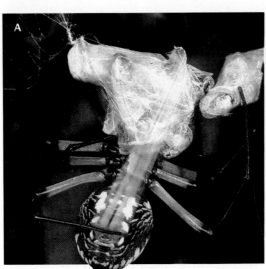 

Figure 3·14

A spider has wrapped its food in silk *(A)*. Notice the stinger of the scorpion*(B)*.

Ticks, mites, and scorpions are other examples of arachnids. Ticks are parasites. They attach to the skin of their host and feed on the host's blood. Ticks in some areas carry diseases such as Rocky Mountain spotted fever. Ticks pick up this disease by biting an infected host, such as a squirrel. Humans can get the disease if they are bitten by a disease-carrying tick.

Dogs and cats that spend time outdoors may pick up ticks and mites. Most mites are parasites. A mite called a chigger affects people. Its bite causes severe itching. Other mites are helpful because they eat insects that destroy crops.

Look at the scorpion in Figure 3·14*C*. How is this arachnid different from a spider? Note the sharp stinger at the end of the abdomen. The stinger contains a poison. The sting of a scorpion is painful but usually not fatal to humans.

CENTIPEDES AND MILLIPEDES

Centipedes and millipedes make up two classes of arthropods. Notice in Figure 3·15 that these animals have a long body with many segments. They have an exoskeleton, jointed legs, antennae, and simple eyes.

Figure 3·15

Centipede *(left)*. Millipede, with inset of millipede curled up in defense *(right)*. What are some differences between these arthropods?

centi- (hundred)
podus (foot)

mille (thousand)

A **centipede** is an arthropod that has one pair of legs attached to most of its body segments. The most common types of centipedes have about 15 pairs of legs. Centipedes have a flat body. A pair of poison claws is attached to the first body segment behind the head. Centipedes use the claws to catch and kill insects or other small animals. Centipedes may hide in damp places, such as under rocks.

A **millipede** is an arthropod that has two pairs of jointed legs on most of its body segments. Most millipedes have 30 to 40 body segments. Millipedes have no poison claws and mostly eat the remains of dead plants. When disturbed, a millipede may curl up as shown in Figure 3·15.

REVIEW

1. What are the traits of arachnids?
2. Give four examples of arachnids.
3. How are arachnids both helpful and harmful?
4. How do millipedes differ from centipedes?

CHALLENGE Suppose you find an arthropod that has two main body parts, no antennae, and four pairs of legs. What class is this animal in? What structures does it have for respiration?

3·6 Echinoderms

Have you ever seen a sand dollar or a starfish, also called a sea star? If so, you have seen an echinoderm. An **echinoderm** is a spiny-skinned invertebrate that lives in the ocean. Sea urchins and sea cucumbers are other examples of echinoderms shown in Figure 3·16.

TRAITS OF ECHINODERMS

Unlike arthropods, echinoderms have an endoskeleton. An *endoskeleton* is a skeleton that is inside an animal's body. This skeleton is made up of hard plates, and it gives support. It also helps to protect an echinoderm from other animals.

The term *echinoderm* means "spiny skin." In most echinoderms, pointed structures called spines cover the animal's body. These spines, which are part of the skeleton, serve as protection.

Echinoderms use structures called tube feet in an unusual type of movement. **Tube feet** are hollow tubes that end in structures like suction cups. The tube feet are found in rows on the underside of the body. Muscles move water through a system of canals inside the body. These canals connect to the tube feet. The movement of water creates suction by which the tube feet attach to surfaces. As the echinoderm moves, some of the tube feet extend and then attach to a surface in the direction of move-

After completing this section, you will be able to

- **describe** the traits of echinoderms.
- **give examples** of echinoderms.
- **explain** how the tube feet of a starfish function.

The key terms in this section are
echinoderm   **tube feet**
radial symmetry

echinos (spiny)
derma (skin)

Figure 3·16

Examples of echinoderms: sand dollar *(A)*, sea urchin *(B)*, and sea cucumber *(C)*.

71

Figure 3·17
Radial symmetry in an echinoderm.

ment. Other tube feet then release their suction, and the animal moves forward.

Echinoderms have radial symmetry (RAY dee-uhl SIHM uh tree). **Radial symmetry** is the arrangement of body parts around a central area. In the starfish, five similar parts extend from the central area of the body. The dotted lines shown in Figure 3·17 show how the starfish can be divided into five mirror-image halves. A starfish body is unlike a human body. Notice that your body has only two mirror-image halves—a left side and a right side. Humans, and other animals with left and right sides, have *bilateral symmetry*.

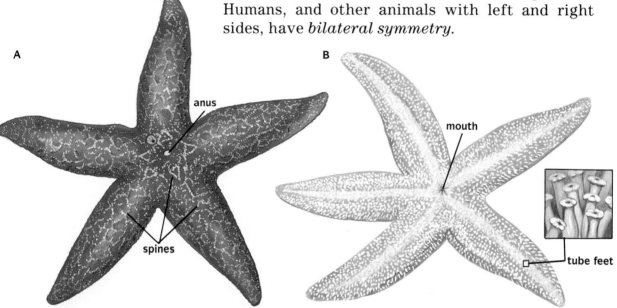

A

B

anus

spines

mouth

tube feet

Figure 3·18
Upper surface of a starfish *(A)*. Lower surface of a starfish *(B)*. What are the suction-cuplike structures called?

THE STARFISH

Look at the starfish in Figure 3·18. The upper and lower surfaces of the starfish are both shown. Notice that the mouth is on the lower surface of the body. On which surface is the anus found? The tube feet are in rows on the underside of each arm.

Starfish use their tube feet in feeding as well as in movement. The starfish use their tube feet to pull open clams and other mollusk shells. The tube feet attach to both halves of a shell, and the starfish pulls on each half. The starfish only needs to open the shell a tiny amount. Once the halves are parted, the starfish pushes its stomach out of its mouth and into the shell. The starfish then digests the soft body of the mollusk.

Starfish are either male or female, and they reproduce sexually. Large numbers of egg cells and sperm cells are released into the water, where the eggs are fertilized. Starfish can also reproduce asexually by regeneration.

REVIEW

1. What are the traits of echinoderms?
2. List four examples of echinoderms.
3. How do tube feet function in movement of an echinoderm?
4. Describe how a starfish feeds on a clam.

CHALLENGE The dried remains of starfish and sea urchins are often sold as souvenirs. What part are the dried remains?

CHAPTER SUMMARY

The main ideas in this chapter are listed below. Read these statements before you answer the Chapter Review questions.

- Arthropods are a very successful animal phylum. The body of an arthropod is made up of a head, a thorax, and an abdomen. Arthropods have jointed legs and a protective exoskeleton. (3•1)

- Insects are arthropods with three pairs of jointed legs. Most insects have both simple eyes and compound eyes. (3•2)

- A growing insect undergoes metamorphosis. Incomplete metamorphosis has three stages: egg, nymph, and adult. Complete metamorphosis has four stages: egg, larva, pupa, and adult. (3•2)

- The many adaptations of insects make them a very successful class of animals. These adaptations include the small size of insects, mouth parts specialized for different food sources, the ability to fly, and the ability to blend in with the environment. (3•3)

- Social insects live in colonies. Members of a colony share work and food. They depend on each other for survival. (3•3)

- Crustaceans are arthropods that have five pairs of jointed legs. The head and thorax of crustaceans are joined into a single body part. (3•4)

- Arachnids, such as spiders, are arthropods that have four pairs of jointed legs. Spiders use book lungs in respiration. (3•5)

- Centipedes are arthropods that have one pair of legs on most body segments. Millipedes are arthropods that have two pairs of legs on most body segments. (3•5)

- Echinoderms are spiny-skinned invertebrates of the oceans. Echinoderms have radial symmetry, and they feed and move by means of tube feet. (3•6)

The key terms in this chapter are listed below. Use each term in a sentence that shows the meaning of the term.

abdomen	centipede	exoskeleton	metamorphosis	radial symmetry
adult	colony	head	millipede	social insect
arachnid	crustacean	insect	nymph	thorax
arthropod	echinoderm	larva	pupa	tube feet

Chapter Review

VOCABULARY

Use the key terms from the previous page to complete the following sentences correctly.

1. An arthropod that has one pair of legs attached to most of its body segments is a/an _____.
2. A spiny-skinned invertebrate that lives in the ocean is a/an _____.
3. In an insect the body part that contains the reproductive and digestive organs is the _____.
4. An arthropod that has three pairs of jointed legs is a/an _____.
5. A series of distinct changes in form through which an animal passes as it grows from egg to adult is called _____.
6. An arthropod that has five pairs of jointed legs is a/an _____.
7. Hollow structures like suction cups and used in movement by echinoderms are called _____.
8. A skeleton that covers the outside of an animal's body is a/an _____.
9. The arrangement of body parts around a central area is called _____.
10. An insect that shares work and food with other insects is a/an _____.

CONCEPTS

Make a table like the one shown. Write the correct information under each heading.

TYPE OF ARTHROPOD	NUMBER OF PAIRS OF LEGS
Insect	
Crustacean	
Arachnid	
Centipede (per body segment)	
Millipede (per body segment)	

Choose the term or phrase that best answers the question or completes the statement.

1. Which of the following is not a trait of all adult arthropods?
   a. a hard exoskeleton
   b. muscles attached to the exoskeleton
   c. a jointed body
   d. pairs of wings
2. One disadvantage to an arthropod's having an exoskelton is that the exoskeleton
   a. is waterproof.   c. does not grow.
   b. is a hard covering.   d. covers the animal's body.

3. Which life stage is not found in incomplete metamorphosis?
   a. egg
   b. pupa
   c. nymph
   d. adult
4. Land-dwelling crustaceans are often found under rocks or logs because
   a. crustaceans must hide to avoid being eaten.
   b. it is cooler under rocks.
   c. these places are moist.
   d. the most food is found under rocks.
5. Radial symmetry describes the arrangement of body parts found in
   a. an insect.
   b. an arachnid.
   c. a centipede.
   d. an echinoderm.

Answer the following in complete sentences.

6. What are the traits of arthropods?
7. Describe traits that help to make insects successful.
8. Explain the differences between a queen bee, a drone, and a worker bee.
9. How do centipedes and millipedes differ in body structure and in food sources?
10. Explain how an echinoderm moves.

---

1. How is the appearance of a walking stick insect an adaptation?
2. Not all the threads of a spider's web are sticky. How might this difference in the stickiness of threads be beneficial to spiders?
3. Compare the skeletons of echinoderms and arthropods. Explain how the skeletons are alike and how they are different.

APPLICATION/ CRITICAL THINKING

---

1. Research and present a report to your class on an ant, wasp, or termite colony. Describe the shelter in which the colony lives and the functions of its members.
2. Locust is the name for several species of grasshoppers that travel in very large groups. Write a brief report on the damage these insects can cause to crops.
3. Chemicals used to kill insect pests have been found to pollute the environment. Find out about the different ways that insect pests can be controlled by natural means. Present a brief report of your findings in class.

EXTENSION

CHAPTER 4

SEED PLANTS

Have you ever walked through the woods or underbrush and later found burs stuck to your clothing? Notice the many tiny hooks on each bur shown in the photograph. These hooks cling tightly to fabric as you pull a bur from your clothing.

Forty years ago a Swiss mountain climber was once again pulling burs from his socks when he had an idea. He wondered whether he could copy the design of the bur. He made a strip of fabric covered with hundreds of tiny hooks. On another strip of fabric, he made hundreds of tiny loops. The two strips stuck together like burs on a sock. This was the beginning of Velcro. Now, Velcro is used not only for fastening clothes, but also for such diverse tasks as attaching gear inside spacecraft and sealing the chambers of artificial hearts.

- *What part of a plant is a bur?*
- *What are other plant parts, and what are their functions?*
- *How do seed plants reproduce?*

4·1 Roots of Seed Plants

Most of the plants that you are familiar with are seed plants. Grasses, trees, cactuses, and roses are all types of seed plants. A *seed plant* is a plant that reproduces by forming seeds.

As with animals, some types of plants are considered successful. Seed plants are the most successful plants on land. They are found in deserts and tropics, on mountains and in valleys, throughout the world. Which of the seed plants shown in Figure 4·1 grow in your area of the country?

Seed plants are most important to humans as a source of food. Animals raised for food also eat seed plants. Thus humans depend either directly or indirectly on seed plants as a food source.

The cells of seed plants are grouped into tissues and organs. You learned that a tissue is a group of cells that are similar in structure and function. One type of tissue found in seed plants is vascular (VAS kyuh luhr) tissue. *Vascular tissue* is made up of tubelike cells. It carries food, water, and minerals within a plant. Recall that an organ is a group of two or more tissues that work together to perform a function. The organs of seed plants include roots, stems, leaves, and flowers.

Figure 4·1

A variety of seed plants: rainbow cactus *(A)*, grass *(B)*, lobster claw *(C)*, and pine tree *(D)*.

KINDS OF ROOTS

A **root** is an organ that anchors a plant in the ground and that absorbs water and minerals from the soil. Plants have either a taproot system or a fibrous root system. A *taproot system* has a single, large root—the taproot—that grows straight down. Smaller roots branch out from the taproot. Taproots anchor a plant firmly in the ground. The dandelion, a common weed, is an example of a plant with a taproot system. Taproots such as carrots, beets, and turnips are used as food by people.

Notice in Figure 4·2 that a *fibrous root system* has many roots that are all about the same size. These roots spread out in all directions near the surface of the soil. Fibrous roots do not anchor the plant as well as do taproots. However, more soil particles cling to fibrous roots than to taproots. Soil is thus held in place.

STRUCTURE AND FUNCTIONS OF ROOTS

Vascular tissue in a root carries water and minerals from the soil to the stem. There are two types of vascular tissue: xylem (zī lehm) and phloem (FLOH ehm). **Xylem** is a vascular tissue that carries water and minerals from the root to the stem and leaves. Locate the xylem in the cross section of the root shown in Figure 4·3. What shape does the xylem form? Surrounding the xylem is the phloem. **Phloem** is a vascular tissue that carries food throughout a plant. Around the xylem and phloem is a tissue that stores food. Surrounding these tis-

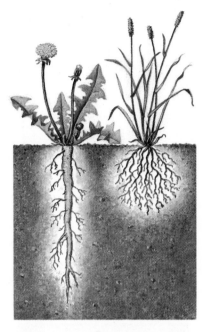

Figure 4·2

Types of root systems: taproot *(left)* and fibrous root *(right)*. Why, do you think, are plants with fibrous root systems often planted on steep slopes?

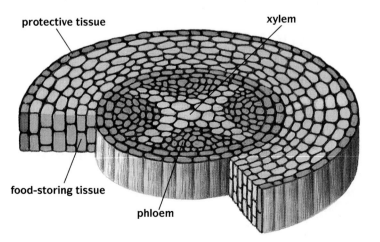

protective tissue

xylem

food-storing tissue

phloem

Figure 4·3

Cross section of a typical root.

sues is an outer tissue layer that covers and protects the root.

Look at the root of the radish seedling shown in Figure 4·4A. At the tip of the root is the root cap. The *root cap* prevents the root tip from being injured as it grows through the soil.

Find the fuzzy areas on the sides of the root in Figure 4·4A. These areas are made up of many tiny root hairs. Figure 4·4B shows an enlargement of these root hairs. *Root hairs* are threadlike extensions of cells on the surface of a root. Root hairs grow in the spaces between soil particles where they absorb water and minerals. Root hairs increase the surface area through which roots absorb materials.

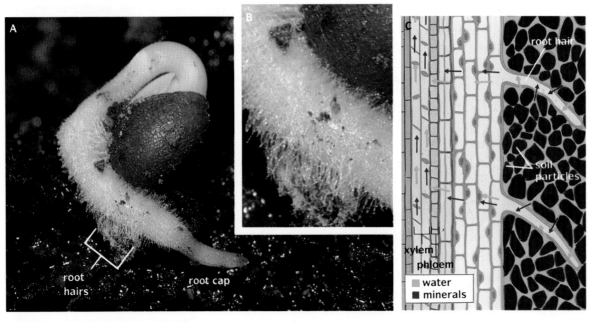

Figure 4·4

Radish seedling *(A)* and magnification of root hairs *(B)*. Water and minerals are absorbed through the root hairs and travel through the root *(C)*.

ADAPTATIONS OF ROOTS

The structure of roots varies in different types of plants. The type of root can be an adaptation of a plant to its environment. Recall that an adaptation is a trait that makes an organism better able to survive in its environment.

A root that grows above the soil and extends out from the stem is one type of adaptation. Orchids develop roots from the part of the stem that is above the ground. These roots can absorb dew and rain

The famine that has existed in several African countries has been worsened by the growth of witchweed, a parasitic plant. Witchweed attaches to the roots of some plants grown for food. These plants include corn, sorghum, and millet. They are the host plants for the witchweed.

Soon after a witchweed seed sprouts, it releases a chemical that diffuses through the soil. When it reaches a nearby host plant, this chemical digests some of the cells on the surface of the root of that plant. These partly digested root cells produce a special chemical that is a signal to the witchweed. The chemical causes the witchweed to grow a special organ by which it attaches to the host plant. The witchweed receives its food through the host's root system.

The witchweed does not kill its host. Rather, the host plant is unable to form fruits and, thus, cannot reproduce. A crop that is attacked by witchweed produces only a few seeds for the next season. These seeds often cannot grow into strong new plants.

Scientists are working on a new technology that could help to stop the witchweed. They are developing a chemical that would force the witchweed to produce its attaching organ before it finds a host plant. Without food from a host, the witchweed would die.

water. Roots that develop along the stems of climbing vines, such as English ivy, anchor the plant to a support. Corn plants may form aboveground roots called prop roots which grow down from the stem into the soil. Like other roots, prop roots absorb water and minerals and support the plant.

The roots of desert plants may spread over a wide area. When it rains, the showers are brief and heavy. The widespread root system of desert plants allows them to take in water quickly.

REVIEW

1. What is the basic structure of a root?
2. What are the functions of roots?
3. How do the functions of xylem and phloem differ?
4. What is the difference between a taproot system and a fibrous root system? Give examples of plants that have these root systems.

CHALLENGE Gardeners suggest that plants that are to be moved be dug out of the ground with a ball of soil left around the roots. Explain why this is a good suggestion.

4·2 Stems and Leaves of Seed Plants

A **stem** is an organ that supports the leaves or flowers of a plant. Vascular tissue within a stem carries food and water to the parts of a plant. Many stems are green and can make food by photosynthesis. Some plant stems store food.

HERBACEOUS STEMS

As shown in Figure 4·5, there are two types of stems: herbaceous (her BAY shuhs) and woody. A stem that is soft and green and that bends easily is called a *herbaceous stem*. Most annuals have herbaceous stems. Annuals are plants that grow, reproduce, and die during one growing season. Dandelions and petunias are examples of annuals.

In herbaceous stems the xylem and phloem are grouped together in *vascular bundles*. The "strings" in a celery stalk are an example of vascular bundles. The bundles extend up and down the plant, from the roots to the stem and leaves. In addition to carrying materials, vascular bundles provide support to the plant.

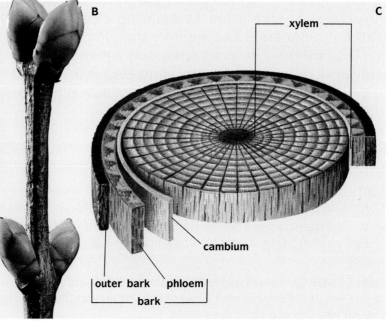

Figure 4·5

Herbaceous stem *(A)* and a woody stem *(B)*. Cross section of a woody stem *(C)*.

WOODY STEMS

A *woody stem* is a stem that contains many xylem cells with thick cell walls. Perennials are plants such as trees and shrubs and have woody stems. Perennials are plants that live for several years. Plants with woody stems grow taller and thicker each year.

In most woody stems the xylem forms a series of rings. Notice in Figure 4·5C that the outermost layer of a woody stem is the bark. The bark itself is made up of two layers: an outer protective layer and an inner layer made up of phloem. The center of the stem is made up of rings of xylem. All the layers of xylem tissue together form wood. As you can see in Figure 4·5C, xylem makes up the bulk of the stem and is the main source of support for the plant. Between the xylem and the phloem is the cambium (KAM bee uhm). **Cambium** is a layer of dividing cells that produce new xylem and phloem cells. The growth of these new cells causes the stem to increase in diameter.

Figure 4·6

Annual rings, formed of spring wood and summer wood *(left)*. Enlargement of rings *(right)*.

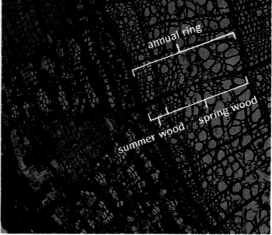

The layers of xylem that grow each year form *annual rings*. An annual ring is made up of one ring of spring wood and one ring of summer wood. Look at Figure 4·6 *right*. How do the cells of summer wood look different from those of spring wood? By counting the annual rings, you can estimate the age of a woody stem.

Figure 4·7

The main parts of a leaf and magnification of stomates.

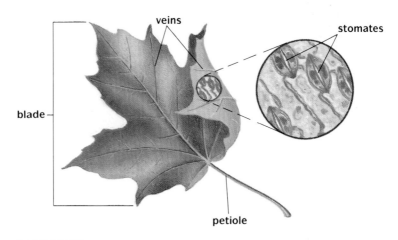

veins

stomates

blade

petiole

LEAVES

A **leaf** is a plant organ in which food is made by photosynthesis. Most leaves consist of two parts. The wide, flat part of a leaf is the **blade**. The stalk that joins the blade to the stem is the **petiole** (PEHT-ee ohl). Find these two structures in Figure 4·7. The lines or ridges on the surface of the blade are the veins. A **vein** is a bundle of vascular tissue that carries materials to and from a leaf.

On the lower surface of a leaf, and sometimes on the upper surface, are small openings called **stomates** (STOH mayts). Carbon dioxide passes into the leaf, and water vapor and oxygen pass out through the stomates.

Leaves may either be broad and flat or be needlelike. Most flowering plants have broad, flat leaves. Maple trees and strawberry plants are examples of broad-leaved plants. Trees such as pines, firs, and spruces have needlelike leaves. The compact shape of the pine leaves, as shown in Figure 4·8B, helps to prevent water loss. Plants with needlelike leaves can thrive in dry climates.

stoma (mouth)

Figure 4·8

Two types of leaves: broad *(A)* and needlelike *(B)*.

REVIEW

1. What are the functions of stems?
2. How do woody stems differ from herbaceous stems in structure and appearance?
3. What are the main parts of a leaf? Give a brief description of each part.

CHALLENGE Two forest rangers are looking at the annual rings of a tree. Some annual rings are narrow, and others are wide. Account for the differences in width.

4·3 Food Making and Energy Release

All organisms need energy to grow and reproduce. Animals get energy by eating food. This food may be in the form of plants or of other animals. But plants produce their own food. By the process called **photosynthesis** (foh tuh SIHN thuh sihs), plants use light energy from the sun to make food.

The energy used by all living things comes originally from the sun. But many organisms cannot use this light energy directly. Plants must first change the light energy to chemical energy in the form of food. By making food, plants make energy from the sun available to other organisms.

STRUCTURE OF LEAVES

The structure of a leaf is adapted to carry out photosynthesis. Find the epidermis in the cross section of the leaf shown in Figure 4·9. The **epidermis** (ehp uh DER mihs) is the protective outer tissue layer of a leaf.

The **palisade** (pal uh SAYD) **layer** is a layer of columnlike cells below the upper epidermis. Below the palisade layer is a layer of loosely packed cells called the **spongy layer**. Locate these layers in Figure 4·9. The cells of the palisade and spongy layers

photo- (light)
syn- (together)

epi- (on)
dermis (skin)

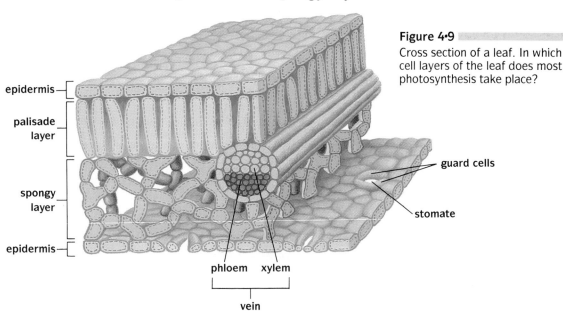

Figure 4·9

Cross section of a leaf. In which cell layers of the leaf does most photosynthesis take place?

epidermis
palisade layer
spongy layer
epidermis
guard cells
stomate
phloem   xylem
vein

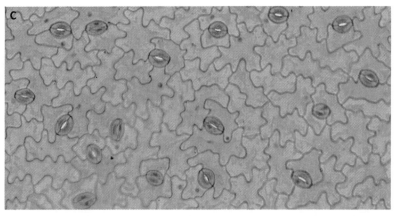

Figure 4·10

Guard cells full of water form an open stomate *(A)*. Guard cells that have little water form a closed stomate *(B)*. Stomates on the lower surface of a leaf *(C)*.

contain many structures called chloroplasts (KLAWR uh plasts). It is within the *chloroplasts* that photosynthesis takes place.

Gases pass into and out of the leaf through the stomates. Notice in Figure 4·9 that a stomate is surrounded by two guard cells. The **guard cells** control the opening and closing of the stomate. When the guard cells are full of water, they swell and bend outward, as shown in Figure 4·10*A*. The space between the guard cells is the open stomate. When the guard cells lose water, they shrink and move together, as you can see in Figure 4·10*B*. The stomate is thus closed. How do you think the closing of the stomate benefits the plant?

PHOTOSYNTHESIS

Photosynthesis is a very complex process. It is summarized in the following equation.

carbon dioxide + water + light $\xrightarrow{\text{chlorophyll}}$ sugar + oxygen

Carbon dioxide and water are the raw materials needed for photosynthesis. Sunlight is the source of energy. *Chlorophyll* (KLAWR uh fihl), a green pigment found in the chloroplasts, captures light energy. In a series of chemical changes, sugar is formed. Oxygen is also given off in this process.

Research has shown that photosynthesis takes place in two distinct stages. Look at Figure 4·11 as you read about these stages. The first stage, the *light reactions*, is a series of chemical changes that require light. In the light reactions, chlorophyll captures the energy of sunlight. Some of this energy is used to split water into oxygen and hydrogen. The oxygen is then released into the air. The rest of the energy captured by chlorophyll is stored as chemical energy.

The second stage, the *dark reactions*, is a series of reactions that do not require light. These reactions use the chemical energy stored during the light reactions. This energy is used to combine carbon dioxide and hydrogen to form sugar.

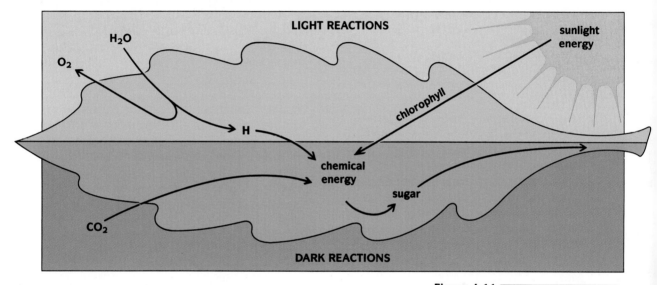

Figure 4·11
Photosynthesis: light reactions and dark reactions.

RESPIRATION

Plants use some of the sugar formed in photosynthesis to supply energy for their life processes. The process by which foods are broken down and energy is released is called **respiration**. Most living things carry out respiration. Respiration is summarized by this equation.

sugar + oxygen → carbon dioxide + water + energy

During respiration, sugar is broken down as it reacts with oxygen. Carbon dioxide, water, and energy are released. Much of the energy that is stored in sugar is released during respiration. Some of this energy is given off as heat, but most of it is stored in another, more usable form of chemical energy. This chemical energy can then be used by the plant for growth and reproduction.

ACTIVITY   How Do Stomates Function?

OBJECTIVE
Observe the structure and function of stomates in a lettuce leaf.

MATERIALS
hand lens, lettuce leaf soaking in distilled water, metric ruler, forceps, dropper, microscope slide, coverslip, microscope, salt water, paper towel, clock or watch

PROCEDURE
A. Use a hand lens to observe both the upper and lower surfaces of a lettuce leaf. Look for small openings on the leaf surfaces.

B. Tear a 5-cm-square piece off the lettuce leaf. Bend the square of lettuce in half. Use forceps to remove a thin layer of epidermis.

C. Use a dropper to place a drop of distilled water on a microscope slide. Place the thin layer of epidermis in the drop. Cover with a coverslip. Observe the epidermis under low power of a microscope. Locate the pairs of bean-shaped guard cells. Make a drawing of the epidermis, showing at least two pairs of guard cells. In your drawing include several epidermal cells. Label a guard cell, a chloroplast, a stomate, and an epidermal cell.

D. Use the dropper to place a drop of salt water next to the edge of the coverslip, as shown in the drawing. Touch a piece of

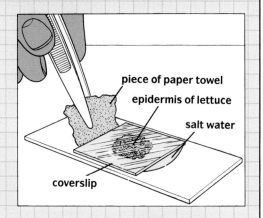

piece of paper towel
epidermis of lettuce
salt water
coverslip

paper towel to the edge of the coverslip on the side opposite the drop of salt water, as shown. The salt water should flow under the coverslip. Wait 5 minutes, and then observe the epidermis under low power of the microscope. Make a drawing of the epidermis. Label the same structures labeled in step **C**.

RESULTS AND CONCLUSIONS
1. How are guard cells different from other epidermal cells?
2. Describe how the guard cells and stomates looked as you observed them in step **C**.
3. Compare the appearance of the guard cells and stomates in step **C** with their appearance in step **D**. How did the salt water affect the guard cells and stomates?

REVIEW
1. Give a brief description of each of the tissue layers of a leaf.
2. What happens during the light reactions and dark reactions of photosynthesis?
3. Compare the processes of photosynthesis and respiration, in terms of the materials used, the products formed, and the use of energy.

CHALLENGE You have been given leaves from two different kinds of plants. One plant is from a very hot, dry region. The other plant is from a warm, moist region. Describe how the structure of the leaves might differ.

4·4 Transport of Materials

All living cells of a plant need energy. The energy is supplied by sugar made during photosynthesis. Water is also needed by all the living cells of a plant. How do the cells throughout a plant get the food and water they need?

In complex plants, vascular tissue moves these materials throughout the plant. Simple plants, however, do not have vascular tissue. Materials pass slowly from cell to cell. Some simple plants, such as algae (AL jee), can grow to be quite large. In a large simple plant, it takes a long time for substances to move from one part of the plant to another.

VASCULAR TISSUE

All complex plants, including ferns and seed plants, have vascular tissue. As you have learned, vascular tissue includes xylem and phloem. Recall that xylem carries water and minerals up from the roots. Phloem carries sugar made in the leaves to the other parts of the plant.

Figure 4·12 shows the location of the vascular tissue in a plant. Notice that both the xylem and the phloem extend from the tips of the roots to the tips

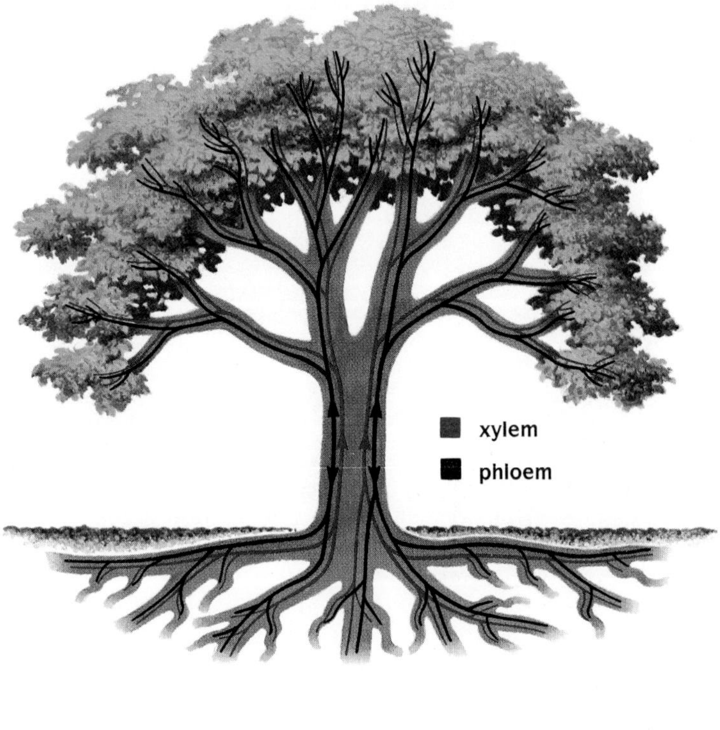

After completing this section, you will be able to

- **compare** transport in simple and complex plants.
- **describe** transpiration and **identify** the cause of wilting.

The key term in this section is **transpiration**

■ xylem
■ phloem

Figure 4·12
The location of xylem and phloem in a plant. Notice that phloem carries materials both up and down. In which direction are water and minerals carried in the xylem?

trans- (across)
spirare (breathe)

of the leaves. Both tissues pass through all parts of the plant.

Xylem cells are joined end-to-end, forming long tubes. After xylem tissue forms, the xylem cells die, leaving behind the tubular cell walls. Water can then flow through these hollow tubes.

Phloem cells also form long tubes, but the cells within these tubes remain alive. In contrast to mature xylem tissue, which consists of empty cell walls, phloem is a living tissue. Excess sugar from the leaves of a plant is carried away by the phloem. The phloem may carry the sugar down to the stem and roots or up to the branches.

TRANSPIRATION

Water enters a plant through the root hairs and passes through the xylem to the stem and leaves. Some of the water is used by the plant. The excess is given off as water vapor, which passes out of the plant through the stomates. The loss of water through the stomates is called **transpiration**. Have you ever visited a greenhouse and noticed that the air inside was very humid? The humid air is due to the large amount of water given off by the plants in transpiration. Figure 4·13 shows water on the inner surface of a glass jar. The water droplets formed as a result of transpiration.

Figure 4·14*A* shows what happens when water is lost through transpiration more quickly than it is

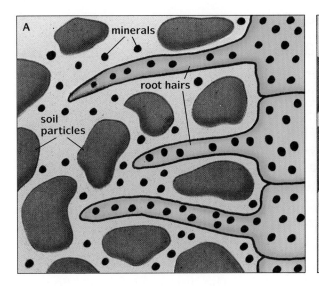
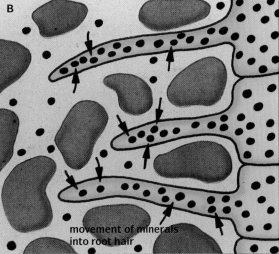

Figure 4·15
Active transport of minerals into root hairs.

absorbed by the roots. As the plant cells lose water, the leaves, stems, and flowers droop, in a condition called *wilting*. How does the plant in Figure 4·14 look after watering?

ACTIVE TRANSPORT

Most of the minerals needed by plants are dissolved in the water that is in soil. However, minerals are often more crowded inside the root hairs than in the soil. For this reason, the minerals cannot simply flow into the root. But root hairs can absorb minerals from the soil even under these conditions. Plants can use energy to bring substances into the root hairs. This movement of substances from an area where they are less crowded to an area where they are more crowded is called *active transport*. Figure 4·15 shows active transport of minerals into root hairs.

REVIEW

1. How does transport of materials in simple plants differ from that in seed plants?
2. What occurs during transpiration?
3. What causes wilting?

CHALLENGE You have learned that some of the water that is absorbed by plants is lost through the leaves. Design an experiment to find out how much water is lost through a plant's leaves in a given period.

4·5 Reproduction in Seed Plants

A **seed** is the product of sexual reproduction in a seed plant. There are two types of seed plants. One type, which includes plants such as pines and spruces, forms seeds within a cone. A cone is a reproductive structure made of overlapping, woody scales. The most common type of seed plant, however, is the flowering plant. Flowering plants form seeds within a reproductive organ called a **flower**.

FLOWER STRUCTURE

Figure 4·16 shows the parts of a typical flower. Locate each flower part as you read about it. A **sepal** (SEE puhl) is a leaflike part found at the base of a flower. Above the sepals are colored sructures called **petals**. The petals surround and protect the reproductive parts of a flower.

A **stamen** (STAY muhn) is a male reproductive structure of a flower. A stamen is made up of two parts. The long stalk is called a filament (FIHL uh-muhnt). The anther, the sac at the end of the stamen, produces and holds pollen grains. How many stamens are shown in Figure 4·16?

A **pistil** (PIHS tuhl) is a female reproductive structure of a flower. There may be one or more pistils, depending on the type of plant. Find the

Figure 4·16

Structure of a typical flower. What are the parts of the pistil?

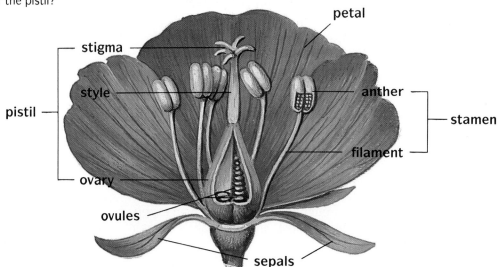

92

OBJECTIVE

Observe the structure of a flower.

MATERIALS

gladiolus flower, forceps, hand lens, dropper, water, microscope slide, scalpel, coverslip, microscope

PROCEDURE

A. Locate the green sepals of a gladiolus flower. Observe the petals just inside the sepals.

B. Use forceps to remove the petals and sepals. Find the long, slender stamens. Identify an anther and a filament. Use a hand lens to look at the structure of the stamens.

C. Locate the pistil in the center of the stamens. Identify the stigma, style, and ovary of the pistil.

D. Make a drawing of the stamens and pistil. Label the following parts: stamen, anther, filament, pistil, stigma, style, ovary.

E. Use a dropper to place a drop of water on a microscope slide. Use the forceps to remove one anther and place it in the water. Use a scalpel to cut open the anther. **Caution:** Always use great care in handling a scalpel. Direct the edge of the blade *away* from your body. Work on a firm surface. Hold the anther with the forceps, and shake the anther so that pollen grains fall into the water on the slide. Remove the anther, and cover the water and pollen grains with a coverslip. Examine the pollen under low and high power of a microscope. Make a drawing of several pollen grains.

F. Use the forceps to remove the pistil from the flower. Use the scalpel to cut open the ovary at the base of the pistil. Locate the ovules, and examine them with the hand lens. Count the number of ovules.

RESULTS AND CONCLUSIONS

1. Which does the flower have in greater quantity, pollen grains or ovules? How might this difference in number be an advantage for pollination?

2. Describe the stamens you examined. What two structures make up a stamen?

3. Describe the shape of the pollen grains you observed.

pistil at the center of the flower. Notice that the pistil is made up of three parts: the stigma (STIHG-muh), the style, and the ovary (OH vuhr ee). The upper part of a pistil is the stigma, a sticky structure on which pollen grains land. The enlarged base of a pistil is the ovary. Inside the ovary are ovules, small round structures from which seeds develop. The stalk that joins the stigma and the ovary is the style.

POLLINATION

In flowering plants the male and female reproductive cells develop within the flower. Sperm cells are produced by pollen grains. Egg cells are produced in the ovules.

Millions of pollen grains are produced in the anther. When ripe, the anther splits open, releasing the pollen grains. For a seed to develop, pollen must pass from the anther to the pistil. This process is called *pollination*.

Most flowers are pollinated by insects, but some are pollinated by other animals or by the wind. The flowers of most grasses and many trees are pollinated by the wind. Wind-pollinated flowers, such as those of the alder shown in Figure 4·17*A*, usually are small and lack brightly colored petals. Wind-pollinated flowers also lack a strong, sweet scent. The large amounts of pollen produced by wind-pollinated flowers cause some people to sneeze and to have itchy, watery eyes.

Figure 4·17

The alder *(A)* has wind-pollinated flowers. How does the bee *(B)* pollinate flowers?

Flowers that are pollinated by insects or birds usually have brightly colored petals. These flowers produce a sweet substance called nectar. Animals such as bees, ants, and birds are attracted by the petals or the nectar of the flowers. As these animals enter a flower, they may brush against the anthers. Notice the pollen grains stuck to the bee in Figure 4·17*B*. As the bee enters other flowers, it may transfer pollen to those flowers.

SEED AND FRUIT FORMATION

Once a pollen grain reaches the stigma, it begins to grow a pollen tube. This tube grows through the style to the ovary. Locate the pollen tubes in Figure

4·18*A*. A sperm travels down a pollen tube and joins with an egg cell inside an ovule. The joining of egg cell and sperm is called *fertilization*.

After fertilization the ovules grow into seeds. The main parts of a seed are the embryo, stored food, and a seed coat. An **embryo** is the earliest stage of growth in a many-celled organism. In Figure 4·18*B*, notice the tiny leaf, stem, and root that make up the embryo. The part of the seed called a *cotyledon* (kaht uh LEE duhn) contains stored food. The embryo uses this food until the plant grows and makes its own food by photosynthesis.

While the ovules develop into mature seeds, the ovary develops into a fruit. A **fruit** is a ripened ovary that contains one or more mature seeds. The fruit protects a seed from disease and insects. You have probably eaten many types of fruits, such as peaches and apples. Figure 4·19 shows some of the stages in the growth of cherry fruits. Many foods that are often called vegetables are actually fruits. Cucumbers and tomatoes are two such fruits.

Fruits sometimes help to scatter seeds away from the parent plant. Animals, wind, and water can carry fruits, as well as seeds, over long distances. What is the advantage to a plant of scattering its seeds?

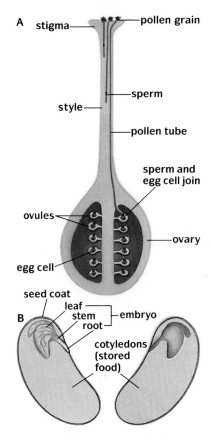

Figure 4·18

Growth of pollen tubes *(A)*; parts of a seed *(B)*.

Figure 4·19

Cherry blossoms (*A* and *B*), developing cherries *(C)* and ripe cherries *(D)*.

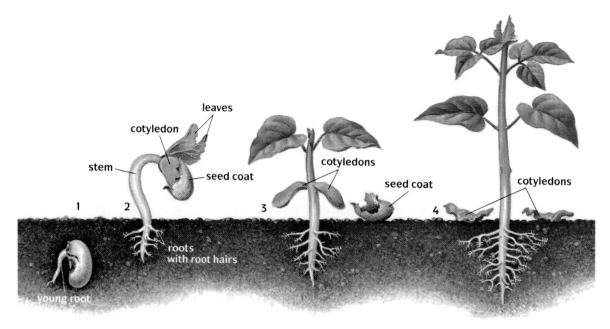

Figure 4·20

Stages in the germination of a bean seed. When can cotyledons drop off without harming the plant?

GERMINATION

Seeds germinate when conditions are right for growth. *Germination* is the growth of a plant embryo into a young plant. Water, oxygen, and proper temperature are needed for seeds to germinate. Look at Figure 4·20 as you read about germination.

1. Water enters the seed, and the seed swells; this causes the seed coat to split. A young root pushes out through the seed coat.
2. Root hairs and side roots develop. A short stem pushes the cotyledons and small leaves aboveground. Photosynthesis begins.
3. The roots and stem lengthen as leaves grow larger and open. The seed coat falls off. Cotyledons shrivel up as the stored food is used.
4. New leaves grow. The cotyledons fall off. The seedling will develop into a mature plant.

REVIEW

1. What are the main structures of a flower? Describe each flower part.
2. How are flowers pollinated?
3. What are the steps of seed formation after a flower has been pollinated?
4. Describe the germination of a seed.

CHALLENGE What might happen to a seedling if the cotyledons were to fall off before the young leaves developed?

4·6 Plant Growth and Behavior

PLANT HORMONES

Growth in plants differs from growth in animals. Most animals grow only when they are young. But many plants continue to grow throughout their life cycle. They grow taller and become larger in diameter. Growth occurs in the tips of roots and stems, in young leaves, and in developing fruits.

Many of the activities of plants are controlled by chemicals called hormones. A **hormone** is a chemical that is produced in one part of an organism and controls an activity in another part of the organism. Hormones are formed in tiny amounts within rapidly growing tissues, such as in the tips of stems and roots. After the hormones are formed, they are carried to other parts of the plant.

The most important plant hormones are the auxins (AWK sihnz). An *auxin* is a hormone that controls plant growth and development. Auxins cause plant cells to lengthen. Some auxins help to start root growth. Auxins may also prevent growth in some parts of a plant.

People working with plants have many uses for plant hormones. Plant hormones may be put on the ends of plant cuttings to start root growth. These chemicals are also used to cause fruit production in

After completing this section, you will be able to
- **identify** the areas where plant growth occurs.
- **define** the term hormone.
- **describe** how growth is related to tropisms and **give examples** of tropisms.

The key terms in this section are
hormone
tropism

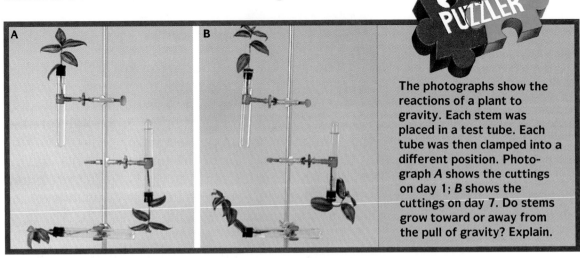

PUZZLER

The photographs show the reactions of a plant to gravity. Each stem was placed in a test tube. Each tube was then clamped into a different position. Photograph *A* shows the cuttings on day 1; *B* shows the cuttings on day 7. Do stems grow toward or away from the pull of gravity? Explain.

plants such as tomatoes and apples. Auxins sprayed on potatoes and onions prevent sprouting. Some hormones that cause plants to grow rapidly are used as weed killers. How do you think this type of hormone would kill weeds?

TROPISMS

Hormones also help plants respond to their environment. Hormones cause growth in certain areas of the plant in response to light or other factors. The growth of a plant toward or away from some outside factor is called a **tropism** (TROH pihz uhm).

trope (a turning)

Tropisms result from the actions of hormones. An outside factor can cause hormones to collect in one part of a plant. These hormones can cause cells in that part of the plant to grow longer. If the cells grow longer on one side of a stem than on the other side, the stem will bend.

Figure 4·21

A plant responds to light by growing toward the light source *(A)*. Auxins collect on the side of the plant away from the light source *(B)*, causing the stem to bend *(C)*.

The growth of a plant toward light is called *phototropism* (foh toh TROH pihz uhm). In Figure 4·21 you can see what happens inside a plant stem to cause it to grow toward light. When light strikes the plant stem, auxins collect in the cells on the side of the stem away from the light. The cells on this shady side grow longer than the cells on the lighted side. As the cells on the shady side grow longer, the stem bends toward the light.

Plants also show several other tropisms. The response of a plant to gravity is called *geotropism* (jee oh TROH pihz uhm). Roots grow toward the pull of gravity. The growth of plants toward water is called *hydrotropism* (HĪ droh TROH pihz uhm). How do you think hydrotropism might benefit a plant?

REVIEW

1. In what parts of plants does growth occur?
2. What is a plant hormone?
3. How do hormones cause stems to grow toward light?
4. Name and describe three types of tropisms.

CHALLENGE Design an experiment to find out whether plant roots respond to light.

CHAPTER SUMMARY

The main ideas in this chapter are listed below. Read these statements before you answer the Chapter Review questions.

- Roots anchor and support plants, absorb water and minerals, and carry materials to the stem. Some roots store food. Adaptations of roots help plants survive. (4·1)
- Stems support leaves, fruits, and flowers, and carry food, water, and minerals to all parts of a plant. (4·2)
- The two types of stems are herbaceous stems and woody stems. A leaf is a plant organ in which food is made. Gases move in and out of leaves through stomates. (4·2)
- The energy needed by all life forms is supplied directly or indirectly by organisms that carry on photosynthesis. Using light energy, plants combine water and carbon dioxide during photosynthesis. Sugar and oxygen are produced. In respiration, sugar joins with oxygen, producing carbon dioxide and water, and releasing energy. (4·3)

- Transport of materials in seed plants occurs in the xylem and phloem. Wilting occurs when water is lost by transpiration more quickly than it is absorbed through the roots. (4·4)
- The flower is the reproductive organ of most seed plants. Pollination is the transfer of pollen from the anther to the pistil. Seeds form in the ovary of a flower, which ripens into a fruit. A seed consists of an embryo, stored food, and a seed coat. Seeds are spread by wind, water, and animals. Germination is the growth of a plant embryo into a young plant. (4·5)
- Growth occurs only in certain parts of a plant. Chemicals called hormones help to control the growth of plants. A tropism is the growth of a plant toward or away from some outside factor. (4·6)

The key terms in this chapter are listed below. Use each term in a sentence that shows the meaning of the term.

blade	guard cells	phloem	sepal	tropism
cambium	hormone	photosynthesis	spongy layer	vein
embryo	leaf	pistil	stamen	xylem
epidermis	palisade layer	respiration	stem	
flower	petals	root	stomates	
fruit	petiole	seed	transpiration	

Chapter Review

VOCABULARY

Write the letter of the term that best matches the definition. Not all the terms will be used.

1. A tissue that carries water and minerals from the root to the leaves
2. The layer of cells that produce xylem and phloem in a stem
3. The part of the leaf that joins the blade to the stem
4. The process by which plants make their own food by using sunlight energy
5. The process by which foods are broken down and energy is released
6. A ripened ovary that contains seeds
7. The loss of water through the stomates of leaves
8. The male reproductive structure of a flower
9. Plant growth in response to an outside factor
10. A leaflike part at the base of a flower

a. cambium
b. flower
c. fruit
d. hormone
e. petiole
f. phloem
g. photosynthesis
h. respiration
i. sepal
j. spongy layer
k. stamen
l. transpiration
m. tropism
n. vein
o. xylem

CONCEPTS

Complete the following sentences.

1. The two types of vascular tissue in plants are _____ .
2. The bulk of a woody stem is made up of tissue called _____ .
3. In the light reactions of photosynthesis, chlorophyll captures _____ .
4. Simple plants differ from complex plants in that simple plants lack _____ tissue.
5. The most important type of plant hormones are the _____ .

Choose the term or phrase that best answers the question or completes the statement.

6. A single large root that grows straight down describes a
   a. root cap
   b. root hair
   c. fibrous root
   d. taproot
7. Which of the following is *not* a leaf part?
   a. vein
   b. petiole
   c. stigma
   d. blade
8. Which of the following is a useful product of respiration?
   a. energy
   b. sugar
   c. oxygen
   d. light

9. Which of the following conditions is usually *not* needed for seed germination?
   a. proper temperature   c. oxygen
   b. food outside the plant   d. water
10. The growth of plants toward water is called
   a. phototropism.   c. hydrotropism.
   b. geotropism.   d. auxin.

Answer the following in complete sentences.

11. What are the functions of roots?
12. Distinguish between woody stems and herbaceous stems.
13. Name the types of cells found in a leaf, and give the function of each.
14. Explain how guard cells control the opening and closing of stomates.
15. Compare the function of xylem with that of phloem.
16. Name three ways in which fruits and seeds are scattered.
17. List and describe three types of tropisms.

APPLICATION/ CRITICAL THINKING

1. Explain how cambium is related to an increase in the diameter of a woody stem.
2. Explain how a meat-eating animal depends on plants.
3. You have found a plant with tiny, unscented flowers. The petals of the flowers are not colored. What is the most likely way in which this plant would be pollinated? Explain your answer.

EXTENSION

1. Look for foods and seasonings in your house that come from seed plants. Name the part of the plant from which the foods and seasonings come.
2. Germinate a corn seedling, and allow the root to grow about 2.5 cm. Make a mark with ink about every 0.5 cm on the growing root. Measure the distance between the marks each day for a week. Which part of the root grows most rapidly?
3. Take photographs of wild flowers common in your area. Learn something about each type of flower. Give a slide presentation to your class, sharing information about each of the flowers shown.

CHAPTER 5

GENETICS

*H*ave you ever seen a goldfish like the one in the photograph? Notice the strange bumps on its head and the long, flowing tail. This goldfish was specially bred for these features. Several generations earlier, a male fish and a female fish having slightly longer or larger tails than normal were mated. The resulting offspring with the largest tails were mated with each other. The desired offspring from successive matings were also mated, resulting in fish with extremely large tails. In the same way, other fish were bred to have bumps and were mated with the fish having long tails.

- *On what scientific principles is this special breeding based?*
- *What is genetics?*
- *How might people benefit from the technology of genetic engineering?*

5·1 Heredity

Have you ever noticed how babies and children look like their parents? Look at the boy and his father in Figure 5·1A. In what ways does the boy look like his father?

People expect offspring, or young, to look like their parents. Many animals, such as puppies, also look like their parents. What features do the puppies shown in Figure 5·1B have in common with their mother?

Plants also look like their parent plants. Farmers rely on the fact that offspring will be much like their parents. A farmer might take seeds from a tomato plant that produces large tomatoes. The farmer expects that these seeds will grow into new plants that will also produce large tomatoes.

TRAITS

Organisms *inherit*, or receive, features from their parents. An inherited feature of an organism is also called a **trait**. There is much variety in the kinds of traits that living things have. The presence of five toes on a foot is an inherited trait of humans. A horse has just one toe on each foot. The presence of one toe is an inherited trait of some hoofed mammals, such as horses and zebras.

Figure 5·1

Offspring look like their parents.

The passing of traits from parents to young is called **heredity** (huh REHD uh tee). When organisms reproduce, many traits are passed to their young. Humans inherit many traits other than toe number. Some of these traits can be seen easily. They include eye color, hair color, skin color, and nose shape. Which of these traits did you observe in Figure 5·1A? Many of the things that organisms do are also inherited. Making food is part of the heredity of plants. Migrating is an inherited trait of some species of birds.

hereditas (heirship)

MENDEL

About 130 years ago, heredity was first studied in a scientific way. The scientific study of heredity is called **genetics** (juh NEHT ihks). Gregor Mendel is often called the father of genetics. Mendel was a monk who lived in Europe in the nineteenth century. He had training in mathematics and biology. Mendel studied the traits of pea plants that he grew in the garden of the monastery where he lived. Mendel's findings about the heredity of peas have been shown to apply to other organisms as well.

genesis (origin)

Some of the methods used by Mendel are still used in the modern study of heredity. To study inherited traits, two organisms must be mated. The mating of organisms to test for traits is called a *cross*. The results of a cross are the offspring. The traits of the offspring are then studied.

Figure 5·2
Gregor Mendel (1822–1884), the father of genetics.

Figure 5·3

The same trait appears in many generations when the organisms are purebred for that trait. This pea plant is purebred for green pods *(A)*. What color peas are found in each generation *(B)*?

Mendel made a good choice in using pea plants in his genetics experiments. There are several reasons why pea plants were a good choice. One reason is that it is easy to cross pea plants. Recall that pollination is the transfer of pollen from the male parts to the female parts of a flower. A single pea flower usually pollinates itself in a process called *self-pollination*. Mendel found that he could transfer pollen from one flower to another. This process is called *cross-pollination*. Thus, Mendel could cause mating between different pea plants.

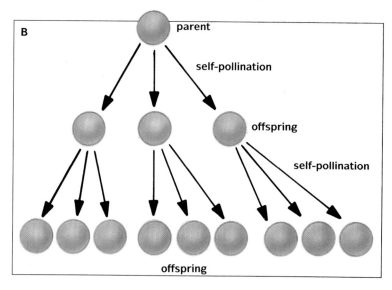

Mendel began his work by finding purebred pea plants. A **purebred** organism results from a cross of parents that have the same form of a trait and whose parents are also purebred for that trait. A self-pollinated, purebred pea plant will show the same form of a trait in all of its offspring. Each generation of purebred offspring that is self-pollinated will produce more purebred offspring. Look at the example shown in Figure 5·3*B*. A pea plant that is purebred for green peas produces only green peas each time it is self-pollinated.

MENDEL'S EXPERIMENTS

In one of his first experiments, Mendel crossed purebred tall pea plants and purebred short pea plants. What type of offspring came from mating

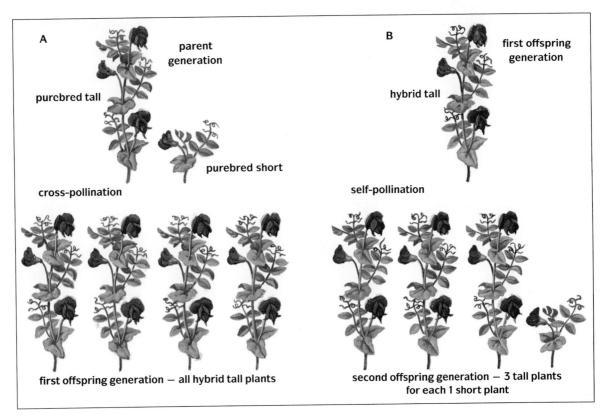

A parent generation

purebred tall

purebred short

cross-pollination

first offspring generation — all hybrid tall plants

B first offspring generation

hybrid tall

self-pollination

second offspring generation — 3 tall plants for each 1 short plant

tall pea plants and short ones? Look at this cross, shown in Figure 5·4. You may be surprised to see that all of the offspring were tall.

The tall plants produced in this cross are called hybrids (HĪ brihdz). A **hybrid** is an organism that results from a cross of parents that have different forms of a trait. Each one of the hybrid plants was as tall as its purebred tall parent. The purebred tall and purebred short parent plants are called the *parent generation*. The tall hybrids are called the *first offspring generation*.

Why were all of the hybrids tall? What happened to the trait for shortness? Mendel hypothesized that the shortness trait must have been present in the tall hybrids but somehow hidden.

In the next experiment, Mendel allowed the tall hybrids to self-pollinate. He then studied the offspring of the tall hybrids. These offspring are called the *second offspring generation*. Figure 5·4B shows the results of this experiment. You can see that there were three tall plants for each short plant.

Figure 5·4
The first and second offspring generations of Mendel's cross of tall and short pea plants.

hybrida (mongrel)

In guinea pigs the trait for black fur color is dominant over the trait for white fur color. Yet both parents of the white guinea pig shown have black fur. What traits do the parents carry? Think about dominant traits and recessive traits. What if one parent was black and the other parent was white? Would it still be possible for the guinea pig shown to be white? Explain.

The shortness trait had not disappeared. It was hidden in the tall hybrids.

Mendel concluded that each tall hybrid carried the traits of both the purebred tall parent and the purebred short parent. He called tallness a dominant trait. A **dominant trait** is one that prevents the showing of another trait. Tallness is a dominant trait in pea plants because it prevents shortness from showing in hybrid plants. Mendel called shortness a recessive trait. A **recessive trait** is one that is hidden in the presence of a dominant trait.

Mendel grew thousands of pea plants over a period of 8 years. The large number of plants grown and the accurate records kept by Mendel made his work the first truly scientific study of heredity.

REVIEW

1. What are some features that might be inherited traits of a dog?
2. What is the difference between heredity and genetics?
3. Describe Mendel's cross of purebred tall pea plants and purebred short pea plants. What type of plants resulted? What happened when these plants were self-pollinated?
4. What is the difference between a dominant trait and a recessive trait? Give an example of each.

CHALLENGE A single, hybrid tall pea plant is allowed to self-pollinate. Five of the seeds produced are planted. Is it possible that none of the resulting offspring will be short? Explain your answer.

5·2 Inheritance of Traits

After completing this section, you will be able to

- **restate** Mendel's basic findings about traits.
- **compare** phenotype and genotype.
- **describe** the use of a Punnett square.

The key terms in this section are
genotype
phenotype

MENDEL'S RESULTS

In his work with pea plants, Mendel studied pairs of traits. Figure 5•5 shows seven pairs of these traits. In each case, two purebred plants with different forms of the same trait were crossed to produce hybrid offspring. Then the hybrid offspring were self-pollinated to produce a second offspring generation. In this second generation there were about three times as many plants with one trait as there were with the opposite trait. He reported these conclusions about traits.

- Organisms inherit traits in pairs. An organism gets one of a pair of traits from each of its parents.
- Some traits are dominant; others are recessive. In hybrids, dominant traits cause recessive traits to be hidden. A recessive trait is shown only when no dominant trait is present.

Mendel used a system of symbols to stand for the various traits of pea plants. He used these symbols to show what traits an organism had and what traits were passed to offspring. Mendel's system is still used. Upper-case letters stand for dominant

Figure 5•5
Mendel studied these seven traits of pea plants.

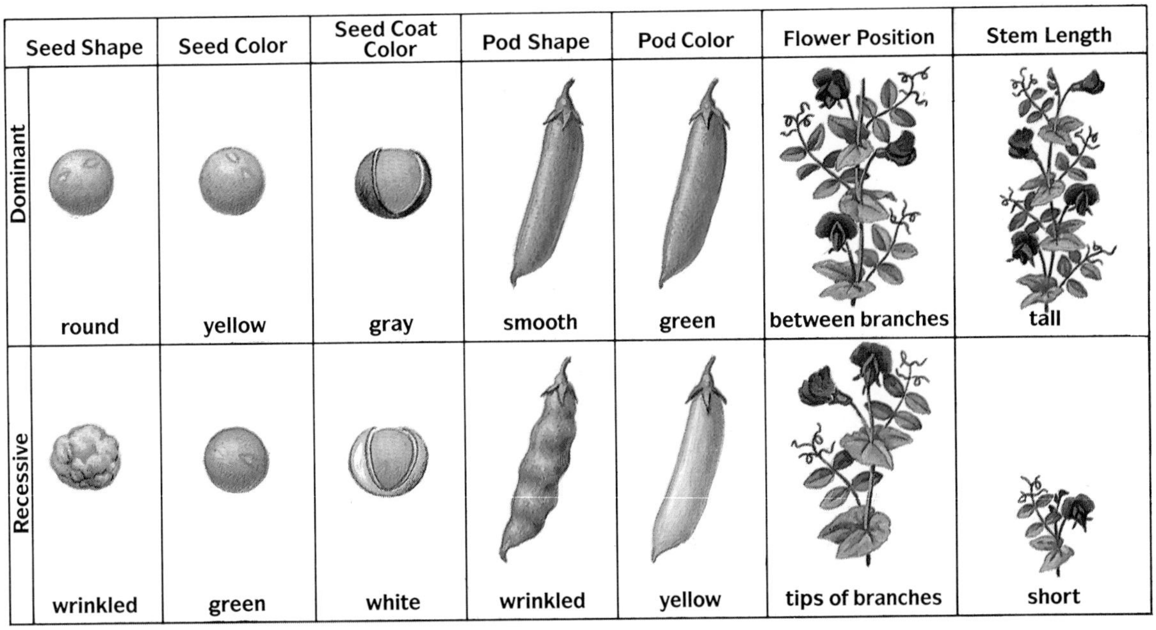

Seed Shape
Seed Color
Seed Coat Color
Pod Shape
Pod Color
Flower Position
Stem Length
Dominant
round
yellow
gray
smooth
green
between branches
tall
Recessive
wrinkled
green
white
wrinkled
yellow
tips of branches
short

traits. Lower-case letters stand for recessive traits. For example, *T* stands for tallness, and *t* stands for shortness. Notice that the same letter is used for the two contrasting forms of a trait.

Recall that an organism inherits traits from each parent. Thus organisms carry traits in pairs. Therefore the letters are used in pairs to show the traits of an organism. For example, *Tt* shows the two traits carried by a hybrid tall pea plant. What does *TT* represent?

Figure 5·6

Plants that look the same may carry different traits.

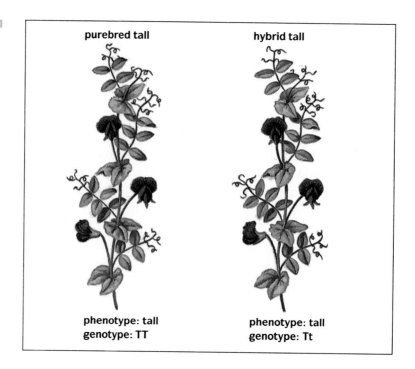

Symbols can also be used to show crosses. An *x* represents a cross, or a mating. The cross of a pure-bred tall pea plant with a purebred short plant can be shown as *TT x* tt. Recall that this cross produces all hybrid tall offspring. These hybrids, shown by *Tt*, are just as tall as the tall parent. Thus two organisms that look the same may differ in their inherited traits.

The appearance of an organism is its **phenotype** (FEE nuh tīp). Two organisms with different traits may have the same phenotype. Compare the two plants in Figure 5·6. They have the same phenotype, but they differ in the traits they carry.

The genetic makeup of an organism, or the traits that it carries, is called its **genotype** (JEEN-uh tīp). The genotype of a purebred tall plant is *TT*. The genotype of a hybrid tall plant is different, *Tt*. But plants with either of these genotypes will have the same phenotype—tall. What is the genotype of a plant whose phenotype is short?

PUNNETT SQUARES

The cross of hybrid tall plants can be shown by using a Punnett square. A *Punnett square* is a table that shows all the possible combinations of traits among the offspring produced in a cross.

Look at the incomplete Punnett square shown in Figure 5·7A. Notice that the traits of one parent are shown at the top of the square. The traits of the other parent are shown at the left side of the square. Figure 5·7B shows the possible results of mating two hybrid tall pea plants. Follow the colored arrows to see how the square is filled in. Each of the four boxes within the square shows one possible combination of traits in the offspring.

A Punnett square also shows the ratio of each type of offspring. A *ratio* is a comparison of two quantities. You can see in Figure 5·7B that one out

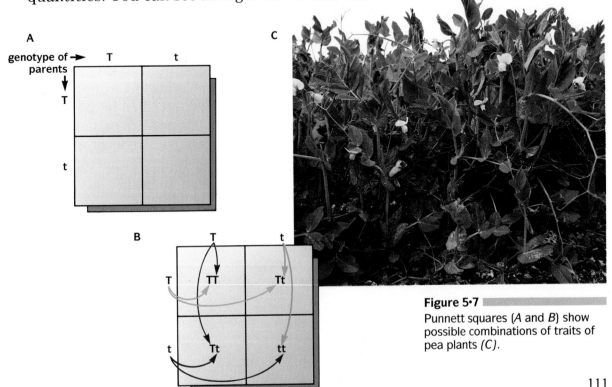

Figure 5·7

Punnett squares (*A* and *B*) show possible combinations of traits of pea plants *(C)*.

ACTIVITY How Is a Punnett Square Used?

Construct Punnett squares and **interpret** the results of a cross.

MATERIAL
metric ruler

PROCEDURE

A. In this activity you will use Punnett squares to find the genotype of a tall pea plant. Draw two Punnett squares.

B. A tall pea plant of unknown genotype is crossed with a purebred short pea plant.
  1. What are the possible genotypes of the tall pea plant?
  2. What is the genotype of the purebred short pea plant?

C. In one Punnett square, write the genotype of each parent plant. Assume that the tall parent is purebred.

D. In the other Punnett square, write the genotype of each parent plant, but this time assume that the tall parent is hybrid.

E. Complete each Punnett square to show the possible genotypes of the offspring of each cross. See Figure 5·7 if you need help.

F. The cross of the purebred short pea plant with the tall pea plant resulted in 213 seeds. All the seeds were planted, and 114 tall and 99 short plants resulted.

RESULTS AND CONCLUSIONS

1. Are any short offspring shown in the first Punnett square? If so, what ratio?
2. Are any short offspring shown in the second Punnett square? If so, what ratio?
3. Which square better fits the data given in step **F**?
4. What is the genotype of the tall parent plant? How do you know?

of every four offspring is expected to be purebred tall. Two of every four are expected to be hybrid tall. One of every four is expected to be purebred short. However, a Punnett square does not show what will or must happen in a single cross. The Punnett square gives the results expected from many matings.

REVIEW

1. What were Mendel's basic findings about traits?
2. What is the difference between genotype and phenotype?
3. What information is needed to set up a Punnett square? What do the central boxes of a Punnett square show?

CHALLENGE If a purebred tall pea plant is crossed with a hybrid tall pea plant, can any of the offspring be short? Explain your answer.

5·3 Chromosomes, Genes, and Heredity

It is now known that information within cells controls heredity. This information that allows traits to be passed from parents to offspring is stored in a substance called *DNA*. The information in DNA controls not only heredity but all the life processes of cells. Figure 5·8 shows a greatly enlarged model of DNA. This basic structure of DNA is the same in all living things.

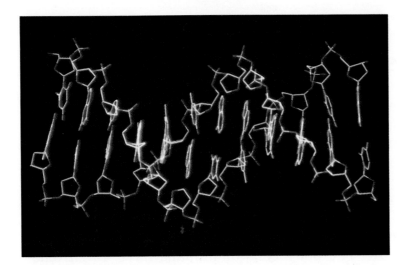

Figure 5·8
The structure of DNA as shown by computer.

CHROMOSOMES

DNA is found within cell structures called chromosomes (KROH muh sohmz). **Chromosomes** are threadlike cell structures that contain DNA and that control heredity. Many traits are carried by each chromosome. A section of a chromosome that carries the information for a single trait is called a **gene**. The part of a pea plant chromosome that carries the tallness trait is the gene for tallness. A chromosome can be thought of as a series of genes.

In most cells of an organism, chromosomes exist in pairs. Note in Figure 5·9 that genes for the same traits are carried in the same position on both chromosomes of the pair. The two chromosomes of a pair can carry genes for the same form of a given trait or for different forms of that trait.

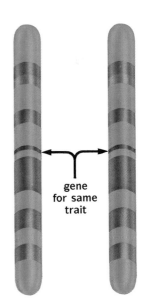

gene for same trait

Figure 5·9
Genes for a given trait are located in the same position on a pair of chromosomes.

113

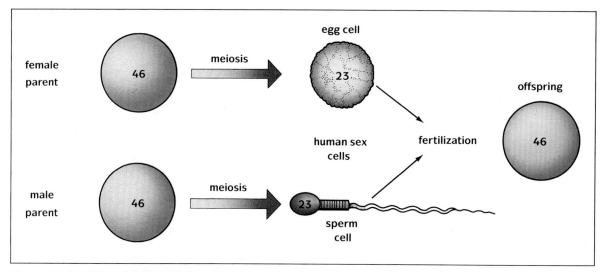

Figure 5·10

Sex cells have half the number of chromosomes as body cells have. How many chromosomes are there in the offspring?

SEX CELLS

There are two general types of cells found in many-celled organisms. Those cells that function in reproduction are called *sex cells*. All other cells are called *body cells*. Unlike body cells, sex cells have single copies of each chromosome.

The sex cells of males are called *sperm*, and the sex cells of females are *eggs*. Eggs and sperm both form by a kind of cell division called *meiosis*. In meiosis the number of chromosomes is reduced by half. The body cells of humans have 46 chromosomes, in 23 pairs. Each sex cell receives one chromosome from each pair. As you can see in Figure 5·10, human sperm and eggs each have 23 chromosomes, half as many as human body cells have.

When sex cells join in fertilization, they form the first body cell of a new organism. The new body cell gets half of its chromosomes from each parent. Thus an organism gets half of its traits from each parent, just as Mendel had thought.

REVIEW

1. How are genes and chromosomes related to heredity?
2. What is the difference in the number of chromosomes in body cells and in sex cells?
3. Describe the process that forms sex cells.

CHALLENGE What would happen if sex cells had the same number of chromosomes as body cells?

5·4 Sex Chromosomes

The sex of an animal is determined by its chromosomes. The chromosomes of a male differ from those of a female. In humans the difference is in only one of the 23 pairs of chromosomes. The two chromosomes that determine sex are called **sex chromosomes**.

Look at the chromosomes of a human male, shown in Figure 5·11. Locate the two chromosomes marked *X* and *Y*. The **X chromosome** is a sex chromosome found in the cells of both males and females. The **Y chromosome** is a chromosome found only in the cells of males. Each body cell of a male contains both an X chromosome and a Y chromosome. Each body cell of a female contains two X chromosomes.

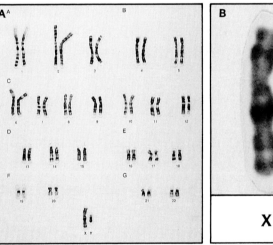
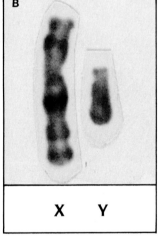

Figure 5·11
The 23 pairs of chromosomes of a human male *(A)*. Which chromosome is larger, the X chromosome or the Y chromosome *(B)*?

INHERITANCE OF SEX

Recall that sex cells are formed by meiosis, which reduces the number of chromosomes in half. Because female body cells contain two X chromosomes, each egg cell receives a single X chromosome. Body cells of males, however, contain both an X chromosome and a Y chromosome. Thus, half of the sperm cells receive an X chromosome, and half receive a Y chromosome.

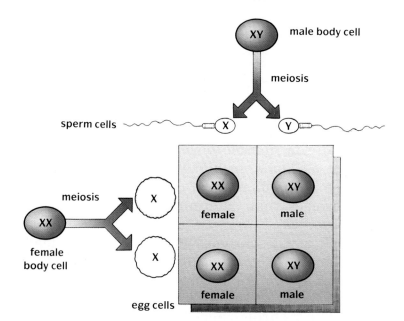

Figure 5·12

The sex of the offspring is determined by the sex chromosome in the sperm.

Look at the Punnett square in Figure 5·12. It shows how sex is inherited. When an egg cell combines with an X-carrying sperm cell, a female offspring develops. When an egg combines with a Y-carrying sperm cell, a male offspring develops. Thus, it is the presence of the X or Y chromosome in the sperm that determines the sex of the offspring. Notice that half of the sperm carry an X chromosome and half carry a Y. Thus there is a 50 percent chance that an egg will be fertilized by an X-carrying sperm. There is also a 50 percent chance that an egg will be fertilized by a Y-carrying sperm.

Because females have two X chromosomes, they have two copies of each gene found on the X chromosome. Look back at Figure 5·11B. Notice that the X chromosome is much larger than the Y chromosome. Some, but not all, of the genes found on the X chromosome are also found on the Y chromosome. Thus, males have only one copy of some genes.

SEX-LINKED TRAITS

A **sex-linked trait** is a trait that results from a gene found on the X chromosome but not on the Y chromosome. An example of a sex-linked trait in humans is a type of *color blindness*, the inability to see certain colors. A person having red-green color blindness cannot distinguish between red and green. Figure 5·13 shows one chart used to test for color blindness. What number do you see in the chart? A person with normal vision will see the number 29 in the chart. A color-blind person may see the number 70.

In humans, genes for red-green color vision are found on the X chromosome but not on the Y chromosome. Normal color vision is a dominant trait. Color blindness is recessive. Study the symbols used in Figure 5·14 showing the heredity of color vision. The trait for color vision is written as a smaller letter next to the X chromosome. Since there is no gene for color vision on the Y chromosome, no letter is written next to the Y. The genotype of a normal male is written as X^CY. The genotype of a color-blind male is written as X^cY.

The Punnett square in Figure 5·14 shows how color blindness is inherited. Both parents have normal vision. However, the mother carries one gene for normal vision and one for color blindness.

Figure 5·13
A test for red-green color blindness.

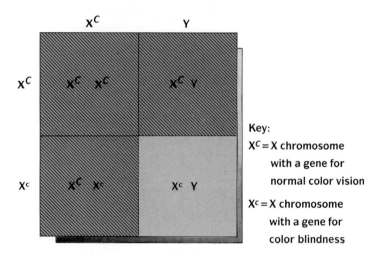

Figure 5·14
Color blindness is a sex-linked trait. Notice that both daughters have normal vision. Are their genotypes the same?

Key:
X^C = X chromosome with a gene for normal color vision
X^c = X chromosome with a gene for color blindness

Notice that unlike the daughters, one of the two sons is color blind. Human males are more likely to be red-green color blind than are females. Unlike a female, a male need only inherit one recessive gene for color blindness to show the trait. Thus, males are more likely than females to show recessive, sex-linked traits, such as color blindness.

Hemophilia (hee muh FIHL ee uh) is another example of a sex-linked trait in humans. *Hemophilia* is a disorder in which the blood does not clot

How Do Chromosomes Determine Sex?

OBJECTIVES

Demonstrate how chromosomes determine sex.

Identify differences in results by using large samples and small samples.

MATERIALS

2 large paper cups, 75 white beads, 25 colored beads, shoebox or other large container

PROCEDURE

A. Make a data table by writing the numbers 1 through 50 on a sheet of paper.

B. Obtain two large paper cups. Label one cup *female parent*. Label the other cup *male parent*.

C. Let a white bead represent an X chromosome. Let a colored bead represent a Y chromosome.

  1. What two beads represent a female?

  2. What two beads represent a male?

D. Place 50 white beads in the cup labeled *female parent*. Place 25 white beads and 25 colored beads in the cup labeled *male parent*.

E. Without looking, take one bead from each cup. Look at the pair of beads, and determine the sex of a child that has this combination of sex chromosomes.

Record the sex of the child next to the number 1 on your data table. Then place the pair of beads in a shoebox.

F. Repeat step **E** until all of the beads have been removed from both cups. Record the sex of the 50 children next to the numbers in your data table.

G. Count the total number of females and the total number of males. Record these totals in your data table. This is a large sample.

  3. How many females and how many males are represented in the large sample?

H. Look at your data table to find the sex of the children for numbers 1 through 4. This is a small sample. Compare the results of your small sample with those of your classmates.

RESULTS AND CONCLUSIONS

1. What was the ratio of females to males in the large sample?

2. What was the ratio of females to males in the small sample?

3. Based on your results and your classmates' results, explain why it is important to use large samples in genetic experiments.

properly. Like other sex-linked traits, hemophilia is caused by a recessive gene on the X chromosome. Why would a male be more likely to have hemophilia than would a female?

REVIEW

1. How do X chromosomes differ from Y chromosomes?

2. How do chromosomes determine sex in humans?

3. What is a sex-linked trait? Give two examples.

4. Why do sex-linked traits show more often in males than in females?

CHALLENGE Is it possible for a son to have inherited red-green color blindness from his father? Explain your answer.

5·5 Applications of Genetics

It is thought that farmers in the Middle East began growing wheat about 10,000 years ago. At first they used wild wheat. In time the wheat that the farmers grew became very different from wild wheat. Figure 5·15 shows wild wheat and a garden type of wheat. Notice that the seeds are much larger in the garden type of wheat than in the wild wheat.

SELECTIVE BREEDING

It is thought that garden wheat was produced from wild wheat by selective breeding. **Selective breeding** is the crossing of organisms with useful traits to make offspring that have the useful traits of both parents. The farmers may have found that large wheat seeds grew into plants that also had large seeds. After many years of choosing the best seeds, the wheat produced was more useful than the original wild wheat.

Selective breeding has become even more successful in recent times. Figure 5·15 shows some results of modern selective breeding. What useful traits do these organisms have?

Figure 5·15

Compare wild wheat *(A)* and garden wheat *(B)*. Selectively bred corn *(C)*, strawberries *(D)*, and sheep *(E)*.

You may have heard of some of the 1600 genetic disorders caused by a defect in a single gene. These include cystic fibrosis, muscular dystrophy, and hemophilia. One genetic disorder that you may not know about is called ADA. It is a disorder that makes the body unable to fight other diseases. A victim of ADA, such as the boy shown here, must not be in contact with other people. Even a minor illness can be fatal to a person born with ADA.

Researchers are developing techniques to cure some genetic disorders. One method, called gene therapy, involves replacing the defective gene with a healthy one.

Gene therapy may provide a cure for ADA. Researchers have identified the defective gene that causes ADA. Using genetic engineering, they have grown copies of the healthy human gene. Their goal is to transfer the healthy gene to the cells of people who have ADA.

Figure 5·16

One form of genetic engineering.

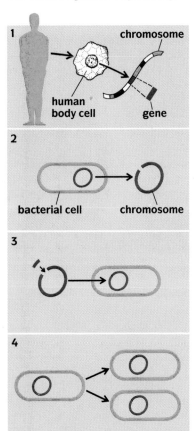

GENETIC ENGINEERING

Recently a procedure called genetic engineering has been developed. **Genetic engineering** is the technology of transferring genes from one organism to another. There are several different methods of genetic engineering. The movement of genes from other organisms into the cells of bacteria is a common form of genetic engineering. Figure 5·16 shows how a human gene can be moved to a bacterial cell. Read the following steps as you look at the figure.

1. A gene is removed from a human chromosome.
2. The circular chromosome of a bacterial cell is split open.
3. The human gene is attached to the bacterial chromosome.
4. Each time the bacterial cell divides, it copies the human gene along with its own chromosome.

Why would scientists want to put a human gene in bacteria? The human gene would be copied each time the bacteria divide. Bacteria divide quickly, as often as every 20 minutes. In a short time there can be many bacteria with copies of the human gene. If the gene directs the making of a substance useful to humans, then all of these bacteria will be able to make that substance. The substance can then be made quickly, in large amounts.

An example of a human substance being made by bacteria is insulin. Insulin controls the way in which the body uses sugar. Some people who cannot make their own insulin can now be treated with insulin made by genetic engineering.

REVIEW

1. What is selective breeding? For what purposes has selective breeding been used?
2. Explain how human genes are placed in bacteria. What is this process called?
3. What advantages are there in having bacteria that contain human genes?

CHALLENGE Most pea plants produce only a few peas in each pod. Devise a method to breed a new type of pea plant that makes more peas per pod.

CHAPTER SUMMARY

The main ideas in this chapter are listed below. Read these statements before you answer the Chapter Review questions.

- Heredity is the passing of traits from parents to young. Genetics is the scientific study of heredity. (5·1)

- Gregor Mendel studied the traits of pea plants by doing crosses. He found that some traits are dominant and some are recessive. (5·1)

- Mendel found that offspring inherit traits in pairs, one trait from each parent. In hybrids a dominant trait prevents a recessive trait from showing. Two organisms with the same phenotype, or appearance, may have different genotypes, or genetic makeups. (5·2)

- A Punnett square shows all possible combinations of genes that two parents can pass to their offspring. (5·2)

- A gene is a section of a chromosome. A gene carries the information for a single trait. Sex cells are formed by meiosis and have half the number of chromosomes found in body cells. (5·3)

- Sex is determined by the sex chromosomes. Sex-linked traits result from genes that are found on the X chromosome but not on the Y chromosome. (5·4)

- Some of the knowledge of genetics has been applied in selective breeding and genetic engineering. (5·5)

The key terms in this chapter are listed below. Use each term in a sentence that shows the meaning of the term.

chromosomes	genotype	purebred	sex-linked trait
dominant trait	heredity	recessive trait	trait
gene	hybrid	selective breeding	X chromosome
genetic engineering	phenotype	sex chromosomes	Y chromosome
genetics			

Chapter Review

VOCABULARY

Write the letter of the term that best matches the definition. Not all the terms will be used.

1. An organism produced by parents that have the same form of a trait
2. A section of a chromosome that carries information for a single trait
3. A kind of sex chromosome found in the cells of both males and females
4. A feature of an organism
5. An organism produced by crossing parents with different forms of a trait
6. A trait that is hidden by the presence of a dominant trait
7. The transfer of genes from one organism to another
8. The scientific study of heredity
9. The crossing of organisms to make offspring with useful traits of both parents
10. A trait that prevents the showing of another trait

a. chromosomes
b. dominant trait
c. gene
d. genetic engineering
e. genetics
f. genotype
g. hybrid
h. selective breeding
i. purebred
j. recessive trait
k. sex-linked trait
l. trait
m. X chromosome
n. Y chromosome

CONCEPTS

Write the correct symbol or symbols for each numbered space in the following Punnett squares.

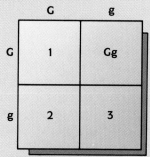

Pea plant seed coat color. G = gray. g = white.

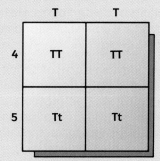

Pea plant height.

Choose the term or phrase that best answers the question or completes the statement.

6. An organism will only show a recessive trait if it
   a. has received the trait from both parents.
   b. has inherited the trait from one parent.
   c. is female.
   d. also carries a dominant trait.

7. Mendel found that
    a. organisms inherit traits in pairs.
    b. genes are parts of chromosomes.
    c. organisms inherit chromosomes in pairs.
    d. self-pollination only works with purebred plants.
8. Chromosomes
    a. each carry a single gene.
    b. are found in pairs in body cells.
    c. are features found only in pea plants.
    d. are found in pairs in sex cells.
9. X chromosomes
    a. are smaller than Y chromosomes.
    b. are found only in females.
    c. are found only in males.
    d. carry more genes than do Y chromosomes.
10. Selective breeding is used to
    a. improve the quality of crops.
    b. control population size.
    c. study genetic engineering.
    d. prevent cross-pollination.

Answer the following in complete sentences.

11. What is the difference between a purebred organism and a hybrid organism?
12. In a genetic experiment with pea plants, what do the symbols TT x tt mean?
13. Explain how two organisms can have the same phenotype but different genotypes.
14. Name the two sex chromosomes, and explain how they differ.
15. What is genetic engineering? What are its benefits?

---

1. Explain why it is important that Mendel used thousands of plants in his experiments.
2. Describe the offspring that will be produced by crossing a hybrid tall pea plant *(Tt)* with a short pea plant *(tt)*.
3. Green pea pods, *G*, are dominant. Yellow pea pods are recessive. What symbol is used to represent yellow pea pods? Explain why. Give the genotype of a plant that is hybrid for green pods.
4. What offspring will be produced by self-pollinating a pea plant hybrid for green pods?

APPLICATION/
CRITICAL
THINKING

---

1. Hybrid seeds of peas that carry a recessive trait and a dominant trait are available. Ask your teacher to help you get these seeds. Use the seeds to repeat some of Mendel's experiments. Write a report on your results.
2. Prepare a short report about hemophilia. What famous people have been affected by this disorder? How have treatments for this disorder changed through history?

EXTENSION

EVOLUTION

Do you recognize the animal with the huge jaws shown in the photograph? It is a great white shark. The great white shark is possibly the most feared of all animals that live in the ocean. The great white shark, which may grow to 6 m long, feeds on sea lions, tuna, and other sharks. It can also attack humans and has even attacked small fishing boats.

Notice that the shark has several rows of teeth. As a tooth wears down or is lost, another tooth replaces it. The shark is also unusual in that its skeleton is composed of cartilage.

Sharks are especially interesting to scientists who study living things of the past. Unlike many other animals, sharks have changed very little over millions of years. Remains of sharks that lived more than 300 million years ago have been found. Scientists have studied the remains and found that those sharks were very similar to sharks alive today.

- *How do scientists study living things of the past?*
- *What causes animal and plant species to change over time?*
- *What are some possible causes of extinction of a species?*

6·1 Change and Mutation

ad- (to)
aptus (fitted)

It is thought that there are several million species of living things on the earth. These many kinds of living things live in many different environments. Some live in wetlands, and some in deserts. Others live in saltwater or freshwater environments. Living things are found at the tops of mountains and in the depths of oceans. And each species is specially suited for living in its environment.

ADAPTATIONS

Organisms often have special features that allow them to function in a given environment. An inherited trait that makes an organism better able to live in its environment is an **adaptation** (ad apTAY shuhn).

There are different kinds of adaptations. Some are special structures. For example, monkeys have hands with separate fingers that are useful for grasping. Monkeys spend much of their time in trees. Their hands are well adapted for grasping branches. The bird shown in Figure 6·1*A* hunts for small fish while wading in shallow water. What adaptations does this bird have for wading? A cactus has a waxy coating that helps to keep water inside the plant. Think about the kind of environment in which a cactus lives. How is the waxy coating an adaptation?

Figure 6·1

This bird hunts for fish while wading in shallow water *(A)*. Cactus plants can survive long periods of drought *(B)*.

126

In some animals, adaptations take the form of camouflage (KAM uh flahzh). *Camouflage* is an adaptation of special coloring or shape that allows an animal to blend in with its environment. This adaptation helps to conceal an organism from its enemies. Can you find the fish in Figure 6·2A?

Figure 6·2

The left-eyed sand dab feeds at the bottom of a body of water, hidden by its protective coloring *(A)*. The serviceberry plant is adapted by having brightly colored berries *(B)*.

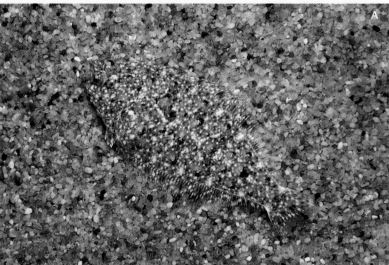

Although some organisms are adapted to their surroundings by being camouflaged, others are adapted by being colorful. Notice the brightly colored berries on the plant in Figure 6·2B. Birds are attracted by the bright color of the berries. The birds eat the berries but cannot digest the seeds inside. The seeds are later discharged, perhaps at a distant location. Brightly colored berries are an adaptation that allows certain plant species to spread over wide areas.

Adaptations also include special ways in which living things act, or behave. Note that the musk oxen in Figure 6·3A, on the next page, are standing close together. The parts of the animals that touch are not exposed to the cold air of their arctic environment. The way the oxen stand together is another example of an adaptation.

Some adaptations relate to the life processes or chemistry of organisms. Most grasses live on land and are harmed by salt. However as you can see in

Figure 6·3

Types of adaptations. Note how the musk oxen stand close together *(A)*. How can cordgrass live in salt water *(B)*?

Figure 6·3*B*, salt-marsh cordgrass lives with its roots in salt water. This plant survives by pumping salt out through its leaves. Due to this adaptation, cordgrass can survive in a place where other kinds of grasses would die.

MUTATIONS

Living things change over time. These changes may be helpful, harmful, or have no effect on an organism. A change that increases an organism's chances for survival is helpful and may lead to new adaptations.

How do adaptations come into being? Sexual reproduction is one process that leads to change. In Chapter 5 you learned that when offspring are produced, genes from the parents are combined, forming new combinations of genes. Adaptations may arise from the new combinations.

mutare (to change)

The other source of change in living things is mutation (myoo TAY shuhn). A **mutation** is a change in the genes of a cell. If a mutation occurs in a sperm cell or egg cell, that mutation can be passed to offspring. Certain chemicals and some forms of radiation, such as X rays, are known to cause mutations. Organisms having mutations, can appear at any time.

When a harmful mutation does not cause death, it may lower an organism's chances of surviving or of reproducing. For example, one type of mutation results in an organism called an albino. An *albino* lacks coloring matter, called pigment. Notice that one mouse in Figure 6·4 is brown. The other mouse, an albino, is white. Imagine that both of these mice were in a meadow of dry, brown grass. Which mouse would be more likely to be seen and attacked by a hawk flying overhead? Could the mutation that produces an albino mouse sometimes be harmful and other times be helpful?

Sometimes, mutations result in traits that help an organism survive. Suppose a mutation causes a plant to make more seeds than do similar plants. Such a mutation would be helpful, adapting the plant for more successful reproduction.

Mutations as well as new combinations of genes may lead to new adaptations. Within a species the organisms that are best adapted to their surroundings are most likely to reproduce. In time the species will include more organisms that have favorable traits.

Figure 6·4

A deer mouse *(left)* and an albino house mouse *(right)*. The albino mouse is the result of a mutation.

REVIEW

1. What is an adaptation? Give an example of a structure that is an adaptation.

2. What is a mutation? Compare a helpful mutation with a harmful mutation.

3. What are two ways that changes occur in organisms?

CHALLENGE Crop breeders sometimes treat plants with X rays, hoping to produce helpful mutations. How successful do you think this procedure might be? Explain why.

6·2 Evidence of Change Over Time

FOSSIL FORMATION

Scientists have evidence that the earth is about 4.6 billion years old. The oldest traces of life that have been found are about 3.5 billion years old. What traces of past life have been left behind? How do scientists know the ages of such things?

Living things have changed a great deal over long periods of time. Direct evidence that life has changed comes from the study of fossils. A **fossil** is the preserved remains of an organism that lived in the past or a trace left by the organism. Animals often leave tracks in soil. The soil may later harden and become rock. A footprint may then be preserved as a fossil.

The bones of animals and the shells of sea animals may also become fossils. Such fossils are often found in *sedimentary* (sehd uh MEHN tuh ree) *rocks*, as shown in Figure 6·5A. This type of rock forms from particles that fall to the bottom of a body of water, such as an ocean or a lake. Over long periods of time, many layers of these particles may form at the bottom of the ocean or lake. The weight of the upper layers presses down on the lower layers.

Figure 6·5

Layers of sedimentary rock *(A)*. Fossil fish in sedimentary rock *(B)*.

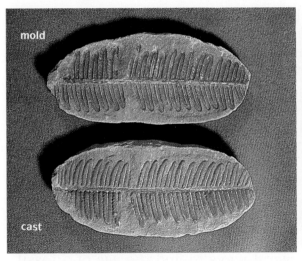

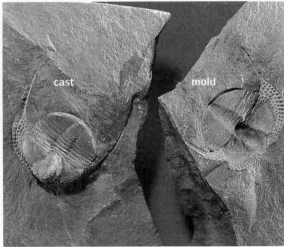

Under this weight the lower layers of particles turn into sedimentary rock. Bones or shells of a dead animal may also fall to the bottom of the ocean or lake. Thus they can become fossils in the sedimentary rock. What type of animal formed the fossil in Figure 6·5B?

Fossils in rock may form in several ways. Sometimes the soft body of an animal or a plant forms a fossil. First the organism dies and is buried by mud, which hardens into rock. Then as the soft body decays, a hollow space is left in the rock. The space has the shape of part or all of the organism. A hollow space in the shape of a once-living thing is called a **mold fossil**.

A mold is sometimes filled by minerals that seep in through the rock. The solid object that forms in the mold is a cast fossil. A **cast fossil** is a fossil that has the same outer shape as the animal or plant part that formed it. You can see examples of mold fossils and cast fossils in Figure 6·6.

In some cases, fossils are the unchanged remains of organisms. Living things are occasionally trapped in substances such as tar or sap that has oozed from trees. For example, insects may get trapped in large drops of sap. When the sap hardens, it turns into a substance called *amber*. Insects inside amber can be preserved as fossils over long periods of time. What type of insect has been fossilized in the amber shown in Figure 6·7?

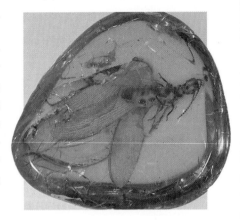

Many thousands of fossils have been found in a tar pit in California. Tar prevented the decay of the bones of animals that fell into the pit. Complete skeletons of many ancient animals have come from this tar pit.

A few complete fossilized animals have also been found trapped in ice in Siberia and Alaska. These animals lived nearly 20,000 years ago. Because they have stayed frozen, the bodies of these animals have been preserved.

DETERMINING FOSSIL AGE

How do scientists know how old a fossil is? There are several ways to find the age of a fossil. One method measures the radioactive elements in a fossil. A radioactive element is an element whose atoms change to other atoms, giving off particles and energy as they change. The use of radioactive elements to find the age of a fossil is called **radioactive dating**.

radius (ray)

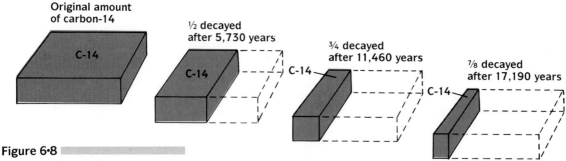

Original amount of carbon-14

½ decayed after 5,730 years

¾ decayed after 11,460 years

⅞ decayed after 17,190 years

Figure 6·8

Carbon-14 is a radioactive substance that is used to find the age of fossils. You can see what happens to carbon-14 over thousands of years.

The rate at which a radioactive element changes is given by its half-life. Half-life is the length of time it takes for half of the atoms of a radioactive element to change to another form. Carbon-14 is a radioactive form of carbon with a half-life of 5730 years. In 5730 years, half the atoms of a sample of carbon-14 will change. Half of the remaining amount will change in another 5730 years. Look at Figure 6·8. How much of the original sample of carbon-14 remains after 11,460 years?

All living things contain about the same percentage of carbon-14. But when an organism dies, the amount of carbon-14 starts to decrease. The age of a fossil can be found by measuring its remaining amount of carbon-14. Carbon-14 is useful for determining the age of fossils up to 75,000 years old. Radioactive elements with longer half-lives are used for dating older fossils.

FOSSIL EVIDENCE OF CHANGE

What has been learned from the many types of fossils that have been found? Fossils give evidence that life has changed during the history of the earth. For example, fossils show that over time there have been changes in the family of animals that includes the horse. Look at Figure 6·9. The leg bones of animals *A*, *B*, *C*, and *D* are fossils. The oldest animal shown is about 60 million years old. This dog-sized animal is thought to have been a distant ancestor of the modern horse. How did the length of the leg bones change over time?

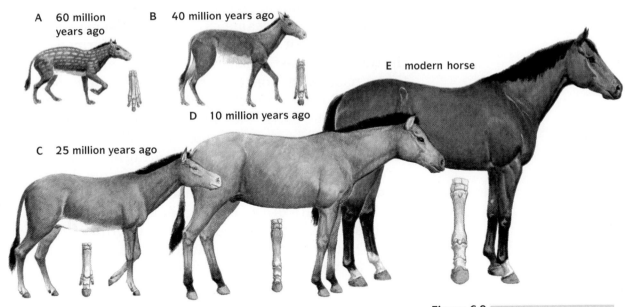

A 60 million years ago
B 40 million years ago
D 10 million years ago
C 25 million years ago
E modern horse

Figure 6·9
Changes in the family of animals that includes the horse. How does the number of toes in *A* differ from the number of toes in *E*?

There are also fossils of many species of organisms that no longer exist. Species of the past that no longer exist are said to be **extinct**. Although many species that once lived are now extinct, dinosaurs are the best-known extinct organisms. Fossils of about 400 different species of dinosaurs have been found. These animals lived on the earth from about 200 million to 65 million years ago. About 65 million

What would you think if you looked up and saw a flying reptile with an 11-m wing-span? Millions of years ago, such a sight was common-place. Today, through technology, you might see a replica of a flying reptile called a pterosaur (TEHR uh-sawr). Pterosaurs, now extinct for 65 million years, are believed to be the largest animals to fly.

Paul MacCready, an engineer, has constructed a model of a pterosaur based

on fossils that were discovered in Texas in 1972. They are the only known remains of the species.

The model not only looks much like the real pterosaur, it also has a computerized brain and can flap its wings.

years ago, the last remaining species of dinosaurs became extinct over a short period of time.

Biologists have long wondered why many species of dinosaurs became extinct at the same time. Iridium has been found in layers of rock formed at the time of the last dinosaurs. Iridium is an element that is usually rare on the earth but more common in meteors. Some scientists hypothesize that a huge meteor hit the earth and exploded about 65 million years ago. This event would have filled the air around the earth with dust, preventing much of the sunlight from reaching the earth. Without light, plants would die, causing animals to starve.

The climate of the earth changed many times. Studies of fossils have shown that over time, organisms adapted to these changes. Organisms that were not well adapted became extinct.

REVIEW

1. What is the difference between a mold fossil and a cast fossil?
2. How are radioactive elements used to find the age of fossils?
3. What do fossils show about life in the past? Use the horse as an example.
4. Describe the hypothesis that the extinction of dinosaurs was caused by a meteor. What evidence supports this idea?

CHALLENGE Give reasons why bones and shells are the most common types of fossils found.

6·3 Theories of Evolution

Fossils show that changes have occurred in living things. However, fossils do not explain why those changes have taken place. Change that occurs in living things over time is called **evolution**. Several ideas about how evolution occurs have been presented.

LAMARCK'S THEORY

In the early 1800s the French scientist Jean Lamarck had an idea about how evolution occurs. He thought that he could explain how giraffes got their long neck and long legs. Note in Figure 6·10*A* that the giraffes are stretching to eat leaves from a tree. Lamarck believed that a lifetime of eating this way would cause the neck and legs of a giraffe to get longer. Such giraffes would then pass on the long neck-long leg trait to their young. Over generations the giraffes' neck and legs would get longer and longer.

Lamarck called a feature that an organism gets during its lifetime an *acquired characteristic*. He thought that evolution occurs by the passing of acquired traits from parents to offspring. His ideas are called the theory of evolution by *inheritance of acquired characteristics*. Lamarck formed these

Figure 6·10

Lamarck's hypothesis on how organisms change over time: short-necked giraffes stretch their necks to reach food *(A)*; over time the giraffes acquired a long neck *(B)*.

135

ideas before the principles of genetics were known. Modern genetics shows that features acquired in a lifetime cannot be passed on to offspring. As you have learned, traits are inherited by the passing of chromosomes in eggs and sperm. Changes in behavior do not affect chromosomes. For this reason, scientists today reject Lamarck's theory.

DARWIN

In the mid-1800s Charles Darwin presented his ideas on how evolution occurs. Darwin had spent 5 years sailing around the world, on the H.M.S. *Beagle* collecting and describing various life forms.

Of special interest to Darwin were the organisms he found on the Galápagos Islands. These islands are in the Pacific Ocean, about 950 km from the coast of Ecuador. Locate these islands in Figure 6·12. Many of the organisms found on these islands are similar to species found in South America. But Darwin noticed that many of the living things on the islands had special adaptations to local conditions. Each of the Galápagos Islands is different in its environment. Some are desertlike, but others have forests. Darwin observed that organisms on each island seemed to be well adapted to the conditions on their own island.

Figure 6·11

Charles Darwin (1809–1882) was an English biologist. He is best known for his theory of evolution.

Figure 6·12

The route taken by Charles Darwin from 1831 to 1836 on the H.M.S. *Beagle*.

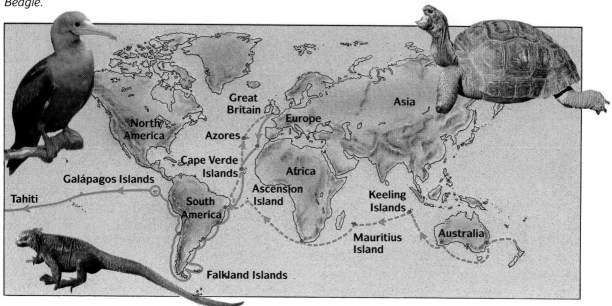

How Can Natural Selection Be Shown?

OBJECTIVE
Determine how individual differences relate to natural selection.

MATERIALS
15 strips each of green, light brown, and red construction paper; fresh grass clippings; clock or watch with second hand

PROCEDURE
A. Make a data table like the one shown.

COLOR OF PAPER	NUMBER OF "INSECTS" PICKED UP			
	FIRST TRIAL	SECOND TRIAL	THIRD TRIAL	TOTAL
Green				
Brown				
Red				

B. Use green, light brown, and red strips of construction paper to represent three types of insects that live in grass. Some types of birds search the grass for insects to eat.

C. Have a classmate thoroughly mix the strips of colored paper with some grass clippings.

D. Try to pick up as many paper strips (insects) as possible in 15 seconds. Have a second classmate act as the time-keeper. Record your results in your table.

E. Repeat steps **C** and **D** two more times.

F. Complete the *Total* column in your table.

RESULTS AND CONCLUSIONS
1. Which color "insect" was captured most often?
2. Which color insect was captured least often? What type of adaptation does this insect have?
3. Which color insect is most likely to survive and reproduce? Explain your answer.

DARWIN'S THEORY

Darwin's main points about how evolution occurs are listed here:

● *Overproduction*   Most organisms have more offspring than can be supported by the environment. Many of these offspring do not survive.

● *Variation*   Many variations in traits are found among the individuals of a species. Some variations make an organism better adapted for survival.

● *Selection*   An organism with favorable variations has a better chance of surviving and reproducing than others of its species. Darwin called this process natural selection. **Natural selection** is the survival of those organisms best suited to their environment. This process is also known as *survival of the fittest*. However, reproduction is just as important as survival. Only through reproduction are favorable traits passed on to the next generation.

Moths are often caught and eaten by birds. The photograph shows two kinds of peppered moths—a dark-colored moth and a light-colored moth. Both kinds of moths are resting on a dark-colored tree trunk. Which moth is more likely to be eaten by a bird? Which kind of moth would be likely to survive over time?

● *Change Over Time*   If organisms with favorable traits reproduce more than do other organisms, those traits will be present in more offspring. After many generations the genetic makeup of the species can change. The species will also be better adapted to its environment. If enough changes occur in a group of living things, a new species may develop.

The evolution of the horse is a good example of evolution. Refer back to Figure 6·9. Animal *A* is the oldest animal shown and is thought to have lived in forests. Modern horses live in flat, grassy areas known as prairies. As forests became prairies, longer, thinner legs and fewer toes became favorable—naturally selected—traits of horses. This streamlining of the horse's leg seems to be an adaptation for running on flat, open ground. Unlike animals living in forests, horses living on prairies could not escape their enemies by hiding. Thus, those horses that could run better were more likely to survive and reproduce.

REVIEW

1. Describe the theory of evolution proposed by Lamarck.
2. Explain Darwin's ideas about how evolution occurs, using the terms *overproduction, variation, selection,* and *change over time.*
3. Describe the theory of evolution by natural selection. Use the horse as an example.

CHALLENGE Explain why "reproduction of the fittest" is a better description of natural selection than is "survival of the fittest."

6·4 Modern Views of Evolution

GENETICS AND EVOLUTION

Most biologists today accept the idea that natural selection is an important cause of evolution. But while many of Darwin's ideas are still accepted, most biologists agree that his ideas do not completely explain evolution. Much new information about evolution has been gathered since Darwin's time. This new information has led to some additions to Darwin's theory.

Look at the mother pig and her piglets in Figure 6·13. What differences do you see among the piglets? Darwin knew that differences among the members of a species had to exist for change to occur. But Darwin had no idea what caused these differences. Genetics, which was developed after Darwin's time, provides two basic causes of differences among individuals.

After completing this section, you will be able to

- **explain** how new findings added to Darwin's theory of evolution.
- **interpret** graphs showing patterns in the rate of evolution of species.

Figure 6·13
A mother pig and her litter of piglets. Notice how different the piglets are from the mother and from each other.

You learned in Chapter 5 that sexual reproduction results in new combinations of genes. Thus sexual reproduction is one cause of differences among organisms.

Mutations are another cause of differences among organisms. Recall that a mutation is a change in the genes of a cell. Some mutations lead to new adaptations. Organisms with new adaptations may be more likely to survive and reproduce than other members of their species. Thus the new adaptations would be passed on to future generations.

PATTERNS OF CHANGE

The theory of evolution by natural selection suggests that changes come about gradually, over time. In some cases, fossils seem to show that such gradual changes have occurred. The development of long-legged animals on the prairies may be an example of gradual change. The graph in Figure 6·14A represents this pattern of evolution.

Figure 6·14

Gradual changes occur in a species over a long period of time *(A)*. Changes can also occur rapidly in a short period of time *(B)*.

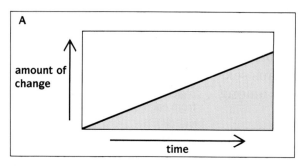

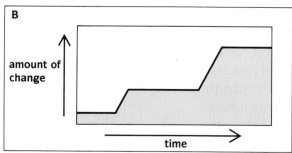

140

Other sets of fossils show a different pattern of change. Look at the graph in Figure 6·14B. Find a part of the graph that shows no change over a long period of time. Find another place on the graph that shows much change taking place in a short time. Some sets of fossils show this pattern of sudden change. A species may show little change over a period of many millions of years. Then in a short period of time, a major change may occur in the species. There is no sure explanation of why such rapid changes take place. Perhaps natural selection can explain both gradual changes and rapid changes in species. Perhaps conditions such as sudden changes in climate also cause rapid change.

REVIEW

1. What are the causes of differences among individuals of a species?

2. Describe two patterns in the rate of evolution of species.

CHALLENGE Suppose that all the members of a certain species are identical. Predict two things that might happen if there were a sudden change in climate in the place where this species lives.

CHAPTER SUMMARY

The main ideas in this chapter are listed below. Read these statements before you answer the Chapter Review questions.

- Living things have adaptations that allow them to survive in their environments. Mutations and new combinations of genes are causes of changes that may result in adaptations. (6·1)
- Fossils are often found in sedimentary rock and sometimes in amber, tar, and frozen in ice. Fossils give evidence that life has changed greatly over time. The age of fossils can be found by radioactive dating. (6·2)
- Lamarck's theory of evolution by acquired characteristics has been rejected by modern scientists. After studying life forms all around the world, Charles Darwin proposed the theory of evolution by natural selection. (6·3)
- Darwin's theory of evolution by natural selection is accepted by most biologists today. The study of genetics has explained why individuals in a species differ from each other. (6·4)
- Fossils show different patterns in the rate of evolution of species. Some changes are gradual, and others are sudden. (6·4)

The key terms in this chapter are listed below. Use each term in a sentence that shows the meaning of the term.

adaptation	extinct	mutation
cast fossil	fossil	natural selection
evolution	mold fossil	radioactive dating

Chapter Review

VOCABULARY

Use the key terms from the previous page to complete the following sentences correctly.

1. The process of change that occurs in species of living things over time is called _____.
2. A trait that allows an organism to get along better in its environment is called a/an _____.
3. A change in an organism's genes is called a/an _____.
4. A fossil that is a hollow space in the shape of a once-living thing is called a/an _____.
5. The theory of evolution by _____ was developed by Darwin.
6. A fossil that has the same outer shape as the organism that formed it is a/an _____.
7. Species of organisms of the past that no longer exist are now _____.
8. A trace of a once-living organism is called a/an _____.
9. The use of radioactive elements to find the age of a fossil is called _____.

CONCEPTS

Choose the term or phrase that best answers the question or completes the statement.

1. Which of the following is *not* true of mutations?
   a. Many are harmful.
   b. Some lead to new adaptations.
   c. They result from changes in genes.
   d. They always lead to extinction.
2. Which of the following describe how long life has existed?
   a. Life has existed for about one fourth of the earth's history.
   b. Life has existed for about three fourths of the earth's history.
   c. Life has existed throughout the earth's history.
   d. Life has existed for about 10,000 years.
3. Fossils show that
   a. life has changed during the history of the earth.
   b. mutations cause species to become extinct.
   c. dinosaurs became extinct over a long period of time.
   d. all species that have ever lived are alive today.
4. Which of the following is *not* part of Darwin's ideas?
   a. Mutations are caused by changes in genes.
   b. Organisms produce more offspring than can survive.
   c. Organisms within a species differ from each other.
   d. Organisms with favorable variations are more likely to reproduce.

5. Natural selection is
   a. a cause of overproduction of organisms.
   b. a cause of evolution.
   c. Lamarck's idea.
   d. not accepted by modern scientists.

Identify each statement as True or False. If a statement is false, replace the underlined term or phrase with a term or phrase that makes the statement true.

6. Whales have a thick layer of blubber under their skin. This blubber insulates the whales from the cold water they swim in. The layer of blubber is an example of a/an <u>adaptation</u>.
7. Only mutations that occur in a sperm cell or an egg cell <u>cannot</u> be passed on to offspring.
8. Mold fossils and cast fossils often form in <u>tar</u>.
9. The age of a fossil can be found by <u>radioactive dating</u>.
10. Lamarck believed in the <u>survival of the fittest</u>.

Answer the following in complete sentences.

11. Describe three examples of adaptations.
12. Describe one hypothesis about how dinosaurs became extinct.
13. Describe the theory of evolution by natural selection.
14. What has been learned from genetics that helps to explain evolution?
15. Describe two different patterns in the rate at which species change.

APPLICATION/ CRITICAL THINKING

1. How is the human hand adapted for using tools?
2. Explain why fossilized footprints often are found in places that were once the banks of rivers or the edges of lakes.
3. What would Lamarck have predicted about the muscles of the children of a weight lifter? Why is this prediction incorrect?

EXTENSION

1. Find out what is meant by the term *ice age*. How many ice ages have there been? What effect did ice ages have on humans and other life forms?
2. Write a brief biography of Charles Darwin. He wrote about many subjects in addition to evolution. Find out about the subject matter of some of his books, and include this information.
3. Research the geography and the life forms of the Galápagos Islands. Focus on life forms that are unique to the Galápagos and their adaptations to the special conditions on the islands. Report your findings to the class.

CHAPTER 7

CHANGES IN THE ENVIRONMENT

How do forest fires, such as the one shown in the photograph, affect an area? Not only do they burn trees and destroy the homes of many animals, forest fires can also permanently change an environment. A forest fire may burn down all plant life in an area. When this happens, there is nothing left to hold the soil in place. Sometimes wind and rain wash away all the soil, leaving behind a barren area.

Sometimes forest fires do not destroy so much vegetation that the soil is washed away. In this case new plant life will soon grow back, but it will be different from the vegetation that lived in the area before the fire.

- *What other factors can change the environment?*
- *How do areas change over time?*
- *How does the type of plant life determine the types of animals that can live in a given area?*

7·1 Cycles in Nature

After completing this section, you will be able to

- **describe** how water moves through an ecosystem.
- **describe** the ways in which carbon dioxide and oxygen move through an ecosystem.
- **explain** how nitrogen is made available to living things.

The key terms in this section are
carbon-oxygen cycle
ecosystem
nitrogen cycle
water cycle

The living world is made up of units called ecosystems. An **ecosystem** is an area in which living and nonliving things interact, exchanging energy and materials. Ecosystems can be large, like a forest, or small, like plants growing in a crack in a rock.

A pond is another example of an ecosystem. Such living things as plants, insects, and frogs are part of this ecosystem. Water, soil, oxygen, and sunlight energy are nonliving parts. Plants use sunlight to make food, which is eaten by insects. Insects, in turn, are eaten by frogs. All these organisms use carbon, oxygen, water, and nitrogen in their life processes. These nonliving materials exist in limited amounts and are cycled through the ecosystem.

THE WATER CYCLE

The movement of water through nature is called the **water cycle**. In the water cycle, the sun's energy causes *evaporation*, the process by which water changes from a liquid to a gas. Notice in Figure 7·1 that water evaporates from oceans, rivers, lakes, soil, and the bodies of living things. By the process of transpiration, water from plants' leaves is released to the air. As water in the air cools, the

Figure 7·1
The water cycle.

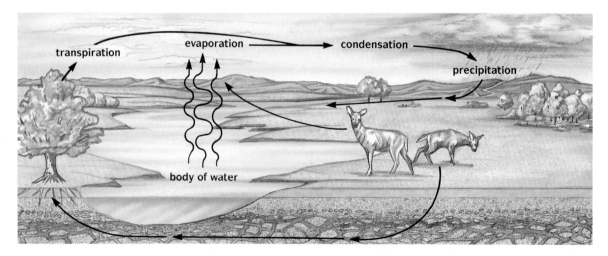

water changes back to a liquid by the process of *condensation* and forms clouds. The water that falls from clouds is called *precipitation* and may be in the form of rain, snow, hail, or sleet.

Water on or in the soil is used by living things. Plants' roots absorb water, and animals drink water and take it in with food. The water in living things is later returned to the ground or air. Plants lose water through their leaves, and animals lose water when they give off wastes. The water cycle is completed when water again evaporates.

THE CARBON-OXYGEN CYCLE

The movement of carbon and oxygen through an ecosystem is called the **carbon-oxygen cycle**. Figure 7·2 shows how these materials are cycled through the environment. Plants take carbon dioxide from the air and use it to make food. What is this process called? This process gives off oxygen as a waste product. Oxygen, in turn, is used by living things in respiration.

Recall that respiration is the process by which living things get energy from food. Respiration gives off carbon dioxide. Carbon dioxide is also given off when once-living things decay. The decay of dead animals and plants is carried on by *decomposers*. Decomposers include bacteria and fungi that live in soil and water. Carbon dioxide is used by plants, completing the carbon-oxygen cycle.

Figure 7·2
The carbon-oxygen cycle.

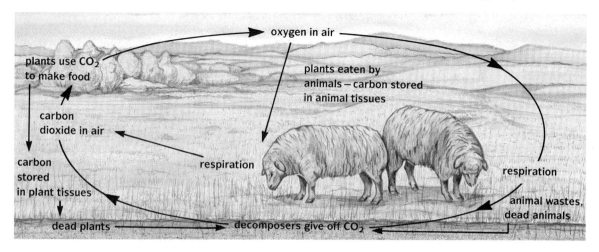

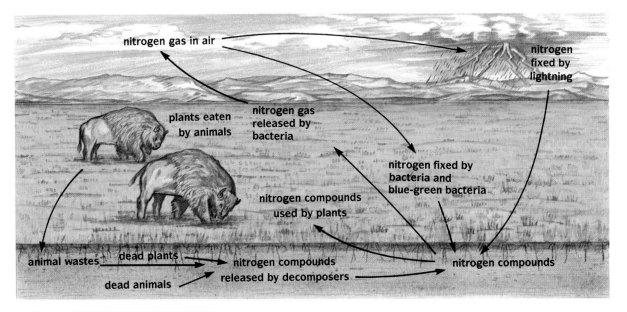

nitrogen gas in air

nitrogen fixed by lightning

plants eaten by animals

nitrogen gas released by bacteria

nitrogen fixed by bacteria and blue-green bacteria

nitrogen compounds used by plants

animal wastes   dead plants

dead animals

nitrogen compounds released by decomposers

nitrogen compounds

Figure 7·3
The nitrogen cycle. How do you think nitrogen fixed by lightning is brought to the ground, where it is used by plants?

THE NITROGEN CYCLE

The **nitrogen cycle** is the movement of nitrogen through an ecosystem. This cycle is shown in Figure 7·3. Although almost 80 percent of the air is nitrogen gas, most living things cannot use nitrogen in this form. The gas must be changed into nitrogen compounds. Nitrogen that is combined with other elements in a compound is called *fixed nitrogen*.

Nitrogen can be fixed into compounds by lightning and by bacteria and blue-green bacteria that live in soil and water. Fixed nitrogen is used by plants to make proteins and is taken in by animals as they eat the plants. Nitrogen from dead plants and animals, as well as from animal wastes, is returned to the soil by decomposers.

The nitrogen cycle is completed by other bacteria. These bacteria change nitrogen compounds into nitrogen gas, releasing it to the air.

REVIEW

1. Describe the water cycle.

2. What life processes are part of the carbon-oxygen cycle?

3. What is fixed nitrogen? Name two ways in which nitrogen is fixed.

CHALLENGE Fertilizers often contain nitrogen compounds. Which of the ecosystem cycles is most affected by the use of such fertilizers? Which step in this cycle is being by-passed?

7·2 Changes in Populations

POPULATION SIZE

A **population** is a group of organisms of one species living in a given area. A population may be all the bald eagles living in a national park, all the people in a town, or all the bass in a lake.

The size of a population is the total number of members in that population. If a lake contains 50 bass, the population size is 50. **Population density** is the number of individuals per unit of space. Suppose an area of 10 km² contains 100 rabbits. The population density is 100 rabbits per 10 km² or 10 rabbits/km². How can two populations have the same size but different densities?

Many factors can change the size of a population. The size increases if new individuals move into an area or if there is a high birth rate. The **birth rate** is the ratio of the number of births in a year to the number of individuals in a population. The human birth rate in six regions for 1983 is shown in Figure 7·4. What is the highest birth rate shown?

After completing this section, you will be able to

- **compare** population size and population density.
- **describe** the factors that affect the size of a population.

The key terms in this section are
birth rate
death rate
limiting factor
population
population density

Figure 7·4
The human birth rate varies from one area to another.

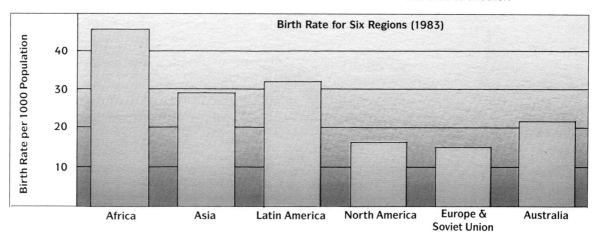

Birth Rate for Six Regions (1983)

Birth Rate per 1000 Population

40
30
20
10

Africa | Asia | Latin America | North America | Europe & Soviet Union | Australia

The movement of members out of a population decreases its size. Deaths also decrease its size. The **death rate** is the ratio of the number of deaths in a year to the number of individuals in a population.

If conditions are favorable, one bacterium could produce over 200,000 offspring in just 6

149

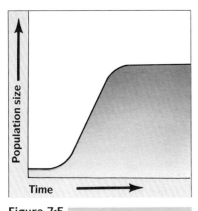

Figure 7·5

Many populations show a growth pattern like the one shown here.

hours. In contrast, elephants breed very slowly. Yet if conditions are favorable, it is thought that one pair of elephants could have 19 million descendants in 750 years. Why is it that bacteria and elephants do not cover the earth? The graph in Figure 7·5 can help to answer this question. The graph shows a typical growth pattern of a population. Notice that growth is slow at first and then becomes very rapid. Later the growth levels off, resulting in a stable population size.

LIMITING FACTORS

When population size is stable, the birth rate is about equal to the death rate. Although there may be small changes during certain years, the population generally stays about the same size.

Certain factors in the environment, such as a lack of food or water, keep a population from growing. A factor that keeps a population from increasing in size is called a **limiting factor**. Figure 7·6 shows the effects of low rainfall as a limiting factor.

Some limiting factors are related to population density. These factors include disease, predators, and the amount of food, water, and space available. The greater the population density, the greater the effect of the limiting factors on the population.

The availability of food affects the size of a population. As population density increases, animals compete with each other for food. If a deer population is too dense, there will not be enough food. As a result, some deer will starve, and the deer

Figure 7·6
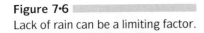
Lack of rain can be a limiting factor.

ACTIVITY — Does Precipitation Affect a Bird Population?

OBJECTIVE
Analyze data to find the effect of precipitation on the hatching of marsh-bird eggs.

MATERIALS
graph paper

PROCEDURE
A. The table below shows the number of eggs laid and the number of eggs hatched in a marsh-bird population over a 6-year period. The table also shows the amount of rainfall and snowfall during the nest-building season for each year. Copy this table.

B. Determine the total precipitation in each year by adding the amount of rainfall and the amount of snowfall. Record the totals in your data table.

C. Find the percentage of eggs hatched in each year. To do this, divide the number of eggs hatched by the number of eggs laid, and then multiply by 100. Record the percentages in your data table.

D. Find out if the percentage of eggs hatched changes with the amount of precipitation. To do this, you will need to graph your results. Mark the x-axis with even numbers from 0 cm to 30 cm to show the total precipitation during each year's nest-building season. Mark the y-axis at 0, 10 percent, 20 percent, and so on to 100 percent.

RESULTS AND CONCLUSIONS
1. In which year was the precipitation the lowest? In which year was it the highest?
2. What seems to be the relationship between the amount of precipitation and the number of eggs hatched? Explain your answer.
3. On the basis of the data, does precipitation seem to be a limiting factor for this marsh-bird population? Explain your answer.

YEAR	NUMBER OF EGGS LAID	NUMBER OF EGGS HATCHED	RAINFALL (cm)	SNOWFALL (cm)	TOTAL PRECIPITATION (cm)	PERCENTAGE OF EGGS HATCHED
1	7	5	3.6	3.8		
2	6	2	6.4	14.2		
3	4	1	19.3	7.6		
4	10	7	8.1	2.0		
5	10	6	7.4	2.5		
6	8	6	5.3	1.5		

population will decrease. Later, with fewer deer competing, more food will be available to each deer. The deer population may then increase again.

Disease can also reduce the size of a deer population. If the deer population is dense, a disease will spread quickly and may greatly decrease the population density. In contrast, if the population density is low, the animals will not be in such close contact, and the disease will have a more limited effect.

Predators also reduce the size of a deer population. A *predator* is an animal that hunts and kills another animal for food. The *prey* is the animal that is hunted. As the density of a deer population rises, wolves and other predators can find and kill deer more easily. Because of the increased food supply, the number of predators will increase. However, if more deer are preyed upon, the number of deer will decrease. The graph in Figure 7·7 shows how the number of predators is related to the number of their prey. You can see that when the number of predators increases, the number of prey decreases. What happens to the number of prey when the number of predators decreases? Why?

Figure 7·7

The timber wolf *(top)* preys on deer *(bottom)*. An increase in the population of a prey species is often followed by an increase in predator species *(right)*.

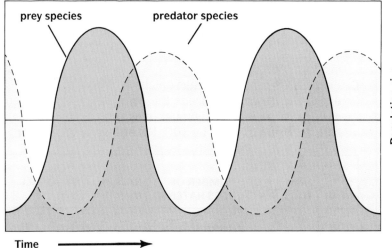

prey species   predator species

Population size

Time

Other limiting factors that do not depend on population density can also affect the size of a population. Forest fires, droughts, severe storms, and the activity of humans can reduce population size, regardless of population density.

REVIEW

1. A pasture that is 2 km² contains six horses. Find the population size and population density of the horses.
2. What ratio does birth rate represent?
3. Name four factors that may limit the size of a population.

CHALLENGE Suppose you planted 200 tree seedlings in a box 1 m² in area and 15 cm deep. How would limiting factors affect the density of the seedling population? Explain your answer.

7·3 Succession

All the organisms that live together in an area make up a *community*. The sequence of changes that occur in a community over time is called **succession**. There are two kinds of succession: primary and secondary.

PRIMARY SUCCESSION

Primary succession occurs in newly formed areas, such as on lava that has cooled after a volcanic eruption. This kind of succession can also occur on sand dunes, on bare rock, and in water. The filling of a pond as it becomes a field is one example of primary succession. Follow the numbered steps in Figure 7·8 as you read about the stages in this type of succession.

1. Many organisms live in and around a pond.
2. As organisms die, they sink to the bottom. Over a long period, the pond begins to fill in.
3. As the pond fills in, a marsh develops.
4. The marsh dries up. Grasses, shrubs, and other plants grow in the field that forms.

After completing this section, you will be able to

- **define** and give examples of primary succession and secondary succession.
- **describe** a climax community.
- **describe** some possible causes of succession.

The key terms in this section are
climax community
pioneers
succession

succedere (go after)

Figure 7·8
Primary succession can change a pond to a field.

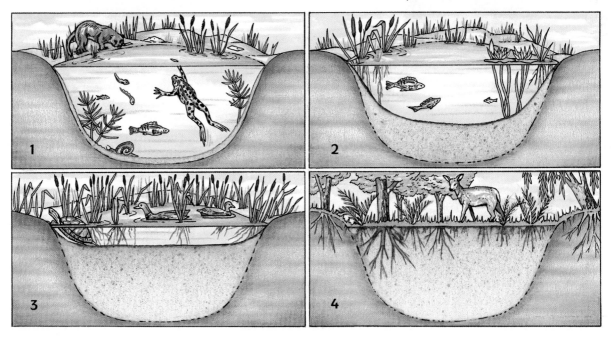

Primary succession is a slow process. It may take many hundreds of years for an area of bare rock to become a forest. The first organisms to grow in an area where primary succession occurs are called **pioneers**. Lichens (LI kuhnz) are often the pioneers on bare rock. A lichen is a plantlike organism made up of an alga and a fungus. Lichens, as shown in Figure 7·9A, release chemicals that break the surface of the rock into small particles. As lichens die, they form a mat of decaying matter. The rock particles and the decaying matter are the beginning of soil. As the amount of soil increases, small plants can grow. In time, larger plants, such as oak trees, will appear.

Figure 7·9

Primary succession started by lichens (A) may result in a climax community like this forest (B).

A forest, such as the one shown in Figure 7·9B, is the final stage of succession in some parts of North America. The final community in a succession is called the **climax community**. A climax community will remain in place unless there is a major change in the climate or in the community itself. For example, a forest fire might burn all the trees in a forest. What other factors could change a forest?

When the plants in an area change, the animals there also change. The plants present during the early stages of primary succession are food for small animals, such as insects. As the numbers and kinds of plants increase, more species of animals can live in the area. A climax community contains many more types of animals than does a community in the pioneer stage.

SECONDARY SUCCESSION

Secondary succession occurs where communities used to exist but were destroyed. Communities can be destroyed by such human activities as logging, strip mining, and plowing. Natural disasters, such as fires and earthquakes, can also destroy communities. Without plants to hold soil in place, the soil may be carried away by water. But if the soil is not lost, secondary succession will occur.

Figure 7·10 shows an example of secondary succession. Plants will grow back in an abandoned field after plowing has destroyed the natural community. During secondary succession, larger plants replace smaller plants. Such changes go on until a climax community again forms.

Figure 7·10
How has a cornfield changed 1 year *(left)*, 10 years *(middle)*, and 30 years *(right)* after being abandoned?

CAUSES OF SUCCESSION

Succession is often caused by the living things that make up a community. The community growing at one stage of succession changes the environment. This change interferes with the survival of that community. Pine seedlings, for example, need light. They grow quickly in a sunny field. But as the pines grow larger, they shade the ground and make the area unsuitable for the growth of new pine seed-

OBJECTIVE
Observe succession in a vacant lot.

MATERIALS
field guides or taxonomic keys, notebook, hand lens

PROCEDURE

A. Observe the plants in a vacant lot. Use field guides or taxonomic keys to help you identify the plants. **Caution:** Do not touch any plants that have not been identified as safe. Some plants may irritate your skin.

B. Make a list of the five most common species of woody plants you see. Rank each species according to how numerous it is. Record this information in your notebook.

C. Repeat step **B** for the five most common herbaceous plants on the lot.

D. Look for animals in the vacant lot. Use field guides or taxonomic keys to help you identify the animals. Make a list of those you find. Look for evidence of animal species you do not observe directly. Evidence might include feathers, tracks, and fur. Record what you see.

E. Examine the surfaces of rocks for further evidence of plant and animal life. Record what you see.

RESULTS AND CONCLUSIONS

1. Which does the lot show, primary succession or secondary succession? Explain.
2. Describe any evidence of primary succession you observed.
3. Describe any evidence of secondary succession you observed.
4. How long do you think it has been since the area was last disturbed? Explain your answer.
5. What species of plants might be growing in the area in 100 years if the area is left undisturbed?

---

lings. Seedlings of trees such as oaks, which grow well in shade, soon outnumber pines. Thus, oaks become part of the climax community.

A climax community is more stable than the communities that came before it. Yet climax communities can also change over time. Before a fungus killed most of them, chestnut trees were a major part of climax community forests of eastern North America. Now other kinds of trees have replaced the chestnut trees.

Figure 7·11
This chestnut tree is dying of a fungus infection.

REVIEW

1. What is succession? How do the two types of succession differ?
2. What is a climax community?
3. Give three examples of events that could start secondary succession.

CHALLENGE What nonliving factors might affect the kinds of climax communities that develop in a given area?

7·4 Land Biomes

If you were to take a trip across North America, you would see many different regions. You might pass through forests, prairies, and deserts. These regions differ in climate. **Climate** is the average weather in an area over a long period. The two factors that most affect climate are temperature and rainfall. Climate, along with soil type, affects the types of organisms that can live in an area. A large region with a distinct combination of climate, plants, and animals is called a **biome**. There are two major kinds of biomes: land biomes and water biomes. Look at the map in Figure 7·12 as you read about land biomes.

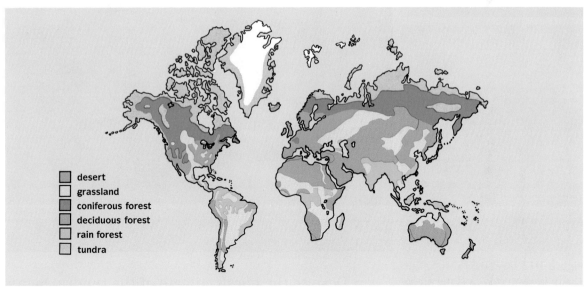

- desert
- grassland
- coniferous forest
- deciduous forest
- rain forest
- tundra

Figure 7·12
Major biomes of the world.

TUNDRA

The **tundra** is a cold, dry land biome in which most plants are low-growing and short-lived. Locate the tundra in Figure 7·12. In winter, tundra temperatures may drop to −40°C. Summer temperatures rarely rise above 10°C. The average rainfall is only 30−40 cm per year.

Winter in the tundra lasts from 6 to 9 months and the ground remains completely frozen. The brief summer growing season lasts about 2 months. During the summer, only the top 10–30 cm of soil thaws. Underneath, the earth remains frozen. The layer of permanently frozen soil is called permafrost. During summer, rain collects above the permafrost and marshes cover the land.

Figure 7·13 *right* shows the tundra in late summer. Notice that all the plants are short. Most of these plants sprout from seeds, grow to maturity, flower, and form new seeds within the brief summer. The seeds can survive the harsh winter that kills mature plants. There are no tall trees on the tundra, but there are a few small woody plants.

Figure 7·13

The ptarmigan *(top)* and the arctic fox *(bottom)* live in the tundra.

Despite the harsh climate of the tundra, many kinds of animals live there. Mammals of the tundra include musk oxen, arctic foxes, wolves, and reindeer. A few species of insects breed in the tundra marshes during the summer. Large numbers of shore birds and waterfowl nest in the tundra during the summer. Many of these birds feed on seeds, which are abundant in late summer, and migrate to warmer areas for the winter. Two birds that remain in the tundra year-round are the snowy owl and the ptarmigan (TAHR muh guhn).

CONIFEROUS FOREST

Look back at Figure 7·12. The band of forest that crosses North America, Europe, and Asia is the coniferous forest. The **coniferous forest** is a biome made up mainly of cone-bearing trees, or conifers, such as pines and spruces.

The climate of the coniferous forest is milder than that of the tundra. Some areas of the coniferous forest receive as much as 125 cm of rain and snow each year. Temperatures range from −30°C in winter to 20°C in summer.

Most trees in this forest biome are conifers with needlelike leaves, such as spruces, firs, and pines. A few broad-leaved trees, such as willows and poplars, grow along stream banks. The top layer of the forest is so dense that little light reaches the forest floor. Ferns and mosses grow beneath the trees. Why would few shrubs grow in the coniferous forest?

The coniferous forest supports many more animals than does the tundra. Some of these animals are shown in Figure 7·14. A large number of insects provide food for birds such as woodpeckers. Mammals such as elk, deer, moose, and squirrels feed on forest plants. These animals, in turn, are food for wolves and foxes.

PUZZLER

Suppose you are hiking up a mountain. At the foot of the mountain you pass through a grassy area. Higher up you see deciduous trees. What kinds of trees would you expect to find farther up? What kinds of plants would grow beyond the tree line—the altitude above which trees cannot grow? Explain. How is traveling up the mountain like moving north from the equator?

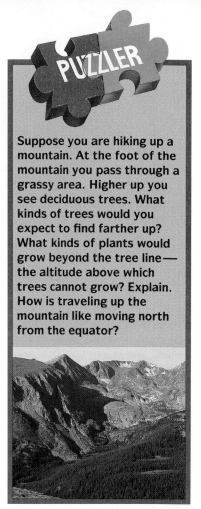

Figure 7·14
Animals of the coniferous forest include the moose *(middle)* and the woodpecker *(right)*.

Figure 7·15

The skunk *(left)* and the newt *(middle)* live in the deciduous forest.

Figure 7·16

The four layers of a forest.

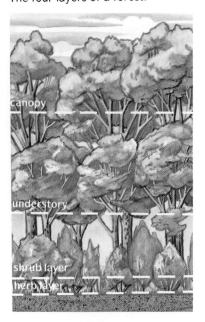

canopy

understory

shrub layer

herb layer

DECIDUOUS FOREST

The **deciduous forest** is a biome in which the main plants are broad-leaved trees that lose their leaves in the fall. Locate this biome in Figure 7·12. The deciduous forest has a moderate climate. There are four distinct seasons of about equal length. What season is shown in Figure 7·15? Winter temperatures may fall to $-20°C$ in some areas. Summers are warm and may reach $30°C$. Yearly precipitation ranges from 75 cm to 150 cm.

The climax community can vary in different areas of the deciduous forest. Some areas have maple and beech trees; other areas have mainly oak and hickory trees.

There are several layers of plants in the deciduous forest, as shown in Figure 7·16. Notice that the highest layer of trees is called the *canopy*. Below the canopy is a layer of smaller trees called the *understory*. Short woody plants that grow beneath the understory form the *shrub layer*. An *herb layer* of small plants with soft, green stems grows close to the ground. Decaying plant matter covers the forest floor.

The layers of plants support a wide variety of animals. Squirrels and birds live in the canopy and understory. Decaying matter on the forest floor provides food and shelter for shrews, lizards, newts, and snakes. Larger animals in the deciduous forest include deer, foxes, and skunks.

RAIN FORESTS

The **tropical rain forest** is a warm, humid biome that has the greatest variety of life forms. There are no distinct seasons in the tropical rain forest. Temperatures are warm throughout the year. Most areas of the tropical rain forest receive at least 220 cm of rain each year.

The climate of the tropical rain forest is ideal for plant growth. The trees of the canopy may be over 50 m tall and may almost completely shade the ground. Notice in Figure 7·17 *center* the many vines growing on and between the trees. Orchids and mosses grow attached to the trees, far above the ground. The soil of the tropical rain forest is usually poor because many nutrients are washed away by the frequent rains.

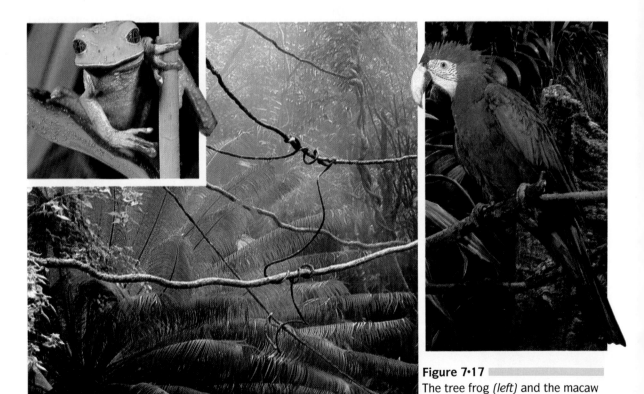

Figure 7·17
The tree frog *(left)* and the macaw *(right)* live in the tropical rain forest.

Figure 7·18
A temperate rain forest.

In the tropical rain forest many animals, including birds, frogs, and mammals, live in the trees. The mammals include monkeys and orangutans. Thousands of insect species also thrive in all parts of this biome.

Another type of rain forest, the *temperate rain forest*, occurs along the North American coast from California to Alaska. Temperatures here are moderate, and rainfall may reach 300 cm per year. Conifers, such as Douglas firs and redwoods, are the main trees of this biome. Figure 7·18 shows redwood trees in the temperate rain forest. Fewer plant and animal species live in this biome than in the tropical rain forest.

GRASSLAND

The **grassland** is a biome with moderate rainfall and grasses as the main plants. Yearly rainfall in this biome is between 25 cm and 75 cm. This amount of moisture prevents deserts from forming but is not enough to allow trees to grow. Another name for the grassland is *prairie*. Locate this biome in Figure 7·12. Note that most areas of the grassland occur far from coasts.

Figure 7·19
Bison *(left)* and the meadow lark *(right)* live in the grassland.

Grouse, meadowlarks, and prairie chickens are birds that nest in the grassland. Gophers and prairie dogs dig burrows under the soil. Owls, snakes, and ferrets prey on these animals. Herds of antelope and bison graze on the prairie.

Prairie like that shown in Figure 7·19 once covered the center of North America. Only a few patches of prairie remain; most of it has been replaced by farmland and by pastures for grazing livestock.

DESERT

A **desert** is a biome that receives less than 25 cm of rain per year. The largest desert area in North America is the Great Basin Desert. It lies between the Rocky Mountains and the Sierra Nevada, as shown in Figure 7·20. Look back at Figure 7·12. Notice that there are other large desert areas in Africa and Asia.

There are both hot desert areas and cold desert areas. In a cold desert, temperatures often drop below freezing during the winter. However, many desert areas can have very high daytime temperatures. Daytime temperatures of more than 50°C

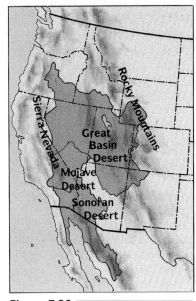

Figure 7·20
North American deserts.

Figure 7·21
The road runner *(left)* and the collared lizard *(right)* live in the desert.

Since the 1950s, tropical rain forest areas have been cleared at alarming rates. Clearing the land provides areas for growing crops and raising cattle. But cleared land has no ground cover. Heavy rains can erode the soil, making the land unproductive. As a result, the land is abandoned. Thus the forest areas have been destroyed for no purpose.

The tropical rain forest provides habitats for about half of the living species on the earth. When these areas are cleared, millions of plants and animals are killed. Not only are living things lost, but the foods, medicines, fuels, timber, and other products that the forest provides are also lost.

Technology may help to save the tropical rain forest. New farming methods include agroforestry—the science of growing crops *with* a forest rather than *instead* of a forest. Also, cattle may be raised in some areas that have already been cleared and abandoned.

have occurred in desert areas of California. However, temperatures fall sharply after sundown.

Despite the lack of water, the desert is home to many organisms. Many desert plants have spinelike leaves and waxy coatings that reduce water loss. Some desert plants, such as cactuses, can store water. As in the tundra, there are no tall trees in the desert. Why?

Common animals in the desert areas of North America include snakes, lizards, armadillos, and birds. The collared lizard and the road runner are examples of desert animals.

REVIEW

1. What is a biome? What two factors are most important in determining the climate of a biome?
2. What is permafrost? In which biome is it found?
3. How do the coniferous forest, the deciduous forest, and the tropical rain forest differ?
4. How does the grassland differ from the desert?

CHALLENGE Suppose the climate of a grassland area changed and 100 cm of rain began to fall each year. Describe the changes you would expect to see in that grassland area over a 15-year period.

7·5 Water Biomes

Water biomes cover most of the earth's surface. There are two distinct water biomes: marine and freshwater. The *marine biome*, made up of the ocean, contains about 3.5 percent salt. The *freshwater biome* includes bodies of water, such as lakes and rivers, with less than 0.005 percent salt.

MARINE BIOME

The marine biome covers over 70 percent of the earth. Four limiting factors determine which organisms can live in this biome. These factors are light, temperature, pressure, and salinity. *Salinity* is the amount of salt in water. The salinity in different parts of the ocean does not vary much. But light, temperature, and pressure vary greatly. Both the amount of light and the temperature decrease as the depth of water increases. Pressure increases with depth. Why?

Figure 7·22 shows the zones of the marine biome. Locate the *intertidal zone* along the ocean shore. Organisms in this zone live in an ever-changing environment. They are underwater at high tide

Figure 7·22

The marine biome has a wide variety of organisms. Marine plankton *(insets).*

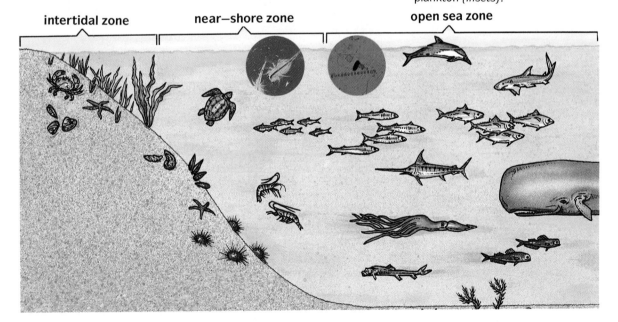

intertidal zone   near—shore zone   open sea zone

and exposed to the air at low tide. They must survive changes in temperature and salinity.

There is enough light in the *near shore zone* to support a variety of organisms. The many tiny organisms, both plant and animal, that float near the surface of the water are called **plankton**. Almost all other organisms in the sea depend in some way on the plant plankton for food.

A third zone in the marine biome is the *open-sea zone*. The upper 100 m of this zone produces the most plant plankton and other food. No plants live below 200 m. Animals there depend on food that drifts down from above.

FRESHWATER BIOME

The freshwater biome includes two types of environments: standing water and running water. Ponds and lakes are standing water. Streams and rivers are running water. Many limiting factors determine which organisms live in fresh water. The most important factors are temperature, current, mineral content, oxygen content, and turbidity. *Turbidity* is cloudiness caused by tiny particles in the water. Turbidity reduces the amount of light.

planktos (wandering)

Figure 7·23

The freshwater biome. Freshwater plankton *(insets)*.

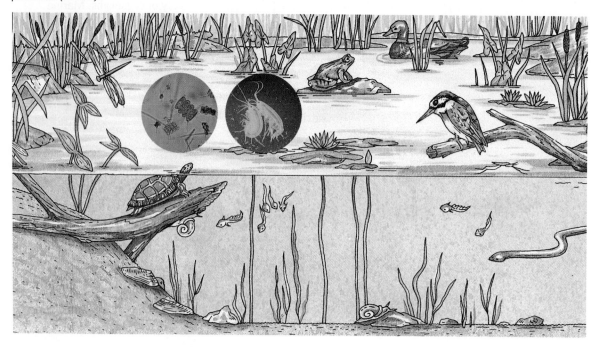

Many kinds of organisms live in standing fresh water. Notice in Figure 7·23 that plants such as water lilies float on the water surface but are rooted in the bottom. Both animal plankton and plant plankton float near the surface of the water.

Running water is quite different from standing water. Because of the current, running water is kept mixed. Thus the amounts of oxygen and minerals are usually more stable in running water than in standing water.

REVIEW

1. Compare the two freshwater environments.
2. What are the limiting factors in a marine biome?
3. Why is the level of oxygen more constant in running water than in standing water?

CHALLENGE Suppose a river were dammed and a lake formed. How would the plant and animal life change?

CHAPTER SUMMARY

The main ideas in this chapter are listed below. Read these statements before you answer the Chapter Review questions.

- Water, carbon, oxygen, and nitrogen move in cycles through ecosystems. These materials are used over and over again. (7·1)

- Population size is affected by birth rate, death rate, and by individuals moving in or out. Limiting factors keep a population from reaching its greatest possible size. (7·2)

- Succession is a sequence of changes in a community over time. Primary succession occurs in newly formed areas. Secondary succession occurs after existing communities are destroyed. Succession also occurs

when a community makes the environment unfavorable for its own survival, resulting in a climax community. (7·3)

- Biomes are largely determined by climate. Major land biomes include tundra, coniferous forest, deciduous forest, tropical rain forest, grassland, and desert. (7·4)

- Water biomes include the marine biome and the freshwater biome. Such factors as salinity, light, temperature, oxygen, and current determine which organisms can live in these biomes. A freshwater biome may have standing water or running water. (7·5)

The key terms in this chapter are listed below. Use each term in a sentence that shows the meaning of the term.

biome	death rate	limiting factor	population density
birth rate	deciduous forest	nitrogen cycle	succession
carbon-oxygen cycle	desert	pioneers	tropical rain forest
climate	ecosystem	plankton	tundra
climax community	grassland	population	water cycle
coniferous forest			

Chapter Review

VOCABULARY

Write the letter of the term that best matches the definition. Not all the terms will be used.

1. The ratio of the number of births per year to the number of individuals in a population
2. A large region with a distinct combination of climate, plants, and animals
3. A factor that keeps a population from reaching its greatest possible size
4. The number of individuals per unit of space
5. The final community in a succession
6. The cold, dry land biome with low-growing plants
7. The biome with less than 25 cm of rain per year
8. The biome with a warm, humid climate and the greatest variety of life
9. The first organisms to grow in an area where primary succession is taking place
10. Tiny organisms that float near the surface of the water

a. biome
b. birth rate
c. climate
d. climax community
e. coniferous forest
f. death rate
g. desert
h. deciduous forest
i. limiting factor
j. pioneers
k. plankton
l. population
m. population density
n. succession
o. tropical rain forest
p. tundra

CONCEPTS

Write the correct term for each numbered biome on the map.

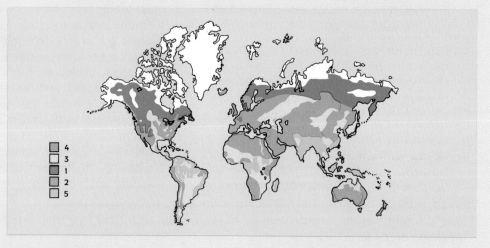

Choose the term or phrase that best answers the question or completes the statement.

6. The energy needed to carry on the water cycle comes from
   a. living organisms.
   b. hydrogen and oxygen.
   c. sunlight.
   d. power plants.

7. Which of the following limiting factors is not affected by population density?
   a. food
   b. disease
   c. volcanoes
   d. predators
8. The growth of lichens on bare rock is an example of
   a. primary succession.
   b. a biome.
   c. secondary succession.
   d. a climax community.
9. Which land biome has the greatest variety of life forms?
   a. tropical rain forest
   b. deciduous forest
   c. temperate rain forest
   d. tundra
10. Almost all animals that live in water depend in some way on which of the following organisms?
   a. plankton
   b. water lilies
   c. plants that root at the bottom of ponds
   d. fish

Answer the following in complete sentences.

11. What are the roles of bacteria in the nitrogen cycle?
12. Describe how the density of a prey population affects the predator population.
13. What events can cause secondary succession to occur?
14. Describe the layers of plants in the deciduous forest.
15. What factors are more stable in running water than in standing water? Explain.

APPLICATION/ CRITICAL THINKING

1. Which population would be more likely to be affected by a disease— one with a density of 5 individuals per square kilometer or one with a density of 30 individuals per square kilometer? Why?
2. Primary succession is a much slower process than is secondary succession. Explain why.
3. Construction projects often cause erosion. Erosion causes the turbidity of the water in lakes and streams to increase. How might this increase in turbidity affect the organisms present? Consider effects on both plants and animals.

EXTENSION

1. In what biome is your city or town located? Find out what organisms are considered to be part of the climax community in your biome. Present your findings to the class.
2. Look for examples of succession in your area. Take photographs of places you believe to be in different steps of succession. Label and display your photographs.
3. There are land biomes in addition to those covered in this chapter. Find out where they are located and what their climates are.

Science in Careers

How much water do the plants in your home and school need? How much sunlight do they need? What soils are best for which plants? A florist can answer these questions.

Florists sell plants and cut flowers. They must know how to care for the plants they keep. They must know under what conditions the flowering plants will bloom. Florists often make attractive arrangements of flowers. Florists also must be able to help customers with plants that are diseased or that have other problems. Florists should know how to recognize certain common plant diseases. A knowledge of how to cure plant diseases is also helpful.

Florists usually work in shops. Some work for hotels and restaurants. Florists may run their own businesses or work for others. Most receive on-the-job training. If you are interested in this career, you will benefit from biology and art courses in high school.

FLORIST

You have learned a lot about how traits are inherited. How are patterns of inheritance determined? Geneticists are researchers who study inheritance.

Many geneticists work with small organisms, such as bacteria and yeasts. The information obtained from these organisms can be applied to other organisms. Geneticists plan and carry out experiments and then record and analyze results. Geneticists working with crops have developed improved varieties of foods, such as corn and wheat. New hybrid fruits and vegetables have also been produced.

Geneticists work for the government, for universities, and for industries. The training varies but includes a 4-year college degree in biology or genetics. An advanced degree is required for some jobs. If you are interested in how traits are inherited and in a career as a geneticist, you should take courses in biology and chemistry in high school.

GENETICIST

People in Science

Dr. Barbara McClintock
GENETICIST

Dr. Barbara McClintock is a geneticist who in 1983 won a Nobel Prize for her work. Although she began her work about 40 years ago, Dr. McClintock's results and conclusions were not widely accepted until recently.

Dr. McClintock studied mutations in corn. She noted that sometimes the color of offspring corn kernels was different from that of the parent kernels. She examined corn cells and found they contained small bits of chromosomes. Dr. McClintock hypothesized that the bits of chromosomes moved about. She suggested that the bits joined other chromosomes in the cells. She thought that the presence of the chromosome bits in cells resulted in the changed color of the corn.

These bits of chromosomes are now known as transposons. They are being studied by many geneticists. Dr. McClintock was a pioneer in the understanding of this aspect of genetics.

Issues and Technology

What Are Benefits and Problems of Genetic Engineering?

For thousands of years, people have been breeding plants and animals for desired traits. This practice began long before the basis for heredity was known. Only in the last half-century have scientists learned that an organism's traits are controlled by genes made up of DNA.

As they have learned more about genetics, scientists have developed techniques to change genetic material within cells. Scientists have been able to isolate genes. The scientists also have been able to move genes from one cell to another and from one species to another. For example, in 1981, scientists moved a gene from a french bean seed into a sunflower.

This new technology, known as genetic engineering, shows great promise in areas such as medicine and farming. New drugs may be developed. Stronger, healthier animals may be bred. Better, more nutritious crops may be grown.

Some people, however, are worried about genetic engineering. They wonder what would happen if scientists accidentally released a dangerous new organism into the environment. Because of such concerns, in 1976 the National Institutes of Health (NIH) began to control genetic engineering. Figure 1 shows a time line on the development of the control of traits in plants and animals.

APPLYING CRITICAL THINKING SKILLS

1. How long ago did the domestication of animals first occur? How long ago did the domestication of plants first occur?
2. When were the first rules of genetics established?
3. In which century did most of the advances in genetics occur?
4. How long after scientists learned that genes are made up of DNA was the first gene cloned?
5. Why did the National Institutes of Health develop genetic engineering guidelines?
6. Many times, technologies become widely used before the problems they can cause are understood. Should the rate at which new developments are put into use be controlled? Why or why not?

Figure 1

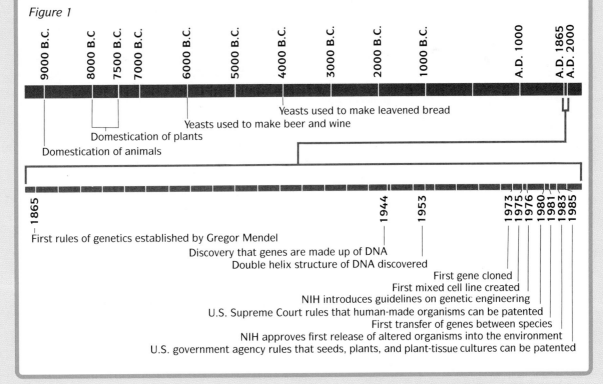

9000 B.C.
8000 B.C.
7500 B.C.
7000 B.C.
6000 B.C.
5000 B.C.
4000 B.C.
3000 B.C.
2000 B.C.
1000 B.C.
A.D. 1000
A.D. 1865
A.D. 2000

Yeasts used to make leavened bread
Yeasts used to make beer and wine
Domestication of plants
Domestication of animals

1865
1944
1953
1973
1975
1976
1980
1981
1983
1985

First rules of genetics established by Gregor Mendel
Discovery that genes are made up of DNA
Double helix structure of DNA discovered
First gene cloned
First mixed cell line created
NIH introduces guidelines on genetic engineering
U.S. Supreme Court rules that human-made organisms can be patented
First transfer of genes between species
NIH approves first release of altered organisms into the environment
U.S. government agency rules that seeds, plants, and plant-tissue cultures can be patented

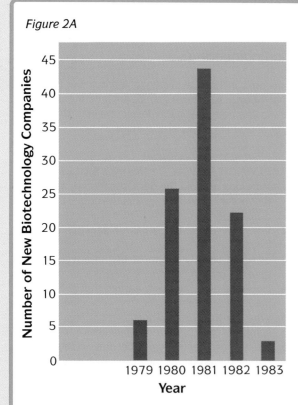

Figure 2A

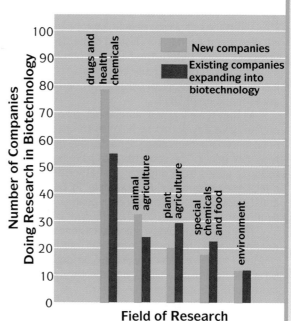

Figure 2B

Diseases, insect pests, and surprise frosts destroy or damage millions of dollars worth of farm crops each year. Genetic engineering could reduce much of this loss. For example, genetic engineers reported in May 1986 that they had given some plants hereditary resistance to viral infection. The researchers took a gene from a virus that attacks tomato and tobacco plants. The researchers transferred the gene to some cells of these plants. These cells then grew into plants resistant to the virus. Scientists hope that the same process can be used to make other crops, such as potatoes and green peppers, resistant to viruses.

Scientists also are working on genetically altered microorganisms that can be used to kill insect pests. An insect pest called a rootworm lives on the roots of corn plants. A certain kind of bacteria also lives on these roots. Scientists have engineered the bacteria to produce a protein that is deadly to the rootworms.

Many different products can be made by using genetically altered organisms. Because of this, many companies have sprung up to produce and sell these products. Figure 2 shows the increase in the number of biotechnology companies in the years from 1979 to 1983. *Biotechnology* refers to genetic engineering and other techniques that use microorganisms. The figure also shows the number of new companies and existing companies involved in different areas of genetic engineering. The same company may be involved in more than one field of biotechnology research.

APPLYING CRITICAL THINKING SKILLS

1. Look at Figure 2A. In which year did the greatest number of new biotechnology companies form? In which year did the least number of new companies form?
2. Why, do you think, did the number of new companies formed decrease after 1981?
3. Do you think the number of new companies will increase or decrease over the next 10 years? Explain your answer.
4. Look at Figure 2B. In which field is the greatest amount of research going on? Why, do you think, is this so?
5. Do you think the amount of research in each field is a good use of money and research time? Which fields should get more interest? Which should get less? Explain your answers.

Genetic engineering has many other possible uses. In addition to improving farming, it may lead to a cure for cancer, a vaccine for AIDS, new kinds of drugs, and new sources of chemicals. But some people worry that this technology could lead to serious problems if the work is not done slowly and carefully.

One concern about genetic engineering is that an altered bacterium or virus could get out of control in the environment. An organism made in the laboratory may have no natural enemies in the outside environment. Thus there would be nothing to control the population growth of such an organism.

People who oppose genetic engineering are quick to point to past cases when foreign organisms were introduced with ill effects. Both the Japanese beetle and the gypsy moth were brought into the United States for useful purposes. The populations of these insects grew rapidly, and they became pests.

Many times in the past, the use of a new technology or substance has had unexpected effects. The development of insect resistance to insecticides is one example of this. *Insecticides* are chemicals that are used to kill insects. Between 1970 and 1980 the number of species resistant to insecticides climbed from 224 to 428. Figure 3 shows the distribution of some insects that have become resistant to a certain insecticide. Some scientists fear that genetically engineered organisms can also become resistant to insecticides.

APPLYING CRITICAL THINKING SKILLS

1. Which resistant insect is more likely to spread out and cover new areas, the mosquito or the cattle tick? Explain your answer.
2. Suppose you were a farmer. If you were offered a choice between using insecticides or using genetically altered organisms to control pests, which method would you choose? Why? What are some of the factors you would consider before making a choice?
3. Consider the possible benefits and risks of genetic engineering. Do you think scientists should change the genes of living things? Why or why not?

Figure 3

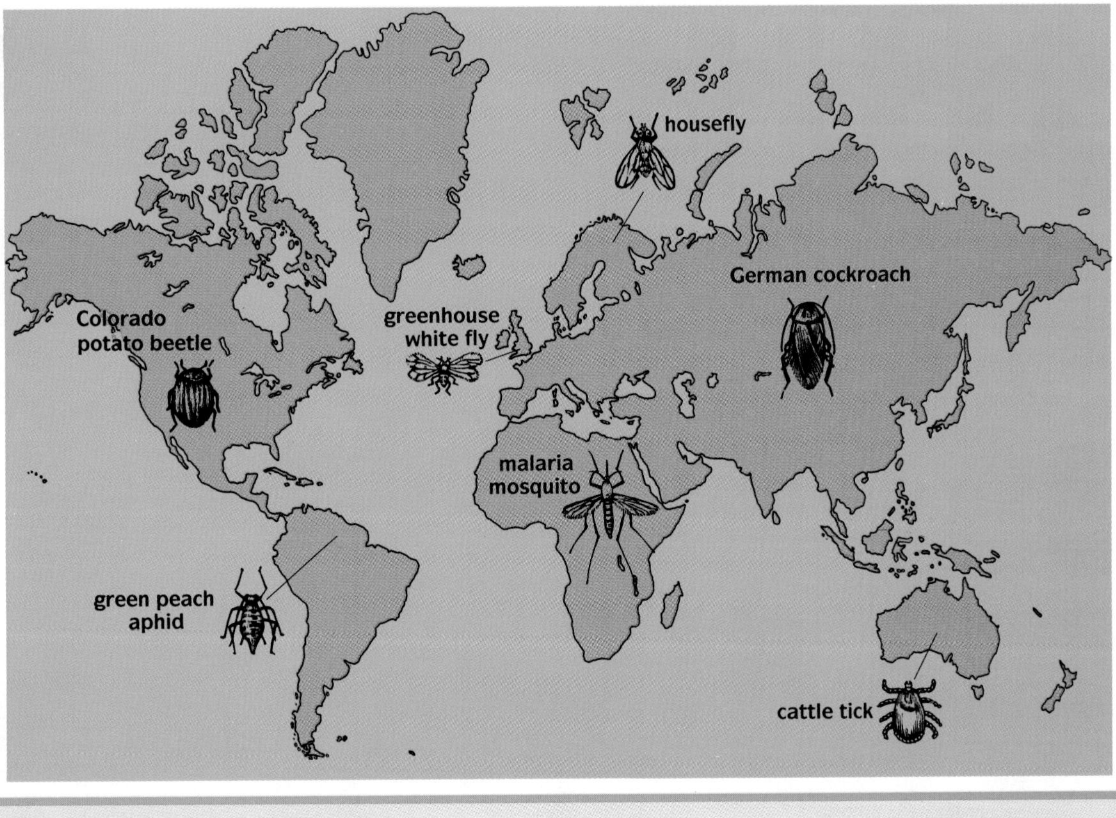

INVESTIGATING
MATTER AND ENERGY

Some kinds of motion, such as a person running, are easy to see. But the motion and energy within tiny particles of matter can be demonstrated by mathematical formulas and by modern equipment. In this unit you will learn about the composition of matter, how matter reacts to forces, and the various forms of matter.

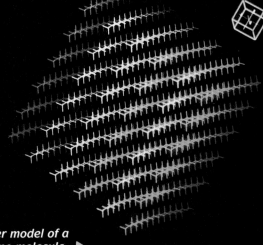

A computer model of a polyethylene molecule. ▶

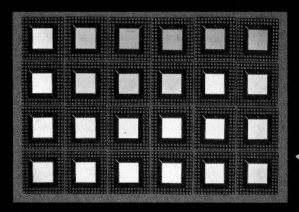

◀ An integrated circuit of a computer.

▼ The human body in motion.

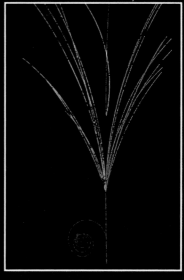

▲ *New kinds of particles are produced when an atom is smashed.*

◀ *Several laser beams are focused to produce white light.*

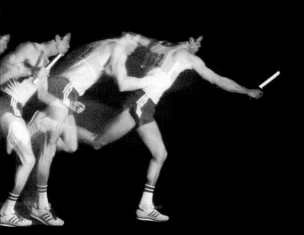

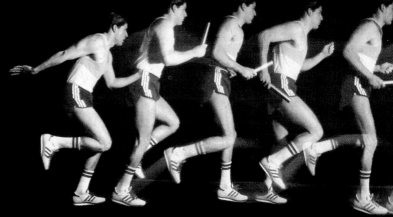

CHAPTER 8

MATTER

The photograph shows a highly magnified image of the surface of graphite. Notice the rows of graphite atoms. Atoms are the building blocks of all matter, including the earth, air, water, and all living things. Atoms are also extremely tiny. It would take more than 100 million atoms to equal the thickness of this page. Despite their small size, atoms are also great sources of energy. Uranium atoms are the fuel for nuclear power plants. Hydrogen atoms are the fuel that produces the sun's energy.

- *What is matter?*
- *How are hydrogen atoms different from uranium atoms?*
- *What is the structure of an atom?*

8·1 The Nature of Matter

KINDS OF MATTER

Everything around you is made of matter. The food you eat, the water you drink, and the air you breathe are all made of matter. **Matter** is anything that has mass and takes up space. Mass is a measure of the amount of matter in a material. Everything you can see, touch, or taste has mass and takes up space. Everything is made of matter.

A sample of matter that has the same makeup throughout is called a substance. Gold, silver, water, salt, and sugar are examples of substances. The particles in gold are the same. The particles in silver are the same. But the particles in gold are different from those in silver.

There are three kinds of matter. They are elements, compounds, and mixtures. An element is a substance that cannot be broken down into simpler substances. Gold, silver, and copper are examples of elements. A *compound* is a substance made of two or more elements that cannot be separated by physical means. For example, water is a compound made of the elements hydrogen and oxygen. Water cannot be broken down into hydrogen and oxygen by physical means. A combination of two or more substances that can be separated by physical means

Figure 8·1

Gold is an element *(A)*. Water is a compound *(B)*. Oil and vinegar dressing is a mixture *(C)*.

Figure 8·2
A mixture can be separated by physical means. What property of iron allows it to be separated from sand?

is called a *mixture*. Figure 8·2 shows a mixture of iron and sand. Notice how the iron can be separated from the sand with a magnet. Examples of common mixtures include air, soil, and salt water.

PROPERTIES OF MATTER

You can use the properties of matter to tell one type of matter from another. A *property* is a characteristic that describes a material. There are two types of properties: physical properties and chemical properties. A **physical property** of a material can be observed without changing the material. Color, odor, and taste are some of the physical properties of matter.

Another physical property of matter is density. **Density** is the amount of mass in a given volume. The SI unit for density is g/cm³. For example, the density of water is 1.0 g/cm³. This means a sample of water occupying a volume of 1.0 cm³ has a mass of 1.0 g.

densus (thick)

The density of a substance is a measure of how tightly the particles of matter in it are packed. The higher the density, the greater the amount of matter in a given volume of that substance. For example, recall that the density of water is 1.0 g/cm³. Mercury has a density of 13.6 g/cm³. A sample of mercury occupying the same volume as a sample of water would have 13.6 times as much mass as the water.

Figure 8·3

The tarnishing of silver is a chemical reaction. What element in air does the silver react with?

The density of a material compared with the density of water is called *specific gravity*. Since the density of mercury is 13.6 times that of water, mercury has a specific gravity of 13.6. The density of silver is 10.5 g/cm^3, or 10.5 times that of water. Thus the specific gravity of silver is 10.5. Notice that specific gravity has no SI unit.

Physical properties, such as density, do not describe how substances can change. Paper changes when it burns. Iron changes when it rusts. The ability to burn and the ability to rust are examples of chemical properties. In each example, new substances are formed. A change that produces one or more different kinds of substances is called a *chemical change*. A **chemical property** of a material describes how the particles of matter react and change with other kinds of matter. Paper burns in the presence of oxygen when heated to a high enough temperature. Thus one chemical property of paper is that it reacts with oxygen and burns.

STATES OF MATTER

Matter exists in four states: solid, liquid, gas, and plasma. A *solid* is matter that has a definite shape and definite volume. A *liquid* is matter that has a definite volume but not a definite shape. Notice in Figure 8·4 that the orange juice takes the shape of the container it is in. A *gas* is matter that has no definite volume and no definite shape. A gas takes the shape of its container. It also expands to fill its container.

Figure 8·4

The amount of orange juice is the same in each of the glasses. What property of a liquid does the orange juice show?

ACTIVITY   How Is Density Determined?

OBJECTIVE
Compare the densities of two liquids.

MATERIALS
safety goggles, laboratory apron, 10-mL graduate, balance and masses, distilled water, rubbing alcohol

PROCEDURE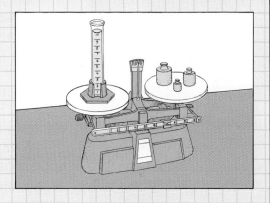

A. Wear safety goggles and a laboratory apron during this activity.

B. Draw a data table like the one shown.

C. Measure the mass of a clean, dry 10-mL graduate. Record the mass in the data table.

D. Add 10 mL of distilled water to the graduate. Record this volume in the table in cm³. (1 mL = 1 cm³) Measure the mass of the graduate and water, and record it in the data table.

E. Repeat steps **C** and **D** with rubbing alcohol.

F. Find the mass of the water and the mass of the rubbing alcohol.

G. Find the density of each liquid by using the following formula.

$$D = \frac{M}{V}$$

Record your answers in the data table.

RESULTS AND CONCLUSIONS
1. What is the density of water?
2. What is the density of the rubbing alcohol?
3. Which of the two liquids is more dense?

LIQUID	VOLUME (cm³)	MASS OF GRADUATE (g)	MASS OF GRADUATE AND LIQUID (g)	MASS OF LIQUID (g)	DENSITY (g/cm³)
Distilled water					
Rubbing alcohol					

When a gas is heated to a very high temperature, it becomes the form of matter called plasma. *Plasma* is a hot gas in which the particles are electrically charged. Matter in the sun and stars is in the form of plasma. But plasma is not found in nature on the earth.

Matter can change from one state to another. For example, ice melts to form water. Ice is water in the solid state. When solid water changes to liquid water, it changes state. It does not become another substance. A change of state is an example of a

Most substances are denser in the solid state than in the liquid state. Water, however, is an exception. This can be shown by the fact that ice floats in water. Explain why water's density decreases when it freezes.

physical change. A *physical change* is a change in which the appearance of matter changes but its chemical makeup remains the same.

The temperatures at which changes of state take place are physical properties. The temperature at which a solid becomes a liquid is called the melting point. The melting point of ice is 0°C. Different substances have different melting points. Copper melts at 1083°C. Solid mercury melts at −39°C. How does this melting point explain why mercury usually exists as a liquid?

When water boils, it changes from its liquid state to its gas state, water vapor. The temperature at which a liquid boils at sea level is the boiling point of the liquid. The boiling point of water is 100°C. Other substances have different boiling points. Liquid nitrogen boils at −196°C. Liquid oxygen boils at −184°C.

Figure 8·5

The melting of ice is a physical change.

REVIEW

1. What is matter?
2. Compare the four states of matter.
3. Give two examples of physical properties and two examples of chemical properties.

CHALLENGE Water boils at 100°C at sea level. In Denver, Colorado, which is about 1.6 km above sea level, water boils at 95°C. What factor or factors might cause water to boil at the lower temperature in Denver?

8·2 The Atom

Can ordinary, everyday metals be changed into silver or gold? In the sixteenth century, scientists called alchemists tried to turn lead into gold. They were unsuccessful because lead is an element different from gold. To understand how elements are different, you must first understand what elements are made of.

Elements are made of small units called atoms. Atoms are the basic units of an element. An **atom** is the smallest particle of an element that has the properties of that element. Thus each atom of iron has the properties of iron. And all iron atoms behave the same. Likewise, all copper atoms behave the same. But copper atoms do not behave like iron atoms.

THE PARTICLES IN THE ATOM

Figure 8·6 shows a model of an atom of carbon. Notice that it contains three types of smaller particles — protons, neutrons, and electrons. The protons and neutrons make up the nucleus. The **nucleus** is the central part of an atom. The nucleus has almost all the mass of the atom. A **proton** is a positively charged particle found in the nucleus. A **neutron** is a particle with no charge, also found in the nucleus.

After completing this section, you will be able to

- **describe** the particles in an atom.
- **relate** the terms *atomic number* and *mass number* to particles in an atom.
- **list** chemical symbols of some atoms.

The key terms in this section are

atom	neutron
chemical	nucleus
symbol	proton
electron	

a- (without)
tomas (cutting)

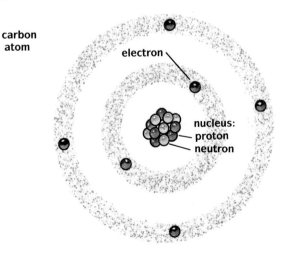

carbon atom

electron

nucleus:
proton
neutron

Figure 8·6

An atom of carbon contains 6 protons, 6 neutrons, and 6 electrons.

The negatively charged particle in an atom is the **electron**. Electrons move around the nucleus. The charge of an electron is equal and opposite to that of a proton. In an atom there are the same number of electrons and protons. Thus the atom has no charge.

The number of protons in an atom determines the atom's identity. Each atom of lead has 82 protons. Each atom of gold has 79 protons. To make an atom of lead into an atom of gold, the number of protons in the lead atom would have to be changed.

The number of protons in an atom is called the *atomic number*. Hydrogen, the simplest atom, has an atomic number of 1. Uranium has an atomic number of 92. How many protons are found in a uranium atom?

Figure 8·7

Uranium is an important energy source *(left)*. The uranium nucleus contains 92 protons *(right)*.

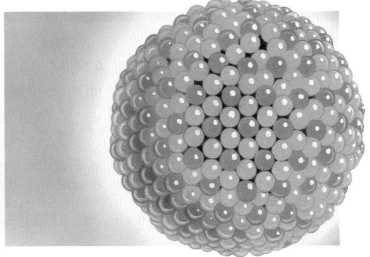

Atoms can also be described by their mass number. The *mass number* is the number of protons and neutrons in an atom. For example, a chlorine atom contains 17 protons and 18 neutrons. Thus the mass number of the chlorine atom is 17 + 18, or 35.

Atoms of the same element always have the same atomic number. But atoms of the same element can have different mass numbers. The mass number can vary because an element can have atoms with different numbers of neutrons. Atoms of the same element with different mass numbers are called *isotopes* (ɪ suh tohps).

CHEMICAL SYMBOLS

A system of chemical symbols is used to stand for atoms or elements. A **chemical symbol** is a notation of one or two letters that represents an atom or element. The chemical symbols of elements with atomic numbers 1–20 are shown in Table 8·1. Notice that the first letter of each symbol is an upper-case letter. If a second letter is used, it is always a lower-case letter. A symbol may be the first letter or first two letters of the name of the element.

Figure 8·8
The elements aluminum *(top)* and phosphorus *(bottom)*. What are the symbols and atomic numbers for these elements?

Table 8·1 *Symbols of Elements with Atomic Numbers 1 – 20*

ELEMENT	SYMBOL	ATOMIC NUMBER
Hydrogen	H	1
Helium	He	2
Lithium	Li	3
Beryllium	Be	4
Boron	B	5
Carbon	C	6
Nitrogen	N	7
Oxygen	O	8
Fluorine	F	9
Neon	Ne	10
Sodium	Na	11
Magnesium	Mg	12
Aluminum	Al	13
Silicon	Si	14
Phosphorus	P	15
Sulfur	S	16
Chlorine	Cl	17
Argon	Ar	18
Potassium	K	19
Calcium	Ca	20

REVIEW

1. What particles make up an atom? Describe each particle.
2. Define the terms *atomic number* and *mass number.*
3. Name the element that each of the following symbols represents: Na, N, Al, P, K.

CHALLENGE Explain why the heavier elements have more isotopes than lighter elements.

8·3 Elements and Compounds

After completing this section, you will be able to

- **distinguish** between elements and compounds.
- **use** a chemical formula to show the makeup of a compound.
- **describe** how covalent and ionic bonds form.

The key terms in this section are
chemical formula
compound
covalent bond
ionic bond
molecule

com- (together)
ponere (put)

Look at the many different kinds of matter around you. If you were to count them, these substances would probably total in the hundreds. But they are mostly made of just a few elements. In fact, only 88 elements make up the billions of different substances that exist on the earth. How can so few elements produce the great variety of substances?

Elements can be thought of as the building blocks that make up all matter. The fact that matter is composed of elements has been known for only the past few hundred years. This is because most elements do not occur alone in nature. Instead they combine to form the many different types of substances. When elements combine, they have different properties from those they have when alone. Thus the elements are difficult to identify.

The chemical combination of two or more elements is called a **compound**. The elements that make up a compound cannot be separated except by chemical means. For example, water is a compound made up of the elements hydrogen and oxygen. Water cannot be broken down into hydrogen and oxygen except by a chemical reaction.

Figure 8·9
Sugar, ammonia, sodium hyperchlorite in bleach, baking powder, and soap are compounds.

Figure 8·10
When wood burns, it is broken down into the element carbon.

The properties of a compound are different from the properties of the elements that make up the compound. For example, the properties of water are not the same as the properties of the hydrogen and oxygen that make it up. At room temperature, water is usually a liquid. Hydrogen and oxygen are gases at room temperature. Liquid water is used to put out fires. Hydrogen burns, and many things burn in oxygen.

The elements in a compound are combined in a definite proportion. Water and hydrogen peroxide are compounds made up of hydrogen and oxygen. But the properties of hydrogen peroxide are different from those of water. Hydrogen peroxide is an antiseptic and is poisonous to drink. In the compound water, two hydrogen atoms combine with one oxygen atom. In the compound hydrogen peroxide, two hydrogen atoms combine with two oxygen atoms. The hydrogen atoms and oxygen atoms are combined in different proportions in each compound.

Almost all common substances are compounds. Water, sugar, and salt are simple compounds. Plastics, rubber, and many of the foods you eat are complex compounds. The human body contains complex compounds called proteins. Proteins make up tissues and muscles in the body.

CHEMICAL FORMULAS

Scientists use chemical symbols and formulas when writing about matter and its changes. Recall that a symbol is used to stand for an element. A formula stands for a compound.

A **chemical formula** is a group of chemical symbols that shows the makeup of a compound. The formula NaCl stands for the compound sodium chloride. The formula shows that the elements sodium (Na) and chlorine (Cl) make up sodium chloride.

Table 8·2 *Formulas of Household Substances*

SUBSTANCE	FORMULA
Sugar	$C_{12}H_{22}O_{11}$
Ammonia	NH_3
Chlorine bleach	NaOCl
Baking powder	$NaHCO_3$
Soap	$C_{17}H_{35}COONa$
Table salt	NaCl
Rubbing alcohol	C_3H_7OH

The formula for water is H_2O. It shows that the elements hydrogen (H) and oxygen (O) are not present in equal amounts. The 2 after the H is a subscript. A subscript shows the proportion of an element in a compound. The 2 after the H shows that there are two hydrogen atoms in the formula for water. Notice that there is no subscript after the O. This means that there is only one atom of oxygen. Thus the formula H_2O represents a compound that has two hydrogen atoms for every oxygen atom.

Most compounds are made up of more than two elements. Look at Table 8·2. The formula for sugar shows that it is made up of the elements carbon, hydrogen, and oxygen. How many atoms of each element are there in the formula?

Figure 8·11

Graphite is made of the element carbon.

CHEMICAL BONDS

Diamond is the hardest substance known to humans. It is made of pure carbon. Graphite is a substance that is also made of pure carbon. Yet it is soft enough to be used as the "lead" in pencils. How can this difference in hardness be explained?

Part of the answer lies in how strongly the atoms in each substance are held together. In both substances the carbon atoms are held together by forces called *chemical bonds*. Chemical bonds can be thought of as the glue that holds matter together. The chemical bonds between carbon atoms are stronger in diamond than in graphite.

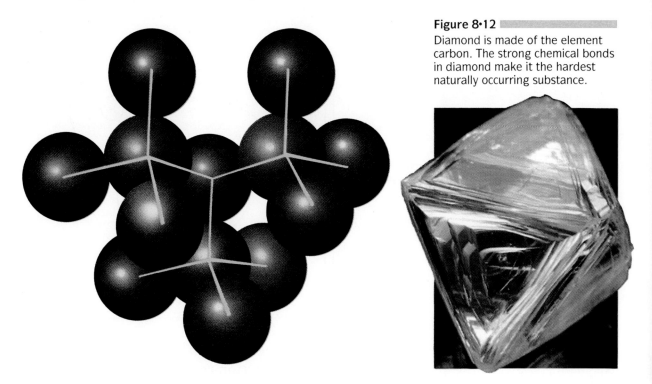

Figure 8·12
Diamond is made of the element carbon. The strong chemical bonds in diamond make it the hardest naturally occurring substance.

Where do chemical bonds come from? They come from the force of attraction between oppositely charged particles. In one type of bond, atoms become charged when one atom loses an electron to another atom. An atom that loses or gains an electron becomes an *ion*. The atom becomes a positive ion if it loses an electron. The atom becomes a negative ion if it gains an electron.

Ions that have opposite charges attract each other. The force of attraction is strong enough to hold the ions together. The force of attraction between two oppositely charged ions is called an **ionic bond**. In the compound sodium chloride, sodium atoms and chlorine atoms are held together by ionic bonds.

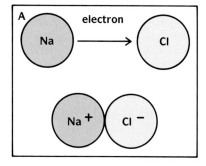

Figure 8·13A shows how an ionic bond forms between a sodium atom and a chlorine atom. The sodium atom loses an electron to a chlorine atom. The sodium atom becomes a positive ion. The chlorine atom becomes a negative ion. The two oppositely charged ions attract each other. The force of attraction between the positive and negative ions holds them together.

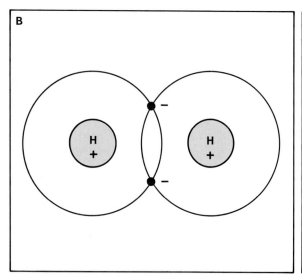

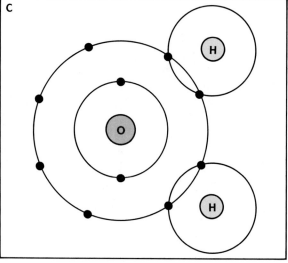

Figure 8·13

The ionic bond in sodium chloride forms when an electron is transferred from a sodium ion to a chlorine atom *(A)*. The covalent bond in H_2 results from the sharing of two electrons between hydrogen atoms *(B)*. The covalent bond in H_2O *(C)*.

In another type of bond, called a **covalent bond,** a force of attraction results when two atoms share electrons. Figure 8·13B shows how a covalent bond forms between two hydrogen atoms in hydrogen gas, H_2. Notice that the two hydrogen atoms share a pair of electrons. Each hydrogen atom has one electron. Each atom "borrows" one electron from the other. The negative charge of the shared pair attracts the two positive hydrogen nuclei. This attractive force holds the two hydrogen atoms together.

The atoms of hydrogen and oxygen in water are held together by covalent bonds. As shown in Figure 8·13C, the oxygen atom shares one of its electrons with one hydrogen atom, and another electron with the other hydrogen atom. Each hydrogen atom shares its electron with the oxygen atom. The result is two covalent bonds.

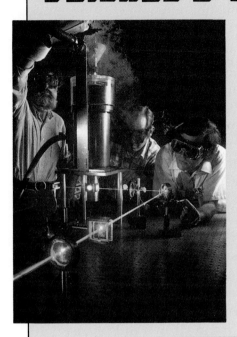

Scientists are developing a computer system that uses molecules to store information. Called a molecular data-storage system, it will be able to store 100,000 times as much information as the best computer systems in use today. This is equal to storing on a 3-inch disk the information found in all of the telephone books in the United States. The key to storing so much information is the extremely small sizes of molecules.

The molecules are first placed in a crystalline material, such as glass. The material is then used as a coating on a tiny chip smaller than a fingernail. Then thousands of different wavelengths of laser beams are used to strike the molecules. Each wavelength of laser beam changes certain groups of molecules. The different molecular structures are used like different letters to represent information.

At present the system works only at very low temperatures, near −273°C At higher temperatures the atoms in the crystalline material vibrate so much that information is lost. To make the system practical, scientists have to find crystalline materials that will work at room temperature.

A combination of two or more atoms held together by a covalent bond is called a **molecule.** A molecule of a substance is the smallest unit that still has the same properties as the substance. A molecule can be made of atoms of the same element. For example, a molecule of hydrogen gas, H_2, contains only hydrogen atoms. A molecule can also be made of atoms of different elements. For example, a molecule of water, H_2O, contains hydrogen and oxygen atoms.

moles (mass)

REVIEW

1. How are elements and compounds different?
2. Give two examples of an element and two examples of a compound.
3. Write the chemical formula of a compound in Table 8·2. Identify the elements and their proportion in the compound.
4. What is an ionic bond? How do ionic bonds form?
5. How does a covalent bond form?

CHALLENGE Can the compound NaCl exist as a molecule? Explain your answer.

8·4 Mixtures

KINDS OF MIXTURES

A **mixture** is a combination of substances that can be separated by physical means. In a mixture, each substance keeps its own properties. Iron has the property of being attracted by a magnet. In a mixture of iron powder and sulfur, the iron keeps its magnetic properties. As shown in Figure 8·14*A*, the iron and sulfur can be identified by their different colors.

If the mixture of iron and sulfur is heated, a compound called iron sulfide, FeS, is formed. Since the iron and sulfur have been chemically combined, they no longer have their own properties. Notice in Figure 8·14*B* that the iron can not be identified.

The raisins in the bread shown in Figure 8·14*C* can be removed by tearing the bread apart. The ability to separate the raisins from the bread by physical means shows one property of a mixture. The parts of a mixture can be separated without a chemical reaction.

If the makeup of samples taken from a mixture varies, the mixture is called *heterogeneous* (heht-uhr uh JEE nee uhs). For example, if you examine

Figure 8·14

A mixture of iron and sulfer *(A)*. A compound of iron and sulfer *(B)*. Raisin bread is a mixture of bread and raisins *(C)*.

ACTIVITY   How Can Substances in Mixtures Be Separated?

OBJECTIVE
Separate the different substances in a mixture.

MATERIALS
safety goggles, laboratory apron, table salt, sand, balance and masses, weighing paper, test tube, rubber stopper, water, graduate, filter paper, funnel, beaker, evaporating dish, ring stand, ring, wire gauze, Bunsen burner, matches, tongs

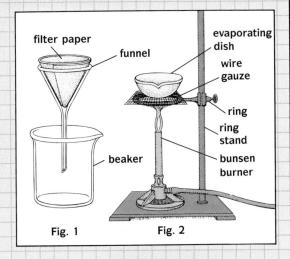

Fig. 1   Fig. 2

PROCEDURE
A. Wear safety goggles and a laboratory apron during this activity.

B. Examine some table salt and sand.

C. Measure 1.0 g of salt and 1.0 g of sand separately.

D. Mix these amounts of salt and sand in a test tube. Stopper the test tube, and shake it well. Examine the mixture of solids.

   1. Can you distinguish the salt from the sand?

E. Remove the stopper from the test tube. Pour water into the test tube, filling it about halfway. Stopper the test tube, and shake it well.

   2. Describe the mixture.

F. Fold a piece of filter paper into quarters. Place it in a funnel. Pour the mixture into the funnel, as shown in Figure 1.

   3. What is left on the filter paper?

G. Transfer some of the remaining solution into an evaporating dish. Set up a ring stand, ring, wire gauze, Bunsen burner, and the evaporating dish as shown in Figure 2.

H. Heat the dish over the Bunsen burner until all the liquid has evaporated. When the dish has cooled, remove it from the ring stand with the tongs.

   4. What is the solid remaining in the evaporating dish?

RESULTS AND CONCLUSIONS
1. What kind of mixture did you have in step **D**?

2. What properties of salt and sand allowed them to be separated by physical means?

various slices of raisin bread closely, you will see that they do not always have the same makeup. Some slices may have more raisins than do other slices. Also, the makeup within each slice can vary.

If all the samples of a mixture have the same makeup, the mixture is called *homogeneous* (hoh-muh JEE nee uhs). Seawater is a homogeneous mixture. It contains salt, calcium, and many other substances dissolved in water.

SOLUTIONS

Most homogeneous mixtures are solutions. A **solution** is a homogeneous mixture of two or more substances. Solutions can be made by mixing substances in solid, liquid, or gas states. The blood in your body is a solution. The gasoline used in cars is a solution. Dental fillings are solid solutions of mercury in silver. A soft drink is a solution of carbon dioxide gas in flavored water.

The substance that is present in the greater amount in the solution is called the *solvent*. The substance present in the smaller amount is called the solute. In a soft drink the flavored water is the solvent, and the carbon dioxide gas is the solute. Some solutions have more than one solute. Seawater is a solution in which many solutes are dissolved in water.

Figure 8·15

A suspension separates if left standing *(left)*. A colloid has suspended particles that can be seen *(right)*.

SUSPENSIONS AND COLLOIDS

In a solution the solute particles cannot be seen. They will not settle to the bottom of the container, no matter how long the solution stands. But if a mixture of oil and vinegar is left standing, the mixture separates, as shown in Figure 8·15. A mixture of oil and vinegar is a suspension. A **suspension** is a heterogeneous mixture in which the particles are temporarily mixed in a liquid. The particles in a suspension can be seen.

A **colloid** (KAHL oid) is a mixture whose properties are between those of a solution and those of a suspension. Smoke, fog, mayonnaise, and raw egg white are examples of colloids. Like solutions, colloids do not separate upon standing. As in suspensions, the particles in colloids can be seen.

REVIEW

1. What is the difference between a homogeneous mixture and a heterogeneous mixture?
2. Give one example of a solution, a suspension, and a colloid.

CHALLENGE A ray of sunlight can be seen in a dark room. How does this show that air is a colloid?

CHAPTER SUMMARY

The main ideas in this chapter are listed below. Read these statements before you complete the Chapter Review.

- Matter is anything that has mass and takes up space. (8·1)
- Matter has four states: solid, liquid, gas, and plasma. (8·1)
- An element is a substance that cannot be changed into simpler substances by simple means. (8·1)
- The smallest piece of an element is called an atom. An atom consists of protons and neutrons, which make up the nucleus, and electrons, which move around the nucleus. (8·2)
- An atom can be described by its atomic number and mass number. (8·2)
- A chemical symbol is a notation of one or two letters that represents an element. (8·2)
- A compound is a substance made of two or more elements that are chemically joined. (8·3)
- A chemical formula is used to show the makeup of a compound. (8·3)

- An ionic bond is a force of attraction between oppositely charged ions. (8·3)
- Covalent bonds are formed when atoms share electrons. (8·3)
- Mixtures are made of two or more substances that can be separated by physical means. Homogeneous mixtures are the same throughout. Heterogeneous mixtures are not the same throughout. (8·4)
- A solution is a homogeneous mixture. The particles in a solution never settle out. (8·4)
- A suspension is a heterogeneous mixture that has particles of a substance temporarily mixed in a liquid. The particles of a suspension will settle if the mixture is left standing. (8·4)
- A colloid has properties between those of a solution and those of a suspension. The particles of a colloid will not settle if the mixture is left standing. (8·4)

The key terms in this chapter are listed below. Use each term in a sentence that shows the meaning of the terms.

atom	compound	matter	physical property
chemical formula	covalent bond	mixture	proton
chemical property	density	molecule	solution
chemical symbol	electron	neutron	suspension
colloid	ionic bond	nucleus	

Chapter Review

VOCABULARY

Use the key terms from the previous page to complete the following sentences correctly.

1. Anything that has mass and takes up space is called _____.
2. A/an _____ is used to represent a compound.
3. Mass divided by volume gives the _____.
4. The central part of an atom is called the _____.
5. The smallest particle of an element that has the properties of that element is called a/an _____.
6. Two or more atoms joined by a covalent bond are called a/an _____.
7. The color of an object is an example of a/an _____.
8. A substance made up of two or more elements that are chemically joined is called a/an _____.
9. Two or more substances that can be separated by physical means are called a/an _____.
10. A mixture in which particles remain suspended and do not settle out is called a/an _____.

CONCEPTS

Write the correct term for each number in the diagram.

1. _____
2. _____
3. _____
4. _____
5. _____

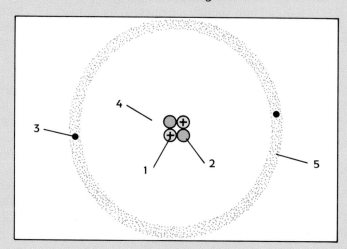

Choose the term or phrase that best answers the question or completes the statement.

6. Which of the following forms of matter occurs naturally in stars?
   a. solid   **b.** liquid   **c.** gas   **d.** plasma
7. An atom contains five protons, five electrons, and six neutrons. What is the mass number of the atom?
   a. 5   **b.** 10   **c.** 11   **d.** 1

8. When an atom becomes an ion, which number of particles changes?
   a. electrons   b. protons   c. neutrons   d. nuclei
9. Substances can be separated by physical means in a/an
   a. element.
   b. compound.
   c. mixture.
   d. atom.
10. Which of the following types of mixtures has samples that always have the same composition?
    a. solution
    b. colloid
    c. suspension
    d. heterogeneous mixture

Answer the following in complete sentences.
11. What are the three states of matter that normally exist on the earth? Give one example of each.
12. Give two examples of physical changes and two examples of chemical changes.
13. List and give the location of each particle in the atom.
14. What is the difference between a covalent bond and an ionic bond?
15. What is the difference between a solute and a solvent? Give an example of each.

APPLICATION/ CRITICAL THINKING

1. Two substances have the same melting and boiling points. You want more evidence to determine whether the two substances are the same. What other properties would you investigate?
2. A student has two blocks with the same volume. One block is made of wood, and the other of cork. The density of the wood is 0.7 g/cm³. The density of the cork is 0.24 g/cm³. How many times heavier than the cork block is the wood block?
3. What tests can be used to find out if a liquid is a solution?

EXTENSION

1. The hydrogen isotopes have the same chemical properties. Do research to find out if they have the same physical properties.
2. Look up the term *electronegativity,* and explain how electronegativity can help to determine the type of chemical bonds that exist in a compound.
3. Find out what an emulsifier is. Present to your class a report on the uses of emulsifiers.

CHAPTER 9

CHANGES IN MATTER

The bright colors in fireworks come from the burning of chemical elements. You may think of burning as a process that destroys matter. However, no matter is lost. In fact, the burning of elements creates new substances.

To understand how elements can form new substances, you must understand how atoms in matter combine to form molecules. You must understand the nature of the chemical bonds that hold matter together. And you must understand how energy is involved when matter changes.

- *Where does the energy in fireworks come from?*
- *What role does oxygen play in burning?*
- *What forms of energy are released when matter burns?*

9·1 Chemical Equations

CHEMICAL REACTIONS

A **chemical reaction** is a process in which one or more substances are changed into one or more different substances. In a chemical reaction the original substances are changed. They cannot be recognized in the new material or materials. For example, iron is a gray solid. Oxygen is a colorless gas. When these chemicals react, they form rust, a reddish-brown solid. Look at the rust shown in Figure 9·1. How does the paint on a car prevent rust?

During a chemical reaction, atoms in substances are rearranged. Chemical bonds are broken, and new bonds are formed. When oxygen combines with iron, the bonds that hold the oxygen atoms together are broken. New bonds form between the iron atoms and the oxygen atoms.

Figure 9·1
The process of rusting is a chemical reaction.

CHEMICAL EQUATIONS

Scientists use chemical equations to describe chemical reactions. A **chemical equation** is a shorthand way to show the changes that take place in a reaction. The reaction between carbon and oxygen can be shown by the following word equation.

carbon plus oxygen yields carbon dioxide

Often, symbols and formulas are used in place of words in a chemical equation. Symbols show the elements in the reaction. Formulas show the number of atoms present. The word equation above can be written by using chemical formulas.

$$C + O_2 \longrightarrow CO_2$$

In this equation, an atom of carbon is shown by C, a molecule of oxygen is shown by O_2, and a molecule of carbon dioxide is shown by CO_2. The arrow is read as "yields."

The starting substances in a chemical reaction are called **reactants**. The new substances that are formed in a reaction are called **products**. In a chemical equation, reactants are written to the left of the arrow. Products are written to the right. In the equation above, carbon and oxygen are the reactants, and carbon dioxide is the product.

THE LAW OF CONSERVATION OF MASS

Careful study of chemical reactions led to the discovery of the Law of Conservation of Mass. The **Law of Conservation of Mass** states that in a chemical reaction the total mass of the reactants equals the total mass of the products. The law also states that the atoms can be rearranged, but the number of atoms on each side of the equation stays the same.

An equation that obeys the Law of Conservation of Mass is called a *balanced equation*.

Water can be separated into hydrogen and oxygen. This reaction is shown by the equation

$$H_2O \longrightarrow H_2 + O_2$$

This equation shows the makeup of a molecule of water. Water is made of two atoms of hydrogen and one atom of oxygen. What is the makeup of one molecule of oxygen? Notice that the number of oxygen atoms on each side of the equation is not the same. Because one oxygen atom cannot form two oxygen atoms, the equation is not correct. However, the formulas for water, hydrogen, and oxygen are correct. These formulas cannot be changed to show the same number of oxygen atoms on each side of the equation.

To make the number of atoms on each side of the equation equal, coefficients are used. A *coefficient* (koh uh FIHSH uhnt) is a whole number placed in front of a symbol or formula to show the number of atoms or molecules in the reaction. Coefficients can be used to change an equation so that the number of atoms on the left side is equal to, or balanced with, the number on the right side. Changing the coefficients is called balancing the equation. Placing a 2 in front of H_2O and a 2 in front of H_2 will balance this equation.

$$2H_2O \longrightarrow 2H_2 + O_2$$

PUZZLER

The flash given off by a flashbulb is caused by the burning of magnesium. Do you think the mass of the flashbulb after the flash is different from that before the flash? What experiment could you do to check your answer?

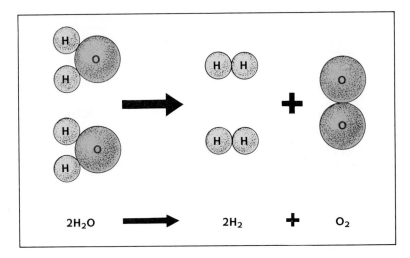

Figure 9·3
When water breaks down into hydrogen and oxygen, the number of atoms of hydrogen and oxygen remains the same.

Figure 9·3 shows two water molecules being separated into hydrogen and oxygen. Compare the number of atoms on each side of the equation.

A balanced equation can also be used to show that the total mass of the reactants is equal to the total mass of the products. The atomic mass of hydrogen is 1. Thus a molecule of hydrogen has a mass of 2. The atomic mass of oxygen is 16. Thus a molecule of oxygen has a mass of 32. Water has a mass of 18. These values are used in the balanced equation for this reaction.

$$2H_2O \longrightarrow 2H_2 + O_2$$
$$2(18) = 2(2) + 32$$
$$36 = 4 + 32$$
$$36 = 36$$

REVIEW

1. What is a chemical reaction?
2. Write a word equation to describe each of the following reactions.
   a. $Fe + Cl_2 \longrightarrow FeCl_2$
   b. $Mg + S \longrightarrow MgS$
   c. $Zn + Cl_2 \longrightarrow ZnCl_2$
3. Tell whether each of the following chemical equations obey the Law of Conservation of Mass.
   a. $H_2O \longrightarrow H_2 + O_2$
   b. $C + O_2 \longrightarrow CO_2$
   c. $KCl + AgNO_3 \longrightarrow AgCl + KNO_3$

CHALLENGE When a piece of wood is burned, the ashes that remain weigh less than the original wood did. Does the Law of Conservation of Mass still hold true?

203

9·2 Synthesis and Decomposition Reactions

After completing this section,
you will be able to

- **distinguish** between a
  synthesis reaction and a
  decomposition reaction.
- **identify** examples of synthesis reactions and decomposition reactions.

The key terms in this section are
decomposition reaction
synthesis reaction

syn- (together with)

SYNTHESIS REACTIONS

A **synthesis reaction** is a reaction in which two or more substances combine to form a compound. This type of reaction can be shown by the following general equation.

$$A + X \longrightarrow AX$$

The A and the X are the reactants. The product is AX. One example of this type of reaction is the reaction between the elements sodium and chlorine. Sodium and chlorine combine to form the compound sodium chloride, which is common table salt. The equation for this reaction is as follows.

$$2Na + Cl_2 \longrightarrow 2NaCl$$

Another synthesis reaction takes place when the element magnesium is burned in air. When magnesium burns, it combines with oxygen from the air. The compound magnesium oxide is formed. The equation for this reaction is as follows.

$$2Mg + O_2 \longrightarrow 2MgO$$

Figure 9·4 shows the flare produced when magnesium reacts with oxygen. The bright flash of light is some of the energy released by the reaction. This reaction causes the flash in flashbulbs.

Figure 9·4

The burning of magnesium is a chemical reaction between magnesium and oxygen.

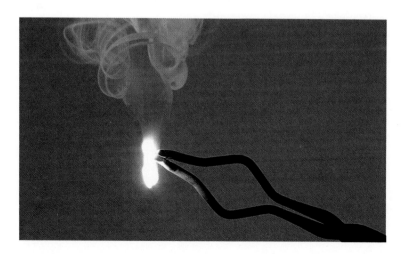

204

Compounds also can combine in synthesis reactions. Ammonia and hydrogen chloride are both compounds. They combine to form ammonium chloride. This compound is used to make fertilizers, dyes, and cough medicines. The equation for the reaction is as follows.

$$NH_3 + HCl \longrightarrow NH_4Cl$$

When sulfur trioxide, SO_3, is mixed with water, the product is sulfuric acid, H_2SO_4. This acid is used in making dyes, explosives, and rayon. The equation for the synthesis of sulfuric acid is shown.

$$SO_3 + H_2O \longrightarrow H_2SO_4$$

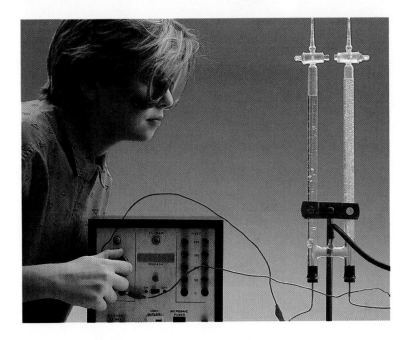

Figure 9·5
Electricity is used to break down water into hydrogen gas and oxygen gas. How can you tell which glass tube contains the hydrogen?

DECOMPOSITION REACTIONS

A **decomposition reaction** is a reaction in which a compound breaks down into two or more substances. Such a reaction can be shown by this general equation.

$$AX \longrightarrow A + X$$

The AX is the reactant. The A and the X are the products. An example of a decomposition reaction is the breakdown of water into hydrogen and oxygen. This reaction is shown in Figure 9·5.

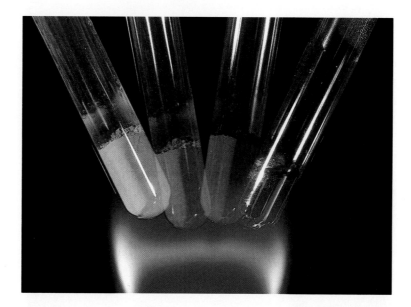

Figure 9·6

When heated, red mercuric oxide decomposes into silver mercury.

Another decomposition reaction is the breakdown of mercury (II) oxide, shown in Figure 9·6. The mercury (II) oxide is the orange-red powder. When heated it breaks down into mercury, which is a shiny liquid metal, and oxygen, a colorless gas. This decomposition reaction can be shown by the following equation.

$$2HgO \longrightarrow 2Hg + O_2$$

Look again at Figure 9·6. Heating breaks the bonds between the mercury and the oxygen. The shiny metal mercury condenses on the upper part of the test tube and then runs back down into the tube. The oxygen atoms form molecules of oxygen gas. They escape from the mouth of the test tube.

REVIEW

1. What is the difference between a synthesis reaction and a decomposition reaction?

2. Identify each of the following as a synthesis reaction or a decomposition reaction.
   a. $2MgO \longrightarrow 2Mg + O_2$
   b. $2Hg + O_2 \longrightarrow 2HgO$
   c. $2SO_2 + O_2 \longrightarrow 2SO_3$
   d. $2KClO_3 \longrightarrow 2KCl + 3O_2$

CHALLENGE Write an equation to show the chemical reaction between water and carbon dioxide. State whether this reaction is synthesis or decomposition.

9·3 Replacement Reactions

In the previous section you learned about reactions in which substances combine and in which substances break down. In this section you will find out about reactions in which two or more substances change places.

SINGLE REPLACEMENT REACTIONS

A **single replacement reaction** occurs when one element replaces another element in a compound. The result is the formation of a new compound. This kind of reaction can be shown by the following general formula.

$$A + BX \longrightarrow AX + B$$

The substances A and B can be metals or other positive ions. The X can be a nonmetal or other negative ion. In compounds that contain metals, metals are written first in the formula. A metal that can replace another metal is said to be the more active of the two metals. In the general equation, A is more active than B.

If an iron nail is placed in a copper sulfate solution, the iron will replace the copper ion. The iron will combine with the sulfate ion to form iron sulfate. The copper will be left uncombined. The equation is as follows.

$$Fe + CuSO_4 \longrightarrow FeSO_4 + Cu$$

After completing this section, you will be able to
- **distinguish** between single replacement reactions and double replacement reactions.
- **give** examples of single replacement reactions and double replacement reactions.

The key terms in this section are
double replacement reaction
single replacement reaction

Figure 9·7
Iron ions from a nail replace the copper ions in copper sulfate solution. This results in copper deposits on the nail.

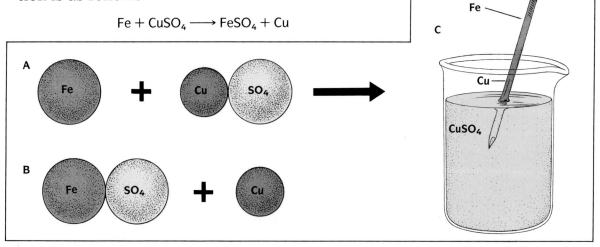

Figure 9·8

Copper is deposited on an iron nail placed in a solution of copper sulfate.

Chemists have done experiments to find out which elements replace others. The results of this work are shown in a list called the activity series. Some of the metals of the activity series are shown in Table 9·1. Notice that potassium is the most active element in the table. The least active element shown is gold. Find aluminum and chromium in the table. Which of these elements is more active? Is copper more active than magnesium?

Table 9·1 *Activity Series*

SYMBOL	NAME	ACTIVITY
K	Potassium	High
Ca	Calcium	↑
Na	Sodium	
Mg	Magnesium	
Al	Aluminum	
Zn	Zinc	
Cr	Chromium	
Fe	Iron	
Ni	Nickel	
Sn	Tin	
Pb	Lead	
H	Hydrogen	
Cu	Copper	
Hg	Mercury	
Ag	Silver	↓
Au	Gold	Low

DOUBLE REPLACEMENT REACTIONS

A **double replacement reaction** occurs when the compounds in a reaction exchange ions. This can be shown by the following equation.

$$AX + BY \longrightarrow AY + BX$$

Substances A and B are positive ions. Substances X and Y are negative ions. In this reaction, compound AX separates into positive A ions and negative X ions. Compound BY separates into positive B ions and negative Y ions. Positive A ions join with negative Y ions. At the same time, positive B ions join with negative X ions. Thus two new compounds, AY

What Are the Types of Chemical Reactions?

OBJECTIVE

Distinguish between different types of chemical reactions, using experimental data.

MATERIALS

safety goggles, lab apron, graduate, water, 3 test tubes, bromothymol blue, test-tube rack, drinking straw, copper (II) sulfate solution, zinc strip, barium chloride solution, potassium sulfate solution

PROCEDURE

A. Wear safety goggles and a lab apron throughout this activity.
B. Draw a data table like the one shown.
C. Measure 10 mL of water into a test tube. Add five drops of bromothymol blue.
D. Using a clean drinking straw, gently blow into the solution. Record your observations in the data table.
E. Measure 10 mL of copper (II) sulfate ($CuSO_4$) solution, and pour the solution into a test tube. Rinse the graduate with water.
F. Place a zinc strip in the solution.
G. After 5 to 10 minutes, examine the zinc. Record your observations.
H. Measure 5 mL of barium chloride ($BaCl_2$) solution, and pour the solution into a test tube. Rinse the graduate with water.
I. Measure 5 mL of potassium sulfate (K_2SO_4) solution. Add this solution to the barium chloride solution in the test tube. Record your observations.

REACTANTS	OBSERVATIONS
H_2O, CO_2	
$CuSO_4$, Zn	
$BaCl_2$, K_2SO_4	

RESULTS AND CONCLUSIONS

1. What evidence is there that chemical reactions took place?
2. Write a balanced equation for each chemical reaction.
3. Which reaction(s) produced a precipitate?
4. Identify each type of reaction that occurred. Explain your answers.

and BX, are formed. Each new compound has a positive ion and a negative ion. The positive ion is written first in the formula.

A double replacement reaction occurs between silver nitrate and sodium chloride. Silver chloride and sodium nitrate are formed. The reaction is shown by this equation.

$$AgNO_3 + NaCl \longrightarrow AgCl + NaNO_3$$

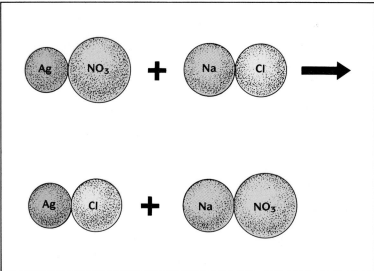

Figure 9·9

When a solution of silver nitrate and a solution of sodium chloride are mixed, a silver chloride precipitate results *(left)*. The double replacement reaction that forms silver chloride *(right)*.

The sodium and silver are the positive ions. The nitrate and chloride are both negative ions.

In this reaction the silver chloride forms a solid material called a precipitate. A *precipitate* is a solid material that separates out of solution. Notice in Figure 9·9 *(left)* that the precipitate sinks toward the bottom of the container.

REVIEW

1. What is the difference between a single replacement reaction and a double replacement reaction?
2. Identify each of the following as a single replacement reaction or a double replacement reaction.
   a. $Mg + H_2SO_4 \longrightarrow MgSO_4 + H_2$
   b. $KI + AgNO_3 \longrightarrow KNO_3 + AgI$
   c. $HCl + NaOH \longrightarrow H_2O + NaCl$
   d. $Al + FeCO_3 \longrightarrow AlCO_3 + Fe$
3. Indicate which is the more active metal in each of the following pairs.
   a. calcium and zinc
   b. chromium and lead
   c. aluminum and sodium
   d. tin and nickel

CHALLENGE Predict which of the following reactions could occur. Write an equation for each reaction that would occur.
a. $Zn + CuSO_4 \longrightarrow$
b. $Al + FeCl_3 \longrightarrow$
c. $Cu + ZnSO_4 \longrightarrow$
d. $H_2 + CuO \longrightarrow$

9·4 Energy in Chemical Reactions

ACTIVATION ENERGY

Reactions need a certain amount of energy before they can start. The amount of energy needed to start a chemical reaction is called **activation energy**. All reactions require activation energy.

Paper burning is a chemical reaction. Energy must be used to start the paper burning. The energy is usually the heat from a lit match. The heat supplies the activation energy needed to start the paper burning. Once the burning begins, the paper continues to burn without the addition of energy.

The amount of activation energy needed to start a reaction depends upon the reactants. The energy given off by a burning match will easily

Figure 9·10
Burning is a chemical reaction that releases energy.

211

ACTIVITY   Does Temperature Change During a Reaction?

OBJECTIVE
Distinguish between an endothermic reaction and an exothermic reaction.

MATERIALS
safety goggles, lab apron, graduate, distilled water, 2 test tubes, test-tube rack, thermometer, balance, ammonium chloride, 2 stoppers, forceps, sodium hydroxide pellets

PROCEDURE
A. Wear safety goggles and a lab apron throughout this activity.
B. Draw a data table like the one shown.
C. Using a graduate, measure 5 mL of distilled water, and pour the water into a test tube.
D. Measure the temperature of the water. Record your result in the data table.
E. Measure 3 g of ammonium chloride, and place it in the test tube.
F. Stopper the test tube, and shake it for 1 minute. Record your observations.
G. Measure the temperature of the solution, and record the result.

H. Measure 5 mL of distilled water, and pour it into a second test tube.
I. Measure the temperature of the solution. Record the result.
J. Using forceps, carefully add 15 sodium hydroxide pellets to the test tube, one pellet at a time. **Caution:** Do not touch the sodium hydroxide pellets.
K. Stopper the test tube, and shake it for 1 minute. Record your observations.
L. Measure the temperature of the solution, and record the result.

RESULTS AND CONCLUSIONS
1. What evidence do you have that energy changes take place when chemicals react?
2. How did you determine which reaction was exothermic and which reaction was endothermic?
3. In the endothermic reaction you observed, what was the source of the energy for the reaction?
4. Which reaction had the greater energy change? Explain your answer.

REACTANT	STARTING TEMPERATURE	OBSERVATIONS	FINAL TEMPERATURE
Ammonium chloride			
Sodium hydroxide			

start paper burning. However, energy from a match will not start wood burning in a campfire like the one shown in Figure 9·10. The wood needs a higher activation energy than does the paper. Why is a campfire or a fireplace fire usually started by first igniting some paper?

When a chemical reaction takes place, energy is absorbed or given off. Energy is absorbed when water is broken down into hydrogen gas and oxygen gas. When water is formed by burning hydrogen gas in oxygen gas, energy is given off. The energy absorbed or given off in a chemical reaction can be in the form of heat, light, or electricity.

ENERGY CHANGES IN REACTIONS

Once started, paper burning gives off energy in the form of heat and light. A reaction that gives off energy is called an **exothermic** (ehk soh THER mihk) **reaction**. In the human body, digested food is broken down to release energy. The energy is used to carry out body functions, such as breathing and moving. For example, when you exercise, your body becomes warmer. The energy is also used to keep the body warm. Thus many chemical reactions in the human body are exothermic.

exo- (outer)
therme (heat)

Figure 9·11
The process by which plants use sunlight is an endothermic reaction.

Some chemical reactions need to take in energy to keep the reaction going. A reaction that takes in, or absorbs, energy is called an **endothermic** (ehn-doh THER mihk) **reaction**. In a process called photosynthesis, green plants use sunlight to make food. Photosynthesis is an endothermic reaction. Energy in the form of sunlight keeps the reaction going.

endo- (inner)

The manufacture of soap is an endothermic reaction. In it, fat or vegetable oil is mixed with lye. The mixture is heated. The heat energy allows the atoms to rearrange to form soap and glycerine. If the heat were taken away, the reaction would stop.

SPONTANEOUS REACTIONS

When solutions of barium chloride and potassium sulfate are mixed, a precipitate forms. This is a spontaneous (spahn TAY nee uhs) chemical reaction. A *spontaneous reaction* takes place with so little energy added to start the reaction that it seems as if no energy is needed.

Many spontaneous reactions give off energy. Chemical reactions inside a battery release energy in the form of electricity. The chemical reaction in a battery is spontaneous. Figure 9·12 shows a variety of batteries and electrical cells. They all give off energy spontaneously. What are batteries used for? Why is a spontaneous reaction important for these uses?

Most chemical reactions do not occur spontaneously. For example, H_2 and O_2 do not react spontaneously to form H_2O. Activation energy is needed to bring the molecules of the reactants together. A spark of electricity can supply this energy.

Figure 9·12
The chemical reactions that produce electricity in batteries are spontaneous reactions.

REVIEW

1. What is the purpose of activation energy in a chemical reaction?
2. How do exothermic reactions and endothermic reactions differ?
3. What is a spontaneous reaction?

CHALLENGE When water or alcohol evaporates from your skin, your skin feels cooler. Is the process of evaporation considered an endothermic reaction? Explain your answer.

9·5 Reactions of Acids and Bases

ACIDS

Acids are an important group of compounds. They are found in many familiar substances, such as fruits, soft drinks, vinegar, and yogurt. Acids are also used widely in the laboratory and in industry.

Acids can be identified by their properties. Acids taste sour. They react with some metals to produce hydrogen gas. They conduct electricity.

Many compounds split into ions as they dissolve in water. These compounds are said to *dissociate* (dih soн shee ayt) in water. An **acid** is a substance that releases hydrogen ions, H^+, when it dissociates in solution. Hydrogen chloride, HCl, dissociates in water as follows.

$$HCl(g) \longrightarrow H^+(aq) + Cl^-(aq)$$

The solution that forms is called hydrochloric acid. Notice the (g) after the reactant. The (g) shows that the state of matter of the reactant is a gas. The solid and liquid states are shown by (s) and (l), respectively. The (aq) shows that the substance formed is in an aqueous, or water, solution.

Acids are among the most useful chemicals known. Sulfuric acid is used more widely in in-

After completing this section, you will be able to

- **list** properties of acids and bases.
- **give** examples of acids and bases.
- **identify** the products of a reaction between an acid and a base.
- **list** some properties of salts.

The key terms in this section are

acid	**neutralization**
base	**salt**

acidus (sour)

Figure 9·13
Tomatoes, smoke from a volcano, and rain all contain acid.

dustry than is any other chemical. Hydrochloric acid is used to remove rust from metals.

Table 9·2 lists some common acids. Notice that all of these acids contain hydrogen. Acids also contain one or more nonmetals, such as chlorine. Acids usually do not contain metals.

Table 9·2 *Common Acids*

NAME OF ACID	CHEMICAL FORMULA	SOURCE
Acetic acid	CH_3COOH	Vinegar
Ascorbic acid (vitamin C)	$(CH_2COOH)_2COHCOOH$	Tomatoes, citrus fruits, vegetables
Carbonic acid	H_2CO_3	Rain water, soft drinks
Hydrochloric acid	HCl	Gastric juice in stomach
Sulfurous acid	H_2SO_3	Acid rain, volcanic smoke

When metals react with some acids, they may be corroded, or eaten away. A *corrosive* (kuh ROH-sihv) *acid* is one that can eat away metals. Sulfuric acid, H_2SO_4, is a corrosive acid. Its reaction with iron is shown in Figure 9·14. Citric acid is not corrosive. Would citric acid react with iron as shown in the figure?

Figure 9·14
A corrosive acid will dissolve a metal.

BASES

Bases are another important group of compounds. Like acids, bases are widely used in the laboratory and in industry. They are used to make soap and other household cleaners. Bases are also used in making fertilizers, explosives, and petroleum products.

A **base** is a substance that releases hydroxide ions, OH⁻, when it dissociates in solution. A *hydroxide* (hī DRAHK sīd) *ion*, OH⁻, contains an oxygen atom and a hydrogen atom. Notice that there is a hydroxide ion in the chemical formula for each base listed in Table 9·3. Most bases also contain a metal. What base in Table 9·3 contains nitrogen, a nonmetal?

Table 9·3 *Common Bases*

NAME OF BASE	CHEMICAL FORMULA
Ammonium hydroxide	NH_4OH
Calcium hydroxide	$Ca(OH)_2$
Potassium hydroxide	KOH
Sodium hydroxide	$NaOH$

Figure 9·15

Sodium hydroxide is used in the production of rayon, a synthetic fiber.

Sodium hydroxide is considered to be a *caustic* (KAWS tihk) *base*. Caustic substances eat away some materials and irritate or damage the skin.

Sodium hydroxide is used to make rayon, a synthetic fiber, shown in Figure 9·15. Sodium hydroxide is also used in the production of paper, detergents, and soaps. It is used in refining petroleum and vegetable oil. The food industry uses sodium hydroxide to remove the peel from fruits and vegetables.

The sandbox tree grows in tropical regions of Central America and South America. This tree is tall, sometimes reaching a height of 36 m. Its toothed leaves form a crown at the top of the tree, and the trunk is covered with short, stiff spines.

Inside the tree is a white, caustic sap. This sap is basic and is harmful to the skin and eyes. The people who cut down these trees wear heavy gloves to protect their hands.

They must also wear face shields because the sap can cause blindness if it gets in someone's eyes.

In spite of its caustic nature, the sap has an odd use. People mix sand with the sap and throw it into lakes and streams. The mixture stuns fish, which are then caught. Surprisingly, fish caught in this manner do not seem to cause any problems for the people who eat the fish.

pH SCALE

The strength of an acid or of a base can be described by using a scale of numbers called the *pH scale*. The pH scale is shown in Figure 9·16. This scale ranges from 0 to 14. An acid has a pH between 0 and 7. A base has a pH between 7 and 14. Pure water, which is neither an acid nor a base, has a pH of 7. Pure water and other neutral solutions have a pH of exactly 7. The pH of a solution can be measured accurately in the laboratory with a pH meter.

Figure 9·16

The pH of common household products.

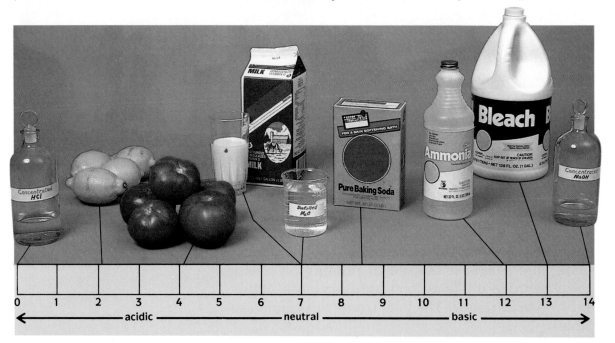

Substances called indicators may be used to find the approximate pH of a solution. An *indicator* is a compound that changes color according to the pH. Figure 9·17 shows the colors of different indicators. Indicators have different colors at different pH levels. Blue litmus paper is an indicator that turns pink in an acidic solution and blue in a basic solution. What color does bromothymol blue turn in an acid? What color does phenolphthalein turn in a base?

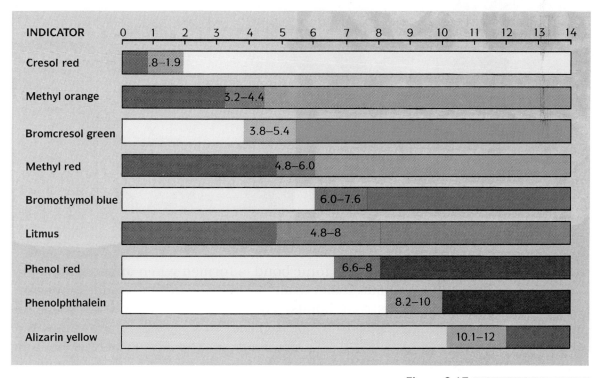

INDICATOR	pH range
Cresol red	.8–1.9
Methyl orange	3.2–4.4
Bromcresol green	3.8–5.4
Methyl red	4.8–6.0
Bromothymol blue	6.0–7.6
Litmus	4.8–8
Phenol red	6.6–8
Phenolphthalein	8.2–10
Alizarin yellow	10.1–12

Figure 9·17
The color changes of some acid-base indicators.

NEUTRALIZATION

If an acid and a base are mixed, H^+ ions from the acid will combine with OH^- ions from the base. The equation for this reaction is as follows.

$$H^+(aq) + OH^-(aq) \longrightarrow H_2O(l)$$

The product of this reaction is water, a neutral substance. The reaction between an acid and a base is called **neutralization** (noo truh luh ZAY shuhn). If the number of H^+ ions from the acid equals the number of OH^- ions from the base, neutralization will be complete. There will be no extra H^+ or OH^- ions left after the reaction is complete.

Neutralization reactions produce water and a salt. A **salt** is a compound formed from the positive metal ions of a base and the negative nonmetal ions of an acid. Most salts are ionic compounds. Recall

Figure 9·18
Crystals of sodium chloride, NaCl.

that an ionic bond is formed when an atom gives its outer electrons to another atom. Ionic bonds are strong bonds. They hold the positive and negative ions of a salt together in a crystal. Crystals have a definite shape, such as the shape of the sodium chloride crystals shown in Figure 9·18. The shape of crystals aids in identifying substances.

Many salt crystals dissolve in water. This is because the water molecules attract the ions that are present in the crystals. Salts dissociate as they dissolve in water.

$$NaCl(s) \longrightarrow Na^+(aq) + Cl^-(aq)$$
$$MgBr_2(s) \longrightarrow Mg_2^+(aq) + 2Br^-(aq)$$

Ions from salts move freely in solution. This is why solutions that contain ions can conduct electricity. Tap water can conduct electricity. How does this show that tap water is not the same as pure water?

REVIEW

1. Name three properties of acids and two properties of bases.
2. Name one acid and one base, and for each one, name a use in industry.
3. What products result from the reaction between an acid and a base?
4. Name three properties of a salt.

CHALLENGE Indigestion is caused by the release of too much gastric juice, an acid in the stomach. Indigestion can be relieved by swallowing or chewing antacid tablets. Explain how antacid tablets work.

CHAPTER SUMMARY

The main ideas in this chapter are listed below. Read these statements before you answer the Chapter Review questions.

- In a chemical reaction, one or more substances are changed into one or more different substances. (9•1)
- The changes that take place in a chemical reaction can be shown in a chemical equation. (9•1)
- In a chemical reaction the atoms can be rearranged, but the total number of atoms stays the same. (9•1)
- A reaction in which two or more substances combine to form a compound is called a synthesis reaction. (9•2)
- A reaction in which a compound breaks down into two or more substances is called a decomposition reaction. (9•2)
- In a single replacement reaction, one element replaces another element in a compound, forming a new compound. (9•3)
- A double replacement reaction occurs when the compounds in a reaction exchange ions. (9•3)

- Energy is absorbed or given off during chemical reactions. A reaction that gives off energy is called an exothermic reaction; a reaction that absorbs energy is called an endothermic reaction. (9•4)
- An acid releases hydrogen ions in water. (9•5)
- Acids taste sour, react with some metals to produce hydrogen, and conduct electricity in solution. (9•5)
- A base releases hydroxide ions in water. (9•5)
- Bases taste bitter, feel slippery, conduct electricity, and dissolve fats and oils. (9•5)
- An indicator is a compound that changes color according to the pH. (9•5)
- Neutralization is a reaction between an acid and a base, producing water and a salt. (9•5)
- A salt is formed from the positive metal ions of a base and the negative nonmetal ions of an acid. (9•5)

The key terms in this chapter are listed below. Use each term in a sentence that shows the meaning of the term.

acid	double replacement reaction	products
activation energy	endothermic reaction	reactants
base	exothermic reaction	salt
chemical equation	Law of Conservation of Mass	single replacement reaction
chemical reaction	neutralization	synthesis reaction
decomposition reaction		

Chapter Review

VOCABULARY

Use the key terms from the previous page to complete the following sentences correctly.

1. The energy needed to start a reaction is called _____.
2. The reaction $2H_2O + O_2 \longrightarrow 2H_2O_2$ is an example of a/an _____.
3. In a/an _____, an active metal replaces a less active metal.
4. A shorthand way of showing a chemical reaction is called a/an _____.
5. A reaction that gives off heat is called a/an _____.
6. The starting substances in a chemical reaction are the _____.
7. The substances formed in a chemical reaction are called _____.
8. A/An _____ is a reaction that absorbs heat.
9. The reaction between an acid and a base is called _____.
10. _____ are substances that give off hydrogen ions, H^+.

CONCEPTS

Identify each statement as True or False. If a statement is false, replace the underlined term or phrase that makes the statement true.

1. The starting substances in a chemical reaction are called <u>products</u>.
2. Substances that give off OH^- ions in solution are called <u>acids</u>.
3. A reaction in which a compound is broken down into two substances is called a <u>synthesis</u> reaction.
4. A <u>single</u> replacement reaction takes place when the compounds in a reaction exchange ions.
5. A <u>salt and water</u> are produced when an acid and a base react.

Choose the term or phrase that best answers the question or completes the statement.

6. In a chemical reaction, which of the following always remains the same?
   a. the number of molecules
   b. the number of atoms
   c. the number of substances
   d. the state of matter
7. Which of the following is an example of a decomposition reaction?
   a. $A + B \longrightarrow AB$ c. $AB + C \longrightarrow AC + B$
   b. $AB \longrightarrow A + B$ d. $AB + CD \longrightarrow AC + BD$
8. Which of the following is an example of a single replacement reaction?
   a. $A + B \longrightarrow AB$ c. $AB + C \longrightarrow AC + B$
   b. $AB \longrightarrow A + B$ d. $AB + CD \longrightarrow AC + BD$

9. Which of the following is required in all chemical reactions?
   a. a high temperature
   b. water
   c. the presence of an acid
   d. activation energy
10. A solution turns blue litmus paper pink. The solution is a/an
    a. acid.
    b. base.
    c. salt.
    d. indicator.
11. Why must chemical equations be balanced?
12. What type of chemical reaction is the rusting of metal? Explain your answer.
13. Using the letters *WX* and *YZ* for the reactants, write an equation for a double replacement reaction.
14. Compare the activation energy in a spontaneous reaction with that in a nonspontaneous reaction.
15. Discuss how pH is used to determine the strength of acids and bases.

---

1. Many photographers keep unused film in the refrigerator. Explain why this makes the film last longer.
2. Explain why aluminum will react with iron chloride but not with magnesium chloride.
3. An unlabeled bottle that is half full of solution has been found near the acids and bases in your lab. How can you determine what kind of substance this unknown liquid is?
4. A solution with a pH of 4.5 is mixed with another solution of unknown pH. The resulting pH is 9.6. State whether the solution with an unknown pH is acidic or basic. Explain your answer.

APPLICATION/ CRITICAL THINKING

---

1. Research the match. Why does a match light when it is struck? What kind of energy changes are involved? Present a report to the class.
2. Research the disease scurvy, and explain why ascorbic acid is essential to the human body.
3. Write a report on the effects of acid rain on plant and animal life. Present your findings to the class.
4. In the human stomach, hydrochloric acid is produced. Find out why the body produces this acid and why it does not damage stomach tissue.

EXTENSION

CHAPTER 10

KINDS OF MATTER

People have used metals since the beginning of civilization. In early times, metals, such as silver, were only the objects of beauty. Later, metals were used in manufacturing. Today, however, metals have many technological uses. Silver, for example, is used as a reflective coating on solar mirrors. It reflects virtually 100 percent of the light that falls on it. Shown in the photograph are rows of silver-coated mirrors. The mirrors track the movement of the sun and focus the sun's rays on a tank of water. Steam from the heated water then drives a generator that produces electricity.

- *What causes the mirrors to become tarnished over time?*
- *Why is silver called a precious metal?*
- *What gives metals their special properties?*

10·1 Groups of Elements

In the 1860s a scientist named Dmitri Mendeleev predicted the properties of many elements that had not yet been discovered. For example, he predicted that one of these elements would have properties very similar to those of aluminum. His prediction was fulfilled years later, with the discovery of the element gallium. Similarly he predicted the properties of other then-unknown elements, such as boron, scandium, and germanium.

Mendeleev observed that many known elements had similar properties. For example, he observed that the elements lithium, sodium, and potassium corroded when they were exposed to air. Other elements, such as fluorine, chlorine, and bromine, were gases and combined with sodium.

Mendeleev organized the known elements in order of increasing atomic mass in a table. He arranged the elements in vertical columns and horizontal rows based on the properties of the elements. He noted how the properties of the elements repeated with each row. Mendeleev left blanks in the table for elements that had not yet been discovered.

Figure 10·1

The elements gallium, boron, scandium, and germanium were predicted by Mendeleev.

THE PERIODIC TABLE

A modern version of Mendeleev's table is called the Periodic Table. The **Periodic Table** is a table of the elements arranged in groups and periods in order of increasing atomic number. A *period* is a horizontal row of elements in the table. A *group* is a vertical column of elements in the table.

Mendeleev had noted how each column contained elements with similar chemical and physical properties. However, he could not explain why groups of elements had similar properties. It was not until the discovery of the structure of the atom that the properties of elements could be explained.

The chemical properties of an element are determined by the number of electrons in the outer energy level of its atoms. The elements in any one group have the same number of electrons in the outer energy level. Thus the elements in any one group have similar chemical properties. For example, each element in Group 1 contains just one electron in its outer energy level. The outer energy levels of these elements are shown in Figure 10·2. How do the elements differ? One common chemical property of Group 1 elements is that they react explosively with water.

Figure 10·2

Each element in Group 1 has one electron in its outer energy level.

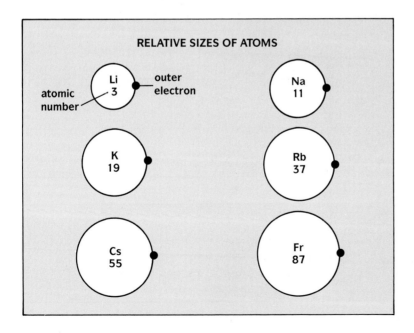

RELATIVE SIZES OF ATOMS

atomic number — outer electron

Li 3

Na 11

K 19

Rb 37

Cs 55

Fr 87

METALS

Elements with three or fewer electrons in their outer energy level are classified as metals. Metals are usually shiny, are good conductors of heat and electricity, and can be pounded into various shapes. Copper, iron, gold, silver, tin, and most other metals are solids at room temperature. Mercury, however, is a liquid metal. No metal is a gas at room temperature.

Over three fourths of the elements in the Periodic Table are classified as metals. Find the heavy zigzag line in the Periodic Table. The elements lo-

Periodic Table of Elements

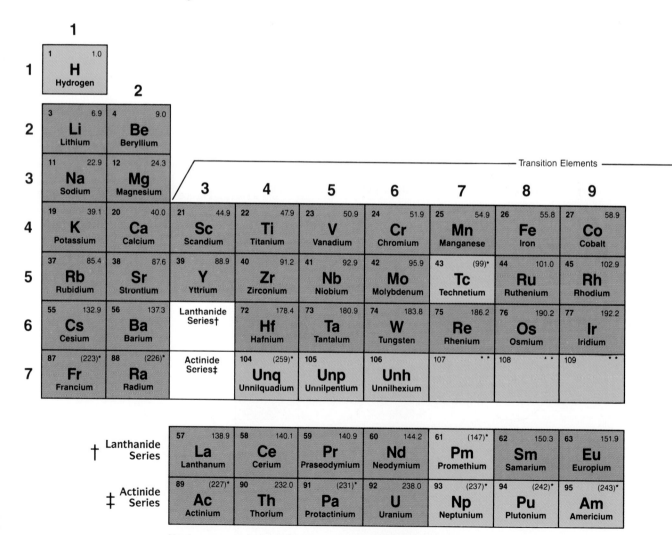

*Atomic masses appearing in parentheses are those of the most stable known isotopes.

cated to the left of the zigzag line are metals. All elements in Groups 1 through 12 and some elements in Groups 13, 14, and 15 are metals.

Metals are elements that are good conductors of electricity and heat. Metals have *luster* (LUHS tuhr), which means they are shiny. Metals are *malleable* (MAL ee uh buhl), which means they can be pounded into many shapes, including thin sheets. Metals are also *ductile* (DUHK tuhl), which means they can be drawn out into a wire. Wire made of metal can bend without breaking. Look at Figure 10·3. What properties of copper are shown in the photograph?

Figure 10·3
The metal copper is malleable and ductile, and has luster.

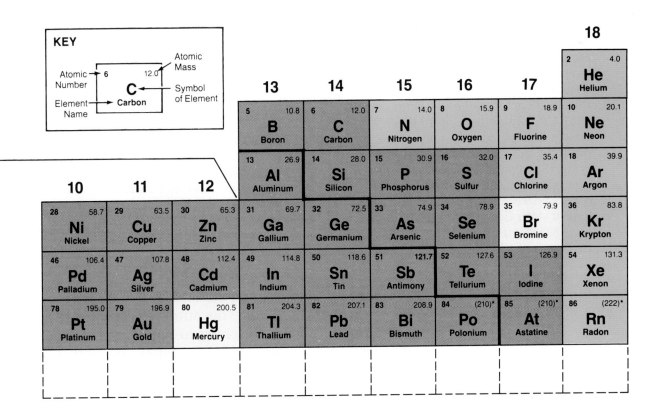

KEY

Atomic Number → 6   12.0 ← Atomic Mass

C ← Symbol of Element

Element Name → Carbon

| 64 157.2 **Gd** Gadolinium | 65 158.9 **Tb** Terbium | 66 162.5 **Dy** Dysprosium | 67 164.9 **Ho** Holmium | 68 167.2 **Er** Erbium | 69 168.9 **Tm** Thulium | 70 173.0 **Yb** Ytterbium | 71 174.9 **Lu** Lutetium |
| 96 (247)* **Cm** Curium | 97 (247)* **Bk** Berkelium | 98 (251)* **Cf** Californium | 99 (254)* **Es** Einsteinium | 100 (257)* **Fm** Fermium | 101 (258)* **Md** Mendelevium | 102 (255)* **No** Nobelium | 103 (256)* **Lr** Lawrencium |

* *No names have been given and no mass data is available.

Atomic masses based on C-12 = 12.0000

ACTIVITY — How Do Metals Differ from Nonmetals?

OBJECTIVE
Distinguish between metals and nonmetals.

MATERIALS
dry cell; insulated wire; wire stripper; light bulb and socket; samples of zinc, carbon, sulfur, magnesium, iron, and copper; watch glass

PROCEDURE

A. Draw a data table like the one shown.
B. Set up the equipment as shown in the diagram. The ends of the wires should have 2 cm of insulation removed. **Caution:** Do not touch the ends of the wires.
C. Obtain a small sample of one of the substances to be tested. Place the sample on a watch glass. Examine the sample to determine if it has luster. Record your observation.
D. Hold an insulated part of the wires, and touch the ends of the wires to the sample. Do not touch the ends of the wires to each other. If the light bulb lights, the element is a conductor. If the light bulb does not light, the element is not a conductor. Record your observation.
E. Repeat steps **C** and **D** for each of the other substances.

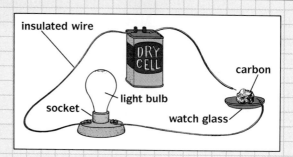

ELEMENT	LUSTER	CONDUCTIVITY
Zinc		
Carbon		
Sulfur		
Magnesium		
Iron		
Copper		

RESULTS AND CONCLUSIONS
1. Do all of the materials that have luster show conductivity?
2. Do all of the materials that show conductivity have luster?
3. Which elements tested are metals?
4. Which elements tested are nonmetals?

Figure 10·4 shows the structure of a metallic solid. In a metallic solid the outer electrons are shared among positively charged metal ions. The electrons do not belong to any particular ion. Notice how closely the metal ions are packed together. The attraction between electrons and the ions forms a bond that holds the metal ions together. The bond that holds the metal ions together in a metallic solid is called a *metallic bond.*

The metallic bond explains why metals are malleable and ductile. Because there are no individual bonds, the ions and electrons can be moved into new positions without breaking the metal.

Figure 10·4
Electrons move freely through a metallic solid.

metal ion

electron

NONMETALS AND METALLOIDS

Elements with five or more outer electrons usually are nonmetals. All elements in Groups 17 and 18 and some in Groups 13 through 16 are nonmetals. Nonmetals are found on the right side of the zigzag line in the table.

Nonmetals are elements that lack luster, that generally do not conduct electricity or heat, and that are not ductile or malleable. Most nonmetals are solids or gases at room temperature. Carbon is a nonmetallic solid, and nitrogen is a nonmetallic gas. Bromine is the only liquid nonmetal.

Some elements have properties of both metals and nonmetals. These elements, which are found along the zigzag line in the Periodic Table, are called **metalloids.** Tellurium is an example of a metalloid.

-oid (like)

REVIEW

1. How are elements organized in the Periodic Table?
2. What are some properties of metals, nonmetals, and metalloids?
3. Give three examples of each of the following: metal, nonmetal, metalloid.

CHALLENGE Why is it unlikely that there are any undiscovered elements today?

10·2 Metals

Metals are usually thought of as being hard, shiny, and heavy. But the metals in Group 1 of the Periodic Table are soft and lightweight. Unlike ordinary metals, such as copper and silver, the Group 1 metals cause burns when touched and react violently with water. Although these properties are unusual for metals, the elements in Group 1 are still classified as metals.

ALKALI METALS

The elements in Group 1 of the Periodic Table are called the **alkali** (AL kuh lī) **metals**. The alkali metals are lithium, sodium, potassium, rubidium, cesium, and francium. The alkali metals have low melting points. For example, cesium melts at 29°C. Alkali metals have luster and are very soft. Look at Figure 10·5(D). How can you tell that sodium is soft? Such softness makes alkali metals very malleable and ductile.

Figure 10·5

Potassium (A), rubidium (B), cesium (C), and sodium (D) are alkali metals.

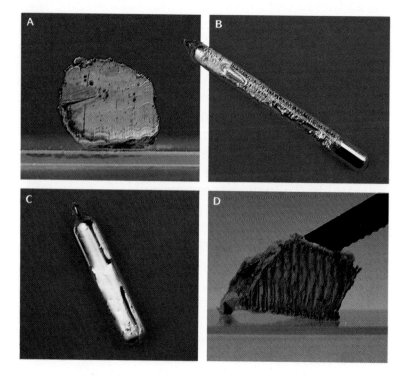

The alkali metals have just one electron in their outer energy level. The electron is located farther from the nucleus in an alkali metal than in other elements. This electron is weakly held and easily lost. Thus, alkali metals tend to be very reactive.

Because alkali metals are so reactive, they are not found alone in nature. They are always combined with other elements in compounds. The alkali metals react violently with water, releasing hydrogen gas as one of the products. If a piece of sodium is dropped into water, the hydrogen released can cause an explosion. Alkali metals also react strongly with water vapor in the air. Alkali metals are usually stored in an oil such as kerosene. The metal does not react with the oil.

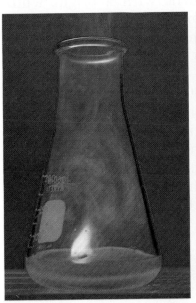 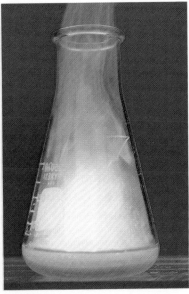 

Figure 10·6
Sodium reacts violently with water *(left and middle)* but not with kerosene *(right)*.

THE ALKALINE EARTH METALS

The elements in Group 2 of the Periodic Table are called the **alkaline** (AL kuh lĭn) **earth metals**. They are beryllium, magnesium, calcium, strontium, barium, and radium. Most alkaline earth metals are found as compounds in rocks.

Alkaline earth metals are reactive, but not as reactive as the alkali metals. The reason for the greater stability is the two electrons in their outer energy level. Their electrons are held closer to the

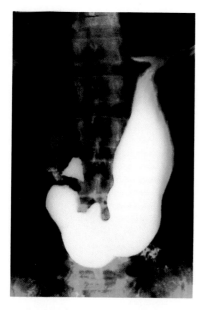

Figure 10·7
Barium in the stomach allows an X-ray photograph to be taken of the stomach.

nucleus and more tightly than the outer electron in alkali metals. Thus the electrons in alkaline earth metals are not lost as easily.

The alkaline earth metals are harder than the alkali metals and have higher melting points. Radium, which has the lowest melting point of the alkaline earth metals, melts at 700°C.

The alkaline earth metals react with water and release hydrogen gas. But the reaction is not as violent as that between alkali metals and water. Magnesium will react with only hot water.

The alkaline earth metals are widely used. Beryllium (buh RIHL ee uhm), a rather rare element, has a very low density. Because beryllium is lightweight and strong, it is used as a material in space vehicles. Magnesium burns with a bright white light and is used in photographic flashbulbs and emergency flares. You may be familiar with some magnesium compounds. Magnesium hydroxide, $Mg(OH)_2$, is commonly called milk of magnesia. Magnesium sulfate, $MgSO_4$, is called Epsom salts.

Calcium is the most common of the alkaline earth metals. It is found in rocks, minerals, and the bones and shells of living things. The lime that is used on lawns contains calcium. Calcium is needed in the human diet for the growth of strong bones and teeth. Calcium in the blood aids in clotting. Good sources of calcium include milk and cheese.

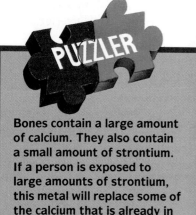

Bones contain a large amount of calcium. They also contain a small amount of strontium. If a person is exposed to large amounts of strontium, this metal will replace some of the calcium that is already in the bones. Why is strontium able to replace calcium?

THE TRANSITION ELEMENTS

The metals to the right of Group 2 in the Periodic Table are called the transition elements. The **transition elements** are the elements located in Groups 3 through 12 in the Periodic Table. These elements are found only in Periods 4 through 7 of the Periodic Table. These ten transition groups once were thought to represent a gradual change, or transition, between the groups on each side of the Periodic Table. Actually the transition elements do not show definite patterns of change in their chemical properties. Transition elements are not as reactive as either alkali metals or alkaline earth metals.

The transition elements contain either one or two outer electrons. Transition elements in different groups can have similar properties. For example, nickel, cobalt, and iron are in different groups. But they are all strongly magnetic. Copper, silver, and gold are in different groups. But they are hard, heavy, and often found free in nature.

The transition elements have many uses. Tungsten (TUHNG stuhn) is used to make filaments for light bulbs. As electricity flows through the tungsten filament, the temperature of the filament increases. The high temperature makes the filament glow. The higher the temperature, the greater the amount of light given off by the tungsten. Tungsten has a melting point of about 3400°C.

trans- (across)

Figure 10·8
Copper, a transition metal, can replace silver ions in the solution.

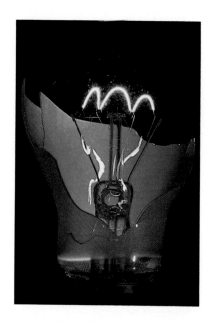

Figure 10·9
The tungsten filament in a broken light bulb.

Transition elements are often combined in mixtures called *alloys*. Alloys are made when metals are heated and mixed together. An alloy has properties different from those of the metals that make up the alloy. For example, silver is a very soft metal. Adding copper to silver makes sterling silver, an alloy that is harder than pure silver or pure copper.

Several alloys are listed in Table 10·1. Notice that no chemical formulas are given. An alloy is a mixture, not a compound. It does not form as a result of a chemical reaction. Thus the makeup of an alloy can vary. What is the composition of bronze?

Table 10·1 *The Composition of Some Alloys*

ALLOY	COMPOSITION	USE
Brass	70% Cu, 30% Zn	Hardware, plumbing
Bronze	90% Cu, 10% Sn	Artwork, domes of buildings
Gold alloy	70% Au, 17% Ag, 10% Cu, 1% Pt, 1% Zn, 1% Pd	Dentistry, jewelry
Pewter	85% Sn, 7% Cu, 6% Bi, 2% Sb	Cups, candlesticks
Solder	60% Pb, 40% Sn	Connecting metal pieces together
Stainless steel	74% Fe, 18% Cr, 8% Ni	Cutlery
Steel	99% Fe, 1% C	Bridges, buildings
Sterling silver	93% Ag, 7% Cu	Jewelry, tableware

The transition elements copper, silver, gold, and nickel are used to make coins. Before 1964, dimes and quarters were made entirely of silver. Newer coins have copper sandwiched between thin layers of silver.

REVIEW

1. How are the alkaline earth metals different from the alkali metals?
2. Identify each of the following elements as an alkali metal, an alkaline earth metal, or a transition element: mercury, magnesium, calcium.
3. Give one use of an alkali metal, an alkaline earth metal, and a transition element.

CHALLENGE Iron, cobalt, and nickel are often found together in meteorites. Explain why these metals are likely to be found together.

10·3 Nonmetals and Metalloids

The elements in Groups 13 through 16 have the most varied properties of all elements in the Periodic Table. The elements found in these groups include nonmetals, metals, and metalloids. Each group is named after the first element in the group.

THE BORON GROUP

Group 13 of the Periodic Table is called the boron group. The elements in the boron group have three electrons in their outer energy level. Except for boron, all the elements in Group 13 are metals. Unlike metals, boron is dull and brittle.

In nature, boron is found only in compounds. Two common compounds of boron are boric acid and borax. Aluminum is in the boron group. Lightweight alloys of aluminum are used for aircraft parts and to make lightweight bicycles, like the one shown in Figure 10·10. Gallium, indium, and thalium have luster and are mildly reactive metals.

After completing this section, you will be able to

- **describe** the properties of elements in Groups 13 through 16 of the Periodic Table.
- **list** uses of elements in Groups 13 through 16 of the Periodic Table.
- **classify** elements in Groups 13 through 16 as metals, nonmetals, or metalloids.

The key terms in this section are
glass
semiconductor

Figure 10·10
Aluminum ore is mined as bauxite. Aluminum is used in lightweight bicycles *(inset)*.

THE CARBON GROUP

The Group 14 elements make up the carbon group. They are carbon, silicon, germanium, tin, and lead. Each atom of the carbon group has four electrons in its outer energy level. The elements of Group 14 have more widely varying properties than do elements in any other group of the Periodic Table. Carbon is a nonmetal, silicon and germanium are metalloids, and tin and lead are metals.

Free carbon, or pure carbon, has two forms: diamond and graphite. Graphite is a soft, black crystalline solid. Notice in Figure 10·11 (*left*) that the carbon atoms in graphite are arranged in layers. Notice also that the distance between the layers is greater than the distance between the carbon atoms within a layer. A weak force holds the graphite layers together.

Figure 10·11

Both graphite and diamond are made of carbon atoms. The bonds between the carbon atoms in graphite form layers *(left)*. The bonds between the carbon atoms in diamond form a three-dimensional structure *(right)*.

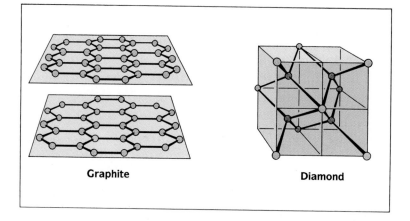

Graphite   **Diamond**

The other form of carbon is diamond. Diamond is a clear, colorless crystal. Look at the diamond structure shown in Figure 10·11 (*right*). Notice that the atoms are closer together in diamond than in graphite. Diamond forms under great pressure in the earth. The pattern of bonds in diamond makes it the hardest substance known.

Silicon, another carbon group element, is the second most abundant element in the earth's crust. However, silicon does not occur naturally as a free element. It is usually found combined with oxygen in the compound silicon dioxide. Silicon dioxide is the main component of sand.

Silicon and its compounds have many important uses. For example, when silicon dioxide melts, it loses its crystal structure. As it cools, it forms a glass. A **glass** is a super-cooled liquid. It flows so slowly that it appears to be a solid.

One of the most important uses of silicon is in the semiconductor industry. A **semiconductor** is a substance that conducts little electricity at low temperatures but conducts more at higher temperatures. Semiconductors are used in televisions, radios, and computers. Semiconductors are also important in solar cells, which are used to convert sunlight to electricity.

THE NITROGEN GROUP

Group 15 is called the nitrogen group. The nitrogen group contains nitrogen, phosphorus, arsenic, antimony, and bismuth. Each of the elements in the nitrogen group has five electrons in its outer energy level. Nitrogen is the smallest atom in Group 15. Nitrogen properties are quite different from those of the other elements in the group. Nitrogen is the only gas in the group. It also is the only element that occurs only in one form, N_2.

Figure 10·12
Silicon is the main element in solar cells, which convert sunlight into electricity.

semi- (half)

SCIENCE & TECHNOLOGY

Many semiconductors are made from the element silicon. However, a new compound called gallium arsenide may replace silicon as the most widely used semiconductor. Gallium arsenide conducts electricity faster than silicon does. It can also withstand higher temperatures.

There are some problems in manufacturing gallium arsenide crystals. Gravity prevents the liquids that form these crystals from mixing properly. The crystals do not form well, and they contain defects. Defective crystals do not conduct electricity or

electric current very well.

Space may provide an answer to these problems. Away from the earth's gravity, there are no mixing

problems, and defects are not likely to occur in the crystals. Some experts say that the chances of producing good crystals are ten times greater in space than on the earth.

Gallium arsenide semiconductors will be used in electronic circuits in complex devices. Companies in the United States and Japan are already producing supercomputers that use semiconductors made of gallium arsenide. As better gallium arsenide crystals are produced, these semiconductors will be used in communications and scientific instruments.

ACTIVITY How Is a Nonmetal Used to Extract a Metal?

OBJECTIVE
Separate a metal from its metal oxide by using carbon.

MATERIALS
safety goggles, balance, spatula, copper (II) oxide, test tube, test-tube rack, powdered charcoal, glass stirring rod, ring stand, burette clamp, Bunsen burner, striker, 250-mL beaker

PROCEDURE
A. Wear safety goggles during this activity.
B. Measure 1 g of copper (II) oxide, and place it in a clean, dry test tube.
  1. Describe the color and appearance of this substance.
C. Measure 2 g of powdered charcoal.
  2. Describe the color and appearance of this substance.
D. Add the charcoal to the test tube, and mix the contents with a stirring rod.
E. Assemble the apparatus as shown in the diagram.
F. Heat the test tube over a low flame for about 1 minute. Then turn up the flame, and heat the test tube strongly for about 10 minutes.
G. Allow the test tube to cool completely. Pour the contents of the test tube into a 250-mL beaker.

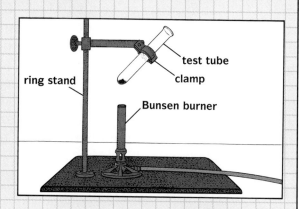

ring stand

test tube clamp

Bunsen burner

H. Place the beaker in a sink, and slowly run cold water into the beaker until all of the unreacted charcoal has floated away.
I. Pour out the water from the beaker, and examine the material left on the bottom.
  3. How does this material differ from the starting materials?

RESULTS AND CONCLUSIONS
1. Identify the reactants in this reaction.
2. Identify the products in this reaction.
3. Write a balanced chemical equation for this reaction.
4. To make steel, carbon and iron oxide are heated together in a blast furnace. Predict what the other products of this reaction would be.

Phosphorus, the second element in the nitrogen group, is a nonmetal not found free in nature. Phosphorus is used in fertilizers, fireworks, and matches. Compounds containing phosphorus, or phosphates, were once widely used in detergents. However, phosphates in wastewater contributed to water pollution. Water plants grow more rapidly in the presence of large amounts of phosphates. Look at the dense plant growth shown in Figure 10·13 (*left*). The plants use up the oxygen in the water.

THE OXYGEN GROUP

Elements in Group 16, the oxygen group, have six electrons in their outer energy level. Oxygen is the most active element of the group and can combine with almost any other element. A compound of oxygen is called an oxide. Oxygen is also the most abundant element in the crust of the earth.

Figure 10·13

Pollution from phosphates causes a rapid increase in plant growth *(left)*. Sulfur deposits around a volcano *(right)*.

Sulfur is the second element in the oxygen group. Large deposits of free sulfur are found in Texas and Louisiana. The major use of sulfur is in the manufacture of sulfuric acid, an important industrial chemical. Selenium and tellurium have both metallic and nonmetallic properties. Polonium is a radioactive element.

REVIEW

1. What are the properties of the elements in Groups 13 through 16 of the Periodic Table?
2. List one use of each of the following: boron, aluminum, carbon, silicon, nitrogen, oxygen, phosphorus, sulfur.
3. State whether the elements listed in question **2** are metals, nonmetals, or metalloids.

CHALLENGE A molecule of nitrogen, N_2, contains a triple covalent bond. How does this explain why nitrogen gas is very nonreactive?

10·4 Other Nonmetals

After completing this section, you will be able to
- **describe** the properties of the halogens and noble gases.
- **list** uses of elements in Groups 17 and 18.
- **describe** the chemical properties of hydrogen.
- **list** uses of hydrogen.

The key terms in this section are
halogens
noble gases

THE HALOGENS

The elements in Group 17 are called **halogens**. These elements combine with metals to form salts. The word *halogen* comes from a Greek word meaning "salt former." Each of the elements in Group 17 has seven electrons in its outer energy level. Group 17 contains only nonmetals. Pure halogens are found as diatomic molecules. Because the halogens are very reactive, they combine with almost all of the elements in the Periodic Table.

Halogen compounds are commonly found in salt deposits, oceans, and natural saltwater wells, also called brine wells. Table 10·2 gives the concentration of some halogen ions in seawater. Which of these halogen ions occurs in the greatest amount?

Fluorine is the most reactive halogen. Fluorine, F_2, is a corrosive, pale yellow gas. Fluorides are compounds that contain fluorine. Probably the most familiar use of a fluoride is in toothpaste and drinking water. Fluoride reduces tooth decay.

Figure 10·14
Seawater contains many halogen compounds.

Table 10·2 *Ions in Seawater*

HALOGEN ION	AMOUNT (g/kg)
Chloride	19.353
Bromide	0.067
Fluoride	0.001

Chlorine, Cl_2, is a poisonous, yellow-green gas. It reacts easily with most elements but is not as reactive as fluorine. Chlorine is used to treat sewage and to purify drinking water. Chlorine is also used as a disinfectant in swimming pools. The process of adding chlorine to water is called chlorination. This process kills bacteria and other living things that may cause disease. In addition, chlorine is used to bleach fabrics.

Bromine, Br_2, is the only nonmetal that is a liquid at room temperature. It is corrosive and causes burns to the skin. In agriculture, bromine is used in chemicals that kill fungi.

Iodine, I_2, is a blue-black solid. In medicine, tincture of iodine is used as a disinfectant for wounds. A *tincture* is a solution in which the solvent is alcohol. Iodine is important in the human diet. Most table salt contains iodine, in the form of sodium iodide or potassium iodide. Astatine is a radioactive element.

Figure 10·15
Chlorine is added to swimming pools to kill bacteria and other disease-causing organisms.

Figure 10·16
Iodine *(left)* and bromine *(right)*.

THE NOBLE GASES

The elements in Group 18 of the Periodic Table are called the **noble gases**. Each has a completely filled outer energy level. Each of the elements except helium has eight electrons in its outer energy level. Helium has two electrons in its outer energy level.

Unlike other gases, the noble gases are not found in nature as molecules. However, scientists are able to produce compounds containing fluorine and the noble gas xenon (ZEE nahn). Now many stable synthetic xenon compounds are known. There are also some krypton (KRIHP tahn) compounds and at least one radon (RAY dahn) compound.

The second element in the noble gases is helium. Helium is the second lightest of all gases. Because it is much less dense than air, it is used in blimps. The noble gas neon is used in some electric lights. When an electric current is passed through the neon gas, the gas gives off a bright orange-red light.

HYDROGEN

Unlike the other elements in the Periodic Table, the element hydrogen does not properly belong to any group. Like an alkali metal, hydrogen has one electron in its outer energy level. Therefore, it is placed on the left side of the table, above Group 1, the alkali metals. But hydrogen is classified as a nonmetal. It is more like the halogens than like the alkali metals. For example, hydrogen is a gas and is found as a diatomic molecule, H_2.

On the earth, hydrogen is found in more compounds than is any other element. Water, petroleum, proteins, and fats all contain hydrogen. Hydrogen gas is colorless, odorless, and tasteless. It is also highly flammable.

REVIEW

1. What are the properties of the halogens and noble gases?
2. List one use of each of the following elements: chlorine, iodine, helium, neon.
3. What are some of the uses of hydrogen?

CHALLENGE Under what conditions might a noble gas be made to combine with fluorine?

CHAPTER SUMMARY

The main ideas in this chapter are listed below. Read these statements before you answer the Chapter Review questions.

- The elements in the Periodic Table are organized according to increasing atomic number. (10·1)
- The elements in the Periodic Table can be classified as metals, nonmetals, and metalloids. (10·1)
- The Group 1 elements are called the alkali metals. The Group 2 elements are called the alkaline earth metals. (10·2)
- The transition elements are metals located in periods 4 through 7 and Groups 3 through 12 of the Periodic Table. (10·2)
- Group 13 of the Periodic Table is the boron group. Except for boron, which is a metalloid, all Group 13 elements are metals. (10·3)
- Group 14 of the Periodic Table is the carbon group. Group 14 elements include metals, metalloids, and nonmetals. (10·3)

- Group 15 of the Periodic Table is the nitrogen group. Living things need nitrogen. (10·3)
- Group 16 of the Periodic Table is the oxygen group. Oxygen is a very active gas and can combine with almost any other element. (10·3)
- The elements in Group 17 are called halogens. The halogens are nonmetals and are very reactive. They combine with metals to form salts. (10·4)
- The elements of Group 18 are the noble gases. Noble gases are not very reactive. (10·4)
- Hydrogen is a nonmetal that does not belong to any group. Hydrogen is placed on the left side of the Periodic Table, above Group 1. (10·4)

The key terms in this chapter are listed below. Use each term in a sentence that shows the meaning of the term.

alkali metals	metalloids	Periodic Table
alkaline earth metals	metals	semiconductor
glass	noble gases	transition elements
halogens	nonmetals	

Chapter Review

VOCABULARY

Use the key terms from the previous page to complete the following sentences correctly.

1. _____ are the elements found in Group 2 of the Periodic Table.
2. The _____ are located in Groups 3 through 12 of the Periodic Table.
3. Elements found in Group 1 of the Periodic Table are called _____.
4. _____ are usually shiny, are good conductors of heat and electricity, and can be pounded into various shapes.
5. A/An _____ is a supercooled, viscous liquid.
6. The elements in Group 18 that do not react easily are the _____.
7. _____ have properties of both metals and nonmetals.
8. Elements that lack luster and are not ductile or malleable are called _____.
9. Elements of Group 17 are known as _____.
10. A/An _____ is a substance that conducts little electricity at low temperatures but more at higher temperatures.
11. The _____ is an arrangement of elements in order of increasing atomic number.

CONCEPTS

Identify each statement as True or False. If a statement is false, replace the underlined term or phrase with a term or phrase that makes the statement true.

1. The elements in the Periodic Table are organized in order of <u>atomic mass</u>.
2. Cesium is an example of an <u>alkaline earth metal</u>.
3. The type of bond that holds a piece of iron together is called a <u>metallic bond</u>.
4. The bonds are <u>stronger</u> in graphite than in diamond.
5. The <u>noble gases</u> have a completely filled outer electron level.

Choose the term or phrase that best answers the question or completes the statement.

6. Which of the following is an alkali metal?
   a. calcium   c. aluminum
   b. oxygen   d. potassium
7. An element has seven electrons in its outer energy level. The element is a/an
   a. alkali metal.   c. transition element.
   b. halogen.   d. noble gas.

8. All organic compounds contain the element
   a. carbon.   c. silicon.
   b. oxygen.   d. nitrogen.
9. Which element does not belong to any group of the Periodic Table?
   a. krypton   c. uranium
   b. francium   d. hydrogen
10. Which element is commonly used in semiconductors?
    a. copper   c. sodium
    b. silver   d. silicon

Answer the following in complete sentences.

11. What is the function of the heavy zigzag line in the Periodic Table?
12. Give two uses for each of the following elements: barium, calcium, magnesium.
13. Classify each element in Group 14 as a metal, metalloid, or nonmetal.
14. Describe two uses of silicon. Is this element a metal, a nonmetal, or a metalloid?
15. Why were the noble gases once called inert gases?

---

1. Make a chart to show the diatomic and triatomic molecules mentioned in this chapter.
2. After repeated pounding, metals become brittle because the movement of the electrons slows down. How could you make these metals malleable again?
3. Why are fluorine and chlorine difficult to remove from the minerals in which they are found?

APPLICATION/ CRITICAL THINKING.

---

1. Write a report on the effects of sodium chloride on the human circulatory system.
2. Research the use of cryogenics in the medical field. Present your findings to the class.
3. Sulfur can exist in different forms. Investigate how to prepare two different forms of sulfur. Plan an experiment to be done as a class project.

EXTENSION

CHAPTER 11

MOTION

The bicyclist shown in the photograph is in motion. But at this very moment, you also are in motion. Since you are on the earth, you are being carried around the sun at a speed of more than 100,000 km/h.

Almost all of the changes you see are caused by motion. Day and night are caused by the turning of the earth on its axis. The changes in weather are caused by the movement of air. The evaporation of water is caused by the motion of molecules.

- *What is motion?*
- *What makes objects move, stop, or change direction?*
- *What makes objects with more mass harder to move?*

11·1 The Nature of Motion

An object is in motion if there is a change in its position compared with the position of a fixed, or stationary, point. The fixed point is called the *reference point*. **Motion** is the change in position of an object as compared with a reference point.

All motion is not the same. Compare the motion of a car to that of a baseball. A car might travel in a straight line for a time and then stop at a traffic light. It might make a turn or move up and down hills, all in the same trip. A baseball's motion is less varied. It might move up, down, in a straight line, or in a curved path. But it cannot stop or start again in the same trip.

VELOCITY

One way to describe motion is to measure how far an object travels. For example, you might say that a car traveled 50 km from a starting point. You might say that you walked 1.5 km from home to school. In each case the description of motion includes a distance. *Distance* is the length of the actual path traveled by an object. *Speed* is the distance an object moves in a given amount of time. To calculate the speed of an object, use the following formula.

$$v = d/t$$

In this formula, v stands for speed, d stands for distance, and t stands for time.

The train in the photograph can travel at speeds up to 255 km/h. Suppose a passenger on the train jumped up while the train was moving forward. What would happen to the passenger? What would the passenger's motion look like to a person watching the train go by?

Sample Problem

A runner travels 10 m in 5 seconds. What is the runner's speed?

1. Write the formula.

$$v = d/t$$

2. Substitute the numbers given in the problem for the symbols in the formula.

$$v = 10 \text{ m}/5 \text{ s}$$

3. Determine the unit that will be part of the answer. The unit to express speed is meters per second (m/s).

$$v = 10/5 \text{ m/s}$$

4. Complete the calculations.

$$v = 2 \text{ m/s}$$

The speed of the runner is 2 m/s.

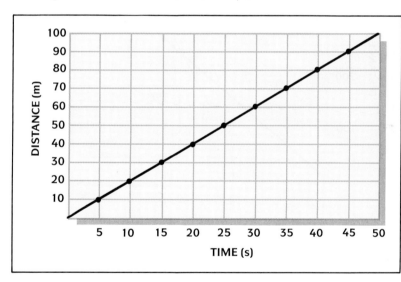

Figure 11·1

The motion of a runner moving at a constant speed is shown as a straight line on a distance-time graph.

Figure 11·1 shows a graph of the motion of a runner traveling at a constant speed of 2 m/s. The straight line shows that the runner's speed is constant. How far does the runner travel in 40 seconds?

Notice that speed is a ratio of two measurements—distance and time. If you state direction as well as speed, you are describing an object's velocity. **Velocity** (vuh LAHS uh tee) is speed

velocitas (swift)

in a definite direction. "Eighty kilometers per hour" is a statement of speed. "Eighty kilometers per hour north" is a statement of velocity.

The difference between speed and velocity can be shown by this example. Two cars traveling at 70 m/s, one north and one south, are said to have the same speed, 70 m/s. Their velocities are different because they are traveling in different directions.

Few objects travel at a constant velocity or speed. The color lines in Figure 11·2 show the changes in speed of a car on a family trip. When the car starts out on city streets, it stops and starts at traffic lights and moves slowly through crowded areas. On the highway the car travels at a greater speed but may stop at a toll booth.

Figure 11·2

How does stopping at a toll booth affect a car's average speed on a trip *(left)*? The average speed of a moving object can be found by connecting the beginning point and the finishing point on a graph *(right)*.

accelerare (quicken)

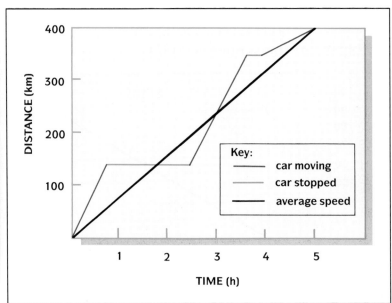

ACCELERATION

Think of a ball dropped from the top of a ten-story building. The ball travels in one direction, down. As the ball falls, it travels faster and faster, that is, its velocity increases. A change in velocity in a period of time is called **acceleration** (ak sehl uh RAY shuhn).

Figure 11·3 *(right)* shows a falling ball photographed at regular intervals. Notice that the dis-

252

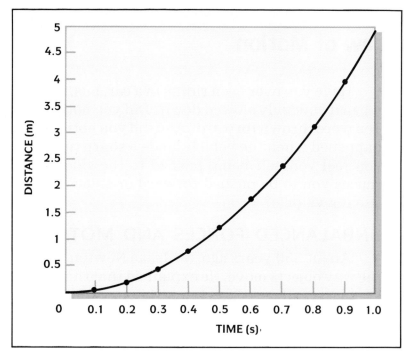

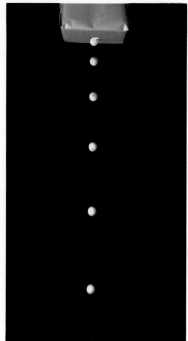

Figure 11·3

An object in free fall increases in speed, or accelerates *(left)*. Acceleration is shown as a curved line on a distance-time graph *(right)*.

tance the ball falls increases with each interval. This means the velocity of the ball is increasing or the ball is accelerating. The acceleration of an object in free fall on the earth is 9.8 m/s². This means in each second the speed of the ball will increase by 9.8 m/s. One second after the ball is released, it will be traveling at 9.8 m/s. After 2 seconds it will be traveling at 19.6 m/s. What will be the speed of the ball after 3 seconds? After 10 seconds it will be traveling at 98.0 m/s. Figure 11·3 *(left)* shows a graph of the motion of the accelerating ball. Notice that the distance between the points on the graph increases with time. This shows that the ball is accelerating. How does this graph compare with the graph of constant velocity in Figure 11·1?

REVIEW

1. What is the difference between speed and velocity?
2. A train travels 85 km in 1.5 hours. What is the speed of the train?
3. What is the difference between velocity and acceleration?

CHALLENGE Assume that the moon travels at a constant speed around the earth. Would the moon's velocity also be constant? Explain your answer.

11·2 Newton's First Law of Motion

Have you ever been riding in a car, bus, or train when it suddenly slowed down? Did you notice how you were thrown forward? And did you notice what happened when the vehicle made a sharp turn? Did you feel yourself being pushed to the side? What causes you to be pushed forward or sideways in a moving vehicle?

UNBALANCED FORCES AND MOTION

About 350 years ago, Sir Isaac Newton studied the way objects move. He explained that the motion of objects follows three laws. **Newton's First Law of Motion** states that an object at rest remains at rest until an unbalanced force acts on it. This law also states that an object moving at a constant speed and in a straight line will continue to do so until an unbalanced force acts on it.

Balanced forces on an object are forces that are equal and opposite. For example, the forces on a basketball being held are balanced forces. Notice in Figure 11·4 that the force keeping the basketball from falling is equal and opposite to the gravitational force on the ball. However, when the person releases the basketball, the gravitational force is no longer balanced by the force being applied. The gravitational force becomes an unbalanced force on

Figure 11·4

What are the forces on a basketball being held *(left)*? Gravity is the force that pulls all objects to the ground *(right)*.

force from student

force of gravity

force of gravity

the basketball, pulling the ball to the floor. An unbalanced force is a force that is not opposed equally by another force on the same object.

Suppose you want to move a book at rest on a desk. According to Newton's First Law of Motion, the object — the book — will remain at rest until an unbalanced force is applied to it. You can provide this force by pushing on the book.

Newton's First Law of Motion also states that once an object is moving, it should continue to move until an unbalanced force acts on it. However, the book does not continue to move at a constant speed. To keep the book moving, you must continue to apply force.

Figure 11·5
An ice skater moves freely because there is little friction between the ice and the skates.

The force needed to keep objects in motion is necessary only because of friction. Friction is a force that tends to slow down a moving object. If friction could be removed completely, no force would be needed to keep objects moving once they were in motion. What keeps the ice skater shown in Figure 11·5 moving?

INERTIA

The tendency of an object to remain at rest or in motion is called **inertia** (ihn ER shuh). The inertia of an object depends on its mass. The greater the mass

ACTIVITY   What Is Newton's First Law of Motion?

OBJECTIVE
Observe how objects resist changes in motion.

MATERIALS
scissors, metric ruler, cardboard, 2 ring stands, masking tape, small cart, 100-g mass

PROCEDURE

A. Cut a piece of cardboard about 20 cm long and 5 cm wide. Tape the cardboard to two ring stands, as shown in the figure. Adjust the position of the cardboard so that the top of a small cart is at least 1 cm higher than the top edge of the cardboard.

B. Place the ring stands and cardboard on the floor.

C. Put a 100-g mass on the front of the cart. Place the cart on the floor about 1 m from the ring stands. *Gently* push the cart toward the cardboard so that the cart strikes it. Note the speed at which the cart moves. Observe what happens to the mass.

D. Repeat step **C**, but this time, push the cart slightly harder so that the speed of the cart is slightly greater. Observe what happens to the 100-g mass.

E. Using masking tape, attach the mass securely to the cart. Push the cart toward the cardboard so that the cart has the same speed as it did in step **D**. Observe what happens to the 100-g mass.

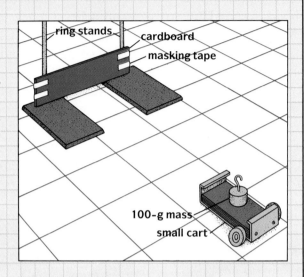

ring stands   cardboard   masking tape   100-g mass   small cart

RESULTS AND CONCLUSIONS

1. Describe what happened to the 100-g mass when the cart hit the cardboard in step **C**.

2. Describe what happened to the 100-g mass in step **D**, when the speed of the cart was increased.

3. Compare the results of steps **C** and **D**.

4. What happened to the momentum of the cart and mass when the cart hit the cardboard?

5. How did the results of step **E** explain why wearing a seat belt can prevent injuries in a car crash?

of an object, the greater the force needed to cause a change in its motion. Suppose you try to move a large car and then a smaller car by pushing them. You will notice that more force is needed to move the large car than the smaller car. Because the large car has more mass than the smaller car has, it also has more inertia. Thus, more force is needed to start it moving. Suppose both cars were moving at the same speed. Which car would need more force to stop it?

The tendency of a passenger to keep moving forward in a moving vehicle when its brakes are applied illustrates Newton's First Law of Motion. Suppose you are riding in a car. It is moving at a constant speed in one direction. You are moving at the same speed and in the same direction as the car. If the brakes are applied suddenly, the car will stop. But you will tend to keep moving forward at the same speed. Look at Figure 11·6. How does a fastened seat belt protect the people in a car crash from this effect?

Figure 11·6
This crash test shows the importance of wearing a seat belt.

MOMENTUM

It takes more force to stop a moving object with a large mass than to stop a moving object with a smaller mass. The force needed to stop a moving object depends on both its mass and its velocity. An object's mass multiplied by its velocity produces a quantity called **momentum**.

Momentum is an indication of the strength of an object's motion. For example, it usually takes more force to stop the motion of a car than to stop that of a bicycle. A moving car has more momentum than a bicycle moving at the same speed, because the car has more mass.

Figure 11·7

The momentum of the cue ball is transferred to the pool ball when they collide. Where did the cue ball get its momentum?

When moving objects collide, momentum can be transferred from one object to another. The *Law of Conservation of Momentum* states that momentum can be transferred between objects but the total momentum is never lost.

Consider what happens when a cue ball strikes a pool ball on a pool table. Notice in Figure 11·7 that the cue ball stops, but the red pool ball moves. As a result of the collision, the momentum of the cue ball is transferred to the pool ball. After the collision, the pool ball moves at the same speed as did the cue ball before the collision. If the moving pool ball hits the side of the pool table, the ball will bounce off with the same speed. Eventually the moving pool ball will slow down and stop moving. What force stops the motion of the pool ball?

REVIEW

1. Use Newton's First Law of Motion to explain how a weather satellite can remain in orbit.
2. What is inertia? Give two examples of the effects of inertia.
3. What property of an object determines how much inertia the object has?
4. How do mass and velocity affect momentum?

CHALLENGE Why do cars skid on curves when the road is icy?

11·3 Newton's Second Law of Motion

Recall that Newton's First Law of Motion states that an unbalanced force on an object causes the object to change its motion. The effect of an unbalanced force on an object is explained in Newton's Second Law of Motion. **Newton's Second Law of Motion** states that an unbalanced force on an object causes the object to accelerate in the direction of the force. Using his second law, Newton showed how force is related to mass and acceleration. According to this law, the greater the force applied to a given object, the greater its acceleration. For a given force, the greater the mass of an object, the smaller its acceleration.

Figure 11·8
How does the large engine and small mass of a race car help it accelerate?

Suppose an empty truck has to pick up a load at a warehouse. The truck is driven to the warehouse and is loaded fully. As the truck leaves the warehouse, the driver notices that it takes longer to reach the same speed as before, when the truck was empty. According to Newton's Second Law of Motion, the fully loaded truck accelerates more slowly because it now has more mass. With the same force

Figure 11·9

A truck with a large mass requires more distance to stop than does a truck with a smaller mass.

applied by the engine, the truck's speed changes more slowly than it did when the truck had less mass. How does the Second Law of Motion explain why larger trucks usually need more distance to stop than do smaller trucks?

Newton's second law is written as a formula.

$$F = ma$$

The F stands for the force applied to an object, the m stands for the object's mass, and the a stands for its acceleration. The formula can be used to find any one of the three quantities—force, mass, or acceleration—when the other two quantities are known. According to this formula, if the force is constant and the mass increases, what will happen to the acceleration?

SCIENCE & TECHNOLOGY

Friction from air is the main force that slows the speed of athletes in sports such as skiing, cycling, speed skating, and running. Air slows these athletes by pushing against them. This effect is called aerodynamic drag.

Recent developments in athletic clothing have reduced aerodynamic drag. For speed sports, clothing should be as smooth as possible.

Studies on cyclists have shown that with clothing and helmets that reduce friction, drag can be decreased by as much as 10 percent. Similar results were found in studies on runners. In tests the use of smooth, tight clothing was shown to reduce the amount of drag by 2 to 6 percent. In some races a change of just 2 percent can change the length of a runner's lead.

REVIEW

1. Use Newton's Second Law of Motion to explain why a free-falling object accelerates.
2. How is the acceleration of an object affected by the force applied to it?
3. If the mass of an object is decreased while the force applied to it remains the same, what will happen to the object's acceleration?

CHALLENGE Using the formula $a = F/m$, explain why all objects in free fall have the same acceleration, regardless of mass.

11·4 Newton's Third Law of Motion

The three main engines and two rocket boosters of a space shuttle provide the force to lift the shuttle off the ground. The force is needed to lift the approximately 68,000-kg mass that makes up the space shuttle.

Notice in Figure 11·10 the burning gases that escape from the engines and rocket boosters. The burning of fuel creates an unbalanced force as the gases escape from the engines and rockets. The unbalanced force is directed toward the ground. How does this unbalanced force lift the shuttle off the ground? The effect of this unbalanced force is explained by Newton's Third Law of Motion.

After completing this section, you will be able to

- **apply** Newton's Third Law of Motion.
- **identify** the action force and reaction force between two objects.
- **distinguish** between a pair of balanced forces and a pair of action and reaction forces.

The key term in this section is
Newton's Third Law of Motion

Newton's Third Law of Motion states that for every action by a force, there is an equal and opposite reaction by another force. If one object exerts a force on a second object, the second object exerts an equal and opposite force on the first object. For example, suppose a book is placed on a desk. Due to the pull of gravity, the book exerts a force on the desk. According to the third law of motion, the desk exerts an equal and opposite force on the book.

Figure 11·10
The space shuttle can lift off of the earth because of Newton's Third Law of Motion.

11·5 Circular Motion

CENTRIPETAL ACCELERATION

In the seventeenth century, Newton explained how an object could be launched into orbit around the earth. He said that an object could be launched into orbit if it could reach a great enough speed. For example, suppose a cannonball were fired in a horizontal direction from the top of a mountain. As you can see in Figure 11·12, if the speed of the cannonball were too slow, it would follow path 1, a curved path, and fall to the earth. At a greater speed the cannonball would follow path 2 and travel farther from the cannon. But the cannonball would still curve toward the surface of the earth, striking it.

At an even greater speed, the cannonball would follow path 3. The cannonball would move so fast that its path would extend past the earth instead of hitting the earth's surface. Notice that the path of the cannonball would still curve toward the earth's surface. But because the earth is round, the surface curves the same amount as the path of the cannonball. Thus the cannonball would never reach the surface. It would travel around the earth.

Figure 11·12

If an object can be made to move fast enough, it can go into orbit around the earth.

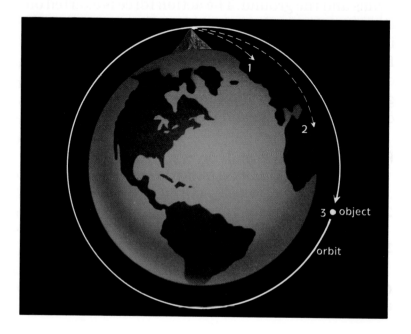

Actually, a cannonball cannot be launched into orbit with a cannon. This is because a cannon cannot accelerate the cannonball to a great enough speed. However, objects can be launched into orbit around the earth by using rockets. An object that moves in orbit around the earth is called a *satellite* of the earth. The moon is a satellite of the earth. What are some human–made satellites that orbit the earth?

Newton's First Law of Motion explains that once an object is in motion, no additional force is needed to keep it moving at a constant speed. Thus a satellite, such as the moon, needs no additional force to keep it moving. Newton's Second Law of Motion is illustrated by the effect of the gravitational force on a satellite. This law explains that an unbalanced force causes an object to accelerate in the direction of the force. As you can see in Figure 11·14, the gravitational force is toward the center of the earth. Thus the acceleration of a satellite is also toward the center of the earth. The acceleration of an object moving in a curved path or circle at a constant speed is called **centripetal** (sehn TRIHP uh tuhl) **acceleration**. The centripetal acceleration is toward the center of the circle in which an object is moving.

Figure 11·13
A weather satellite orbiting the earth.

centrum (center)
petere (seek)

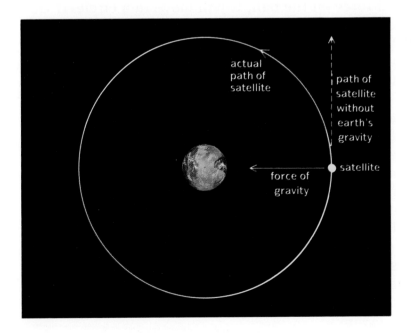

Figure 11·14
A satellite moves at a constant speed, but it also accelerates because it is always changing direction.

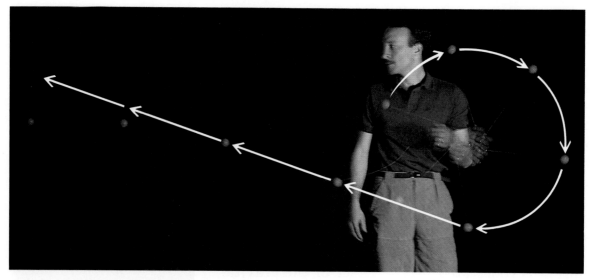

Figure 11·15

When a ball is tied to a cord and swung in a circle, the cord exerts a centripetal force that keeps the ball moving in a circular path. What is the path of the ball when the cord is released?

Figure 11·16

An orbiting spacecraft and all objects in it are in free fall.

CENTRIPETAL FORCE

The force that causes centripetal acceleration is called centripetal force. **Centripetal force** is the force that causes an object moving at constant speed to move in a curved path or circle. Centripetal force is toward the center of the circle in which an object is moving. The earth's gravity is the centripetal force that keeps a satellite moving in a circle.

Suppose you tie a ball to a cord and then swing it in a circle. As long as you keep applying centripetal force on the ball, it will move in a circle. If the cord breaks, you can no longer apply this force. The ball will no longer remain in the circle. It will fly off in a straight line. What would happen to the moon if the earth's gravity no longer acted on it?

The speed needed to keep a satellite in a circular orbit around the earth depends on its distance from the earth. Satellites relatively close to the earth have to move faster than do those farther away. If a satellite does not have the right speed, it may escape from the earth's orbit or fall back to the earth. In 1983 an orbiting space station called Skylab crashed into the earth when it lost speed.

A person orbiting the earth in a spacecraft seems to be weightless. With the gravitational force acting on the person and the spacecraft, both are in free fall. Both fall at the same rate. Therefore the person does not exert a force on the floor of the spacecraft. Nor does the floor of the spacecraft exert a force on the person. The person feels weightless, despite the gravitational force.

REVIEW

1. Use Newton's laws to explain the motion of satellites.
2. How is the motion of a satellite similar to the motion of an object in free fall?
3. How can objects appear to be weightless when they are pulled by the gravitational force?

CHALLENGE Why do astronauts train for weightlessness in an airplane that climbs very high and then dives downward?

CHAPTER SUMMARY

The main ideas in this chapter are listed below. Read these statements before you answer the Chapter Review questions.

- Motion is the change in position of an object as compared with a reference point. (11·1)
- The speed of an object is the distance the object travels in a given amount of time. Velocity is speed in a definite direction. (11·1)
- Acceleration is a change in velocity in a period of time. (11·1)
- Inertia is the tendency of an object to resist any change in motion. (11·2)
- Newton's First Law of Motion states that an object at rest remains at rest and an object in motion remains in motion unless the object is acted on by an unbalanced force. (11·2)
- Momentum is equal to an object's mass multiplied by its velocity. The Law of Conservation of Momentum states that momentum can be transferred between ob-

jects but the total momentum stays the same. (11·2)
- Newton's Second Law of Motion states that an unbalanced force causes an object to accelerate in the direction of the force. The amount of acceleration depends on the mass of the object and the force exerted on the object. (11·3)
- Forces act in pairs. One force is called the action force, and the other is called the reaction force. Newton's Third Law of Motion states that for every action by a force, there is an equal and opposite reaction by another force. (11·4)
- Centripetal force causes a moving object to travel in a curved path or circle. Centripetal force causes centripetal acceleration. (11·5)
- Apparent weightlessness is due to free fall. (11·5)

The key terms in this chapter are listed below. Use each term in a sentence that shows the meaning of the term.

acceleration	inertia	Newton's First Law of Motion
centripetal acceleration	momentum	Newton's Second Law of Motion
centripetal force	motion	Newton's Third Law of Motion
		velocity

Chapter Review

VOCABULARY

Write the letter of the term that best matches the definition. Each term will be used once.

1. Causes objects to resist changes in motion
2. The force that causes an object to move in a circular path
3. The law that states an unbalanced force causes an object to accelerate in the direction of the force
4. Speed in a given direction
5. The law that states for every action by a force, there is an equal and opposite reaction by another force
6. The law that states an object at rest remains at rest if no unbalanced force acts on it
7. The change in position of an object as compared with a reference point
8. A change in velocity
9. An object's mass multiplied by its velocity

a. acceleration
b. centripetal force
c. inertia
d. momentum
e. motion
f. Newton's First Law of Motion
g. Newton's Second Law of Motion
h. Newton's Third Law of Motion
i. velocity

CONCEPTS

Identify each statement as True or False. If a statement is false, replace the underlined term or phrase that makes the statement true.

1. A car travels 100 km in 4 hours. Its <u>acceleration</u> is 25 km/h.
2. "One hundred meters per second north" is a description of an object's <u>speed</u>.
3. A 25,000-kg truck is harder to push than a 2500-kg car. The truck has more <u>inertia</u> than the car.
4. The product of an object's mass and velocity gives the object's <u>acceleration</u>.
5. As the force applied to an object increases and the mass remains constant, the acceleration of the object <u>decreases</u>.

Choose the term or phrase that best answers the question or completes the statement.

6. If the force applied to an object remains the same while the mass of the object decreases, the acceleration of the object will
   a. decrease.
   b. increase.
   c. remain the same.
   d. increase, then decrease.

7. Which is an example of a pair of equal and opposite forces?
   a. balanced and unbalanced
   b. action and reaction
   c. friction and nonfriction
   d. mass and weight
8. A soccer player kicks a ball. The force of the player's foot on the ball is
   a. an action force.
   b. a reaction force.
   c. a balanced force.
   d. a friction force.
9. An orbiting satellite of the earth is the
   a. atmosphere.   c. ozone layer.
   b. moon.   d. sun.
10. An object might appear to be weightless if it is
    a. pulled by gravity.   c. in an airplane.
    b. in free fall.   d. moving rapidly.

Answer the following in complete sentences.
11. Distinguish between speed and velocity.
12. What factors determine an object's inertia?
13. State Newton's three laws of motion.
14. Identify the action and reaction forces in a rocket take-off.
15. Give two examples of centripetal force.

---

1. A horse is attempting to pull a cart. The force that the horse exerts on the cart is equal and opposite to the force that the cart exerts on the horse. Can the horse move the cart? Explain.
2. What factors affect the amount of centripetal force needed to hold an object in a circular path?
3. Why must a spacecraft be "coasting" with the engines off for the astronauts to feel weightless?
4. Use Newton's laws to explain the motion of a car traveling along a curved road.

APPLICATION/ CRITICAL THINKING

---

1. Centrifugal force is sometimes called a fictitious force. Write a report on what centrifugal force is. Compare centrifugal force with centripetal force.
2. Do library research to determine under what conditions Newton's laws of motion are not valid.
3. Prepare a report explaining how astronauts train for long periods of weightlessness.

EXTENSION

CHAPTER 12

ELECTRICITY AND MAGNETISM

*T*he device shown in the photograph is an electronic device called a chip. Its actual size is about one-tenth the size of a postage stamp. Despite its size, the chip can perform 100,000 tasks in one second, using less than a watt of power. Chips are used in television sets, radios, and computers. Because of their small size, chips can be used to make calculators and radios the size of credit cards.

- *What causes electricity to flow?*
- *Why is electricity such a useful form of energy?*
- *How are electricity and magnetism related?*

12·1 Static Electricity

statikos (stand)

Figure 12·1

Objects can become charged when they are rubbed together *(left)*. Electrons are transferred from the sweater to the balloon when they are rubbed together *(right)*.

PRODUCING STATIC ELECTRICITY

Have you ever walked across a carpet and received an electric shock when you touched a doorknob? Do you ever hear electricity crackling when you comb your hair? In both examples, electricity is produced when objects are rubbed together. This type of electricity is called static electricity. **Static electricity** is a type of electricity produced by the separation of negative and positive charges.

Notice in Figure 12·1 what happens when a balloon is rubbed against a sweater. The balloon can become charged and be made to stick to a wall. Figure 12·1 also shows the number of electric charges present in the sweater and the balloon. Notice that before these objects are rubbed together, the number of positive charges and negative charges in each object is equal. As the objects are rubbed together, the balloon gains negative charges. What charge does the balloon then have? The sweater loses negative charges. What charge does the sweater then have?

Your body can become charged when you walk across a carpet. As your shoes rub against the carpet, electrons picked up by the shoes are spread

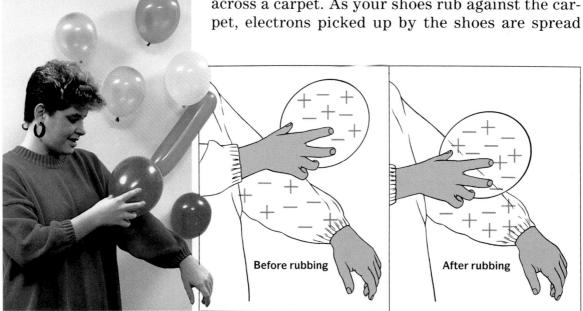

Before rubbing   After rubbing

across your body. As a result, your body becomes negatively charged. What charge does the carpet then have? Static electricity can then be observed if you touch a metal object, such as a doorknob. Some electrons will travel from your body along your fingers to the metal. You will probably feel a shock and hear a crackling sound. Sometimes you will even see a spark. The process of removing the charge on a charged object is called *grounding*.

Some objects lose an electric charge almost as soon as they gain it. This is because electric charges can flow through these substances easily. The charges do not remain in place and build up. A substance that allows electric charges to flow through easily is called a **conductor**. Look at Table 12·1. Which material in the table is the best conductor?

Some substances do not gain or lose an electric charge easily. This is because electric charges do not flow through these substances easily. Thus the charges tend to remain in place. A substance that does not allow electric charges to flow through easily is called an **insulator** (IHN suh lay tuhr).

FORCES BETWEEN CHARGED OBJECTS

Static electricity can exert forces on objects. The girl shown in Figure 12·2 is being electrically charged. Static electricity is causing her hair to stand up. Static electricity can also cause two pieces

Table 12·1 *Conductors and Insulators*

SUBSTANCE	ABILITY TO CONDUCT ELECTRICITY
Silver	Best conductor
Copper	
Aluminum	
Carbon	
Water	
Human body	
Earth	
Plastic	
Glass	
Hard rubber	
Dry air	Best insulator

Figure 12·2
The girl is being electrically charged by a static electricity generator.

of clothing taken from a clothes dryer to stick together. How does static electricity exert forces?

Look at Figure 12·3 *(left)*. One balloon was rubbed with wool and given a negative charge. The other balloon was rubbed with silk and given a positive charge. Notice that the balloons attract each other. Objects with unlike charges attract. Thus two pieces of clothing that attract each other must have opposite charges.

What happens when objects with like charges are brought near each other? Figure 12·3 *(right)* shows two balloons that were rubbed with wool and given negative charges. Notice how the balloons repel each other. Objects with like charges repel.

Figure 12·3
Objects with unlike charges attract *(left)*. Objects with like charges repel *(right)*.

A charged object can also attract a nearby, uncharged object. For example, if you charge a comb by pulling it through your hair, the comb will pick up small pieces of paper. And you already know you can make a balloon stick to a wall by first rubbing the balloon on your sleeve. These attractions take place because a charged object can cause a neutral object to become charged.

Figure 12·4 shows the effect of placing a positively charged glass rod *(A)* just above a small piece of aluminum foil. Notice that negative charges in the foil move up toward the rod. This makes the top of the foil become negatively charged while the bottom of the foil becomes negatively charged. Because substances with unlike charges attract, the positively charged rod attracts the negatively charged top of the foil.

Figure 12·4 also shows what happens when a negatively charged rubber rod *(B)* is brought near a piece of foil. Negative charges in the top of the foil are repelled by the rod, and they move to the bottom. The top of the foil becomes positively charged. Thus the negatively charged rod attracts the positively charged top of the foil.

In each example a charged rod causes electrons to move. The pieces of foil become charged because of the charged rods near them. The process of charging an object through the presence of a nearby charged object is called **induction** (ihn DUHK-shuhn).

The earth's surface is sometimes charged by induction. During a storm, electric charges in a cloud can separate. As you can see in Figure 12·5 *(left)*, the top layer of the cloud becomes positively charged, and the bottom layer becomes negatively charged. The bottom layer then repels negative charges at the earth's surface. What charge does the surface become?

When the build-up of charges in the cloud and in the ground is great enough, electrons flow from

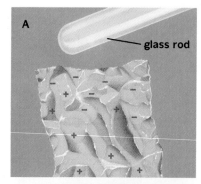

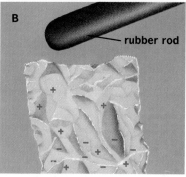

Figure 12·4
A positively charged rod attracts the foil *(A)*. How does a negatively charged rod attract the foil *(B)*?

ducere (to lead)

Figure 12·5
Lightning is caused by the build-up of electric charges in clouds. What causes the cloud to become charged?

How Is Static Electricity Produced?

OBJECTIVES
Explain how static electricity is produced.
Conclude how objects can become charged.

MATERIALS
rubber rod, small strip of aluminum foil, wool cloth, glass rod, silk cloth, pith ball with silk cord attached, ring stand

PROCEDURE
A. Bring a rubber rod near, but not touching, a small strip of aluminum foil.
   1. What do you observe? Explain your observation.
B. Rub the rubber rod with a wool cloth. Bring the rod near the aluminum foil.
   2. What do you observe? Explain your observation.
C. Bring a glass rod near, but not touching, the foil.
   3. What do you observe? Explain your observation.
D. Rub the glass rod with a silk cloth. Bring the rod near the foil again.
   4. What do you observe? Explain your observation.
E. Hang a pith ball from a ring stand. Rub the rubber rod with the wool. Bring the rod near, but not touching, the pith ball.
   5. What do you observe? Explain your observation.
F. Rub the glass rod with the silk. Bring the rod near, but not touching, the pith ball.
   6. What do you observe? Explain your observation.
G. Rub the rubber rod with wool. With the rod, touch the pith ball lightly.
   7. What do you observe? Explain your observation.
H. Rub the glass rod with the silk. With the rod, touch the pith ball lightly.
   8. What do you observe? Explain your observation.

RESULTS AND CONCLUSIONS
1. Describe how an object can become charged.
2. How can a charged object cause another object to become charged?
3. From your observations, can you determine if the charges on the rod and foil and on the rod and pith ball are alike or unlike? Explain your answer.

the cloud to the ground. As the electrons flow, air along their path is heated, resulting in a bright streak of light called lightning. The heating of the air also causes it to expand. If the air expands rapidly enough, a loud sound called thunder can be heard.

REVIEW
1. In what way can two objects become electrically charged?
2. What is the difference between a conductor and an insulator? Give one example of each type of material.
3. What are two ways in which charged objects can interact?
4. How do charged objects attract uncharged objects?

CHALLENGE Explain how static electricity builds up in a clothes dryer.

12·2 Current Electricity

Recall that the separation of negative and positive charges produce static electricity. Moving charges produce *current electricity*. Electrons can move easily through conductors. The flow of electrons, or flow of charges, is called **electric current**.

ELECTRIC CELLS

To move electric charges in a circuit, energy must be supplied. This energy can be supplied by an electric cell. An **electric cell** is a device that changes chemical energy into electrical energy.

An electric cell contains two or more materials called electrodes (ih LEHK trohdz). The electrodes are placed in a conducting mixture called an electrolyte. Chemical reactions take place between the electrodes and the substances in the electrolyte mixture.

An electric cell that contains an electrolyte that is a liquid solution is called a *wet cell*. In a wet cell, when one electrode reacts with the electrolyte, electrons accumulate at the electrode. These electrons flow out of the electric cell, creating an electric current. As shown in Figure 12·6, electrons leave the cell through the electrode called the *anode* (AN ohd). Electrons pass through a conductor and return to the cell through the second electrode. The

After completing this section, you will be able to

- **distinguish** between current, potential difference, and resistance.
- **describe** the parts of a simple electric circuit.
- **compare** a series circuit with a parallel circuit.
- **calculate** the amount of electric power used by an electric device.

The key terms in this section are
ampere
electric cell
electric circuit
electric current
electric power
potential difference
resistance

currere (to run)

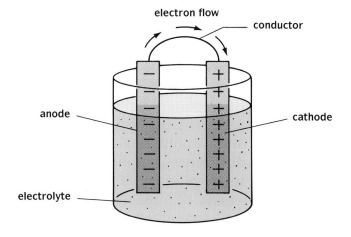

Figure 12·6

An electric cell changes chemical energy into electrical energy. In which direction do electrons flow from a wet cell?

Figure 12·7

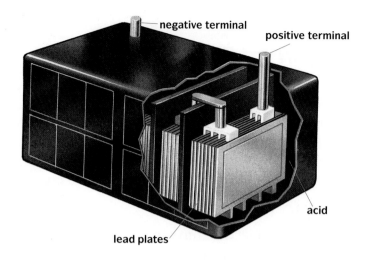

An automobile battery contains wet cells.

electrode through which electrons enter the cell is called the *cathode* (KATH ohd). Most automobile batteries, like the one shown in Figure 12·7, contain six wet cells. How many anodes and how many cathodes does an automobile battery contain?

The electric cells used in toys, flashlights, and calculators are called dry cells. A *dry cell* is an electric cell in which the electrolyte is a paste instead of a liquid. A dry cell is shown in Figure 12·8. The anode is the zinc container, and the cathode is the carbon rod in the center.

ELECTRICAL UNITS

potens (power)

Figure 12·8

A dry cell contains a pastelike material as its electrolyte.

Electric current is a flow of charges. Electric current is measured in electrical units called amperes (AM pihrz), or amps. An **ampere** (A) is a measure of the number of charges that flow past a point in one second. One ampere is equal to 6.25×10^{18} electrons per second.

In an electric cell, electrons accumulate at one electrode. This electrode is described as being a region of high potential. Since the other electrode does not accumulate electrons, it is a region of low potential. The difference in potential between the two electrodes is called the potential difference. Another name for the potential difference is voltage. **Potential difference** is a measure of the energy available to move charges in a circuit. The greater the potential difference, the greater the number of electrons that can flow.

The number of electrons that can flow also depends on the extent to which the conductor opposes their flow. The opposition to the flow of charges in a substance is called **resistance** (rih ZIHS tuhns). Resistance is measured in units called *ohms* (Ω).

ELECTRIC CIRCUITS

To produce a current, there must be a path along which electrons can flow. A path through which an electric current can travel is called an **electric circuit** (SER kiht). An electric circuit in which current flows in a complete path is called a *closed circuit*. If there is a break anywhere along the path of the current, the circuit is no longer complete. An electric circuit that is broken is called an *open circuit*. Electric charges will not flow in an open circuit.

A circuit can be opened or closed by using a device called a switch. Notice in Figure 12·9 *(left)* that when a switch is open, the current's path is broken. Therefore the current cannot flow. When the switch is closed, as in Figure 12·9 *(right)*, the path is complete and the current can flow.

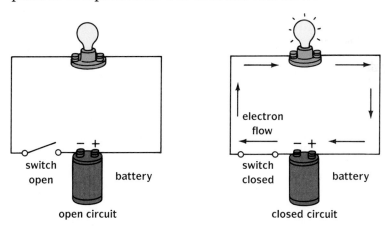

open circuit   closed circuit

A simple circuit is made up of a source of potential difference, a conductor, and a load. The load is any electric device. In the circuit shown in Figure 12·9, the battery is the source of potential difference. It supplies the energy to move the electrons. The wire is the conductor. It provides a path through which the electrons can flow. The light bulb is the load.

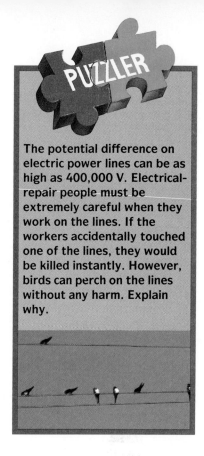
circuire (to go around)

Figure 12·9
When the switch is open, no electrons flow *(left)*. When the switch is closed, electrons flow *(right)*.

Figure 12·10

A series circuit *(left)*. A parallel circuit *(right)*. What effect does a bulb burning out have on the other light bulbs in each type of circuit?

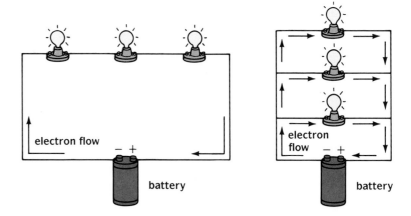

electron flow

battery

electron flow

battery

The two main types of electric circuits are shown in Figure 12·10. The type shown on the left is a series circuit. A *series circuit* is a circuit in which there is only one path for the current. The loads are connected one after the other. If any part of the path is broken, or opened, the current in all parts of the circuit stops.

The other type of circuit, shown on the right, is a parallel circuit. A *parallel circuit* is a circuit in which there is more than one path for the current. In this circuit there are separate paths for the current. When one of the paths is broken, or opened, current can still flow through the other paths.

SCIENCE & TECHNOLOGY

In 1911, scientists discovered that metals would lose all resistance to the flow of electricity at a few degrees above −273°C, or absolute zero. Until recently, however, this property—called superconductivity—has been impractical to use. It has required using liquid helium to cool metal wires to near absolute zero. Now, scientists have produced ceramic materials that can become superconductors at much warmer temperatures, about −73° C. If scientists can produce superconductors that work at higher temperatures, superconductors could affect almost anything that runs on electricity. Computers would become even smaller, faster, and more powerful. High-speed trains would be able to glide almost friction-free on superconducting magnets. Electric appliances could operate at close to 100 percent efficiency. The actual use of superconductors, however, may still be years away. Much research is needed to find out how these materials work.

280

Wires in a circuit must be properly insulated. If uninsulated wires touch, current can pass from one wire to the other at the point where they touch. Because the current takes a shorter path than usual, such a circuit is called a short circuit.

ELECTRIC POWER

The ability of electrical energy to be changed into other forms of energy makes it one of the most useful forms of energy. For example, electrical energy is changed into visible light by light bulbs and into sound energy by stereos. Not all electric devices use the same amount of electrical energy. The amount of electrical energy used each second is called **electric power**.

Figure 12·11
Why does a lighthouse produce more light than does a light bulb?

Electric power is measured in watts. A *watt* (W) is the SI unit of power. The power of a light bulb is measured in watts and is printed on the bulb. The higher the number of watts, the brighter the light bulb will be, and the more energy it will use. A larger unit of power than the watt is called a kilowatt. A kilowatt (kW) is a unit of power equal to 1000 W.

The relationship between electric power and current is shown by the following formula.

$$P = VI$$

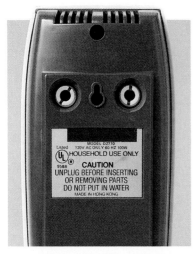

Figure 12·12
Electric appliances with higher power ratings use more electrical energy than do those with lower power ratings.

In this formula the P stands for power, the V stands for potential difference, and the I stands for current.

Sample Problem
How much electric power is used by a color television that uses 1.5 A when the potential difference is 120 V?

1. Write the formula.

$$P = VI$$

2. Substitute the numbers given in the problem for the symbols in the formula.

$$P = 120 \text{ V} \times 1.5 \text{ A}$$

3. Determine the unit that will be part of the answer. Recall that the electrical unit of power is the watt.

$$P = 120 \times 1.5 \text{ W}$$

4. Complete the calculations that are required.

$$P = 180 \text{ W}$$

The color television uses 180 W of power.

Electric power companies bill their customers according to the amount of power used. Each unit of electricity sold is called a kilowatt-hour. A kilowatt-hour (kW-h) is the amount of electrical energy used when one kilowatt of power is used for one hour.

REVIEW

1. What are the differences between electric current, potential difference, and resistance?
2. What are the parts of a simple electric circuit? How does an open circuit differ from a closed circuit?
3. How does a series circuit differ from a parallel circuit?
4. Calculate the electric power of a vacuum cleaner that uses 5 A of current when the potential difference is 120 V.

CHALLENGE Design a circuit with a power source, three light bulbs, wires, and a switch. Arrange the circuit so that only one light bulb can be turned off and on by the switch.

12·3 Magnets and Magnetism

People in ancient civilizations observed that some rocks could attract pieces of iron. These rocks were called magnetic because they were first found in Magnesia, a section of Asia. If pieces of the rocks were hung by thread, they would point north.

A **magnet** is any substance that can attract iron or other magnetic materials. Examples of magnetic materials are cobalt, nickel, iron, and alloys of these metals. Magnets come in many shapes. But no matter what shape a magnet is, its ability to attract magnetic materials is strongest at its ends. These ends are called *poles*. Suppose a magnet is hung by a thread so that one end of it points north. The end of the magnet that points north is called its north pole. The opposite end of the magnet is called its south pole. The north end may be labeled *N* for north and the south end labeled *S* for south.

Figure 12·13 shows what happens when two magnetic poles are brought near each other. When the south pole of one magnet is brought near the south pole of another magnet, the poles repel each other. However, when the north pole is brought near the south pole, the poles attract each other. As with unlike electric charges and like electric charges, unlike magnetic poles attract and like magnetic poles repel.

After completing this section, you will be able to

- **explain** the cause of magnetism.
- **describe** the effects between like and unlike magnetic poles.
- **distinguish** between permanent magnets and temporary magnets.

The key terms in this section are
magnet
magnetic field
magnetism

Figure 12·13
Like poles of magnets repel *(A)*. Unlike poles attract *(B)*.

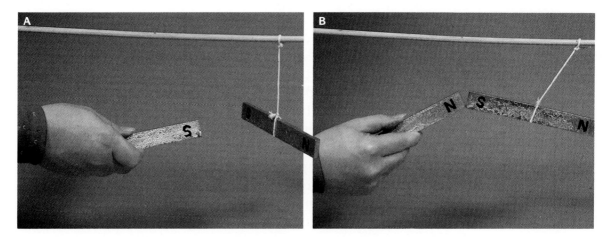

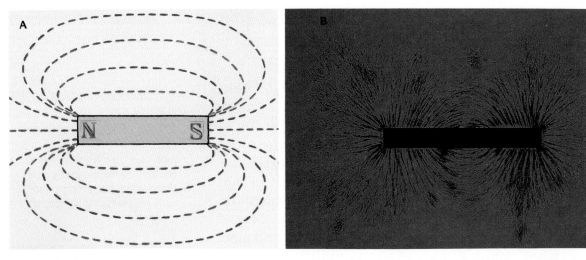

Figure 12·14

Magnetic field lines around a bar magnet *(A)*. Iron filings sprinkled around a magnet shows the magnet's field lines *(B)*. Where is the magnetic field strongest?

The attraction that magnets have for magnetic materials, and the attraction and repulsion between magnetic poles, is called **magnetism** (MAG-nuh tihz uhm). Magnetism is also called magnetic force. The area around a magnet where the magnetic force acts is called its **magnetic field**. The magnetic field of a bar magnet is shown in Figure 12·14 *(A)*. Each line is called a magnetic field line. These lines show where the magnetic force is strongest. The closer the lines, the stronger the magnetic force.

The magnetic field around a magnet can be shown by sprinkling iron filings evenly around the magnet. The magnetic field causes the iron filings to line up along the magnetic field lines. The pattern formed by iron filings around a bar magnet is shown in Figure 12·14 *(B)*. Where is the magnetic force strongest on this bar magnet?

What causes a magnet to have poles and a magnetic field? Recall that all matter is made up of atoms. Most atoms do not have magnetic fields. But in iron and other magnetic materials, the atoms have small magnetic fields. The atoms can be thought of as being tiny bar magnets with tiny magnetic fields. These "magnets" can line up so that their north poles face in the same direction, making a larger magnetic field. When atoms in a magnetic material line up so their magnetic fields combine, the material becomes a magnet.

Studies show that the atoms in magnetic substances act not alone but in groups called magnetic domains. A *magnetic domain* is a region in which the atoms are arranged so that their magnetic fields line up to form a larger magnetic field. In most magnetic materials the domains face in many directions. Their magnetic fields cancel each other. Thus these materials have no magnetism. However, in magnets the domains face in the same direction. This produces an overall magnetic field around the magnets.

The domains in a magnetized piece of iron are shown in Figure 12·15 *(left)*. Notice that they are arranged so that their north poles face in the same direction. The domains in an unmagnetized piece of iron shown in Figure 12·15 *(right)* face in different directions. If these domains can be made to line up, the piece of iron will become a magnet. One way

Figure 12·15
In a magnetized piece of iron, the domains are lined up in the same direction *(left)*. In an unmagnetized piece of iron, the domains are not lined up *(right)*.

of doing this is by repeatedly sliding a magnet over the iron in one direction. This rearranges the domains in the iron so that they line up, creating a magnet.

Another way the domains in an unmagnetized piece of iron can be made to line up is by bringing a magnet near the iron. This causes the domains in the iron bar to line up with the magnetic field lines of the magnet. As a result, the iron becomes a magnet. When the magnet is removed, the domains

How Is a Magnetic Field Mapped?

Draw a diagram of a magnetic field.

2 bar magnets, magnet holder, 4 sheets of paper, iron filings, metric ruler

A. Place one magnet in a magnet holder.
B. Place a sheet of paper over the magnet and holder so that the magnet is at the center of the paper.
C. Lightly sprinkle iron filings on the paper. Tap the paper gently. On another sheet of paper, sketch the pattern of the filings.
D. Return the iron filings to their container.
E. Place two magnets 2 cm apart in the holder so that two unlike poles face each other.
F. Place a sheet of paper over the magnets so that the center of the paper is over the two facing ends of the magnets.
G. Lightly sprinkle iron filings on the paper. Tap the paper gently. On another sheet of paper, sketch the pattern of the filings.
H. Return the iron filings to their container.
I. Place the two magnets 2 cm apart in the holder so that two like poles face each other. Repeat steps **F** through **H**.

1. Where is a magnetic field greatest? How can you tell?
2. What does the sketch you made in step **G** show about the magnetic field between two unlike poles?
3. What does the sketch you made in step **I** show about the magnetic field between two like poles?

Figure 12·16

How do nonmagnets, such as these paper clips, become temporary magnets?

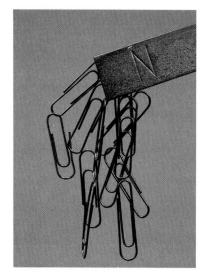

return to their original positions. An object in which the domains return to their original positions when a magnetic field is removed is called a *temporary magnet*. The paper clips shown in Figure 12·16 are acting as temporary magnets.

Some objects stay magnetized even after a magnetic field has been removed. These materials are called *permanent magnets*. In permanent magnets the domains stay lined up because of the strong attraction between their poles. However, permanent magnets can lose their magnetism if their domains are pushed out of line. This can happen if the permanent magnet is heated or hammered.

REVIEW

1. What causes magnetism in a magnet?
2. What happens when like magnetic poles are brought together? What happens if the poles are unlike?
3. What is the difference between a temporary magnet and a permanent magnet?

CHALLENGE Why are iron fences magnetized over time?

12·4 Producing Magnetism from Electricity

Recall that a magnet produces a magnetic field. In 1820 a Danish physicist named Hans Oersted found that an electric current can also produce a magnetic field. He observed that an electric current flowing through a wire can cause a compass needle to change direction. He also noted that the position of the compass needle changes if the current is reversed. The relationship between electricity and magnetism is called electromagnetism (ih lehk troh-MAG nuh tihz uhm).

Figure 12·17A shows the magnetic field produced by a coil of wire through which a current flows. Compare the shape of the magnetic field to that of the bar magnet shown in Figure 12·14. Figure 12·17B shows how the magnetic field changes when an iron bar is placed within the coil of wire. Notice that the magnetic field lines become closer. What does this show about the strength of the magnetic field?

After completing this section, you will be able to

- **compare** the magnetic field produced by a coil of wire with that produced by a straight wire.
- **describe** the factors that affect the strength of an electromagnet.
- **explain** how an electric motor works.

The key terms in this section are
electric motor
electromagnet

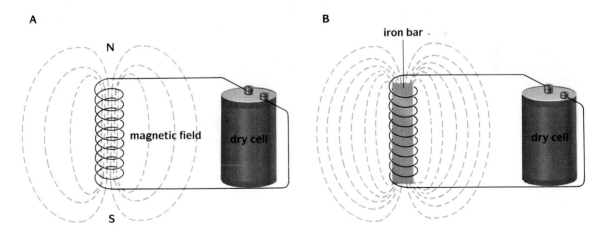

Figure 12·17

A magnetic field produced by an electric current in a coil of wire (A). The strength of the magnetic field can be increased by placing an iron bar in the coil (B).

A coil of wire wound around an iron core is called an **electromagnet**. When current flows in the coil, the magnetic field of the coil causes the domains in the iron core to line up. The iron core becomes a magnet. The magnetic field of the coil and the magnetic field of the iron core combine to produce a stronger magnetic field. When the dry cell is disconnected, the coil and the core lose their magnetism. Thus the magnetism of an electromagnet can be turned on and off. The strength of an electromagnet can be increased by increasing the current or the number of turns in the coil of wire.

Electromagnets have many uses. They are used in doorbells. Electromagnets are also used in earpieces of telephones and in loudspeakers.

A magnetic field can exert a force on a wire carrying an electric current. Michael Faraday, a scientist, observed that a magnetic field could push a current-carrying wire. This effect is shown in Figure 12·18A. A wire is connected to an open switch and to a dry cell. The wire is then placed between the poles of a magnet. When the switch is closed, current flows and the wire moves up. When the switch is opened so that no current exists, the wire returns to its original position.

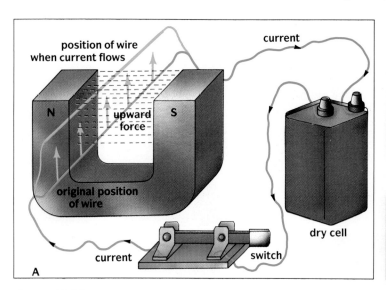

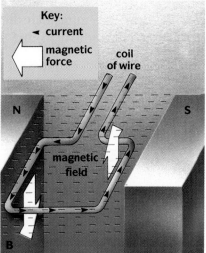

Figure 12·18

A magnetic field exerts a force on a wire through which electric current is flowing (A). A magnetic field can cause a loop of wire carrying electric current to turn (B).

Suppose that the connections of the wire to the battery are reversed. Then when the switch is closed, the direction of the current also reverses, and the wire moves down. This shows that the direction of a magnetic force on a current-carrying wire depends on the direction the current moves.

Figure 12·18B shows what happens when a wire is made into a loop and placed in a magnetic field. When current flows through the loop, a magnetic force is exerted on two sides of the loop. But notice that the current in the sides of the loop flows in opposite directions. This causes the magnetic force on each side of the loop to act in opposite directions. The magnetic force pushes one side upward while it pushes the other side downward. These opposite forces cause the loop to turn.

In an electric motor a magnetic force turns a coil of wire. An **electric motor** is a device that changes electrical energy into mechanical energy. Notice in Figure 12·19 that an electric motor contains a coil of wire set between the poles of a magnet. When current flows through the coil, the magnetic field of the permanent magnet exerts a magnetic force on the coil of wire, causing the coil to turn. In a motor the coil is free to turn all the way around. This turning continues as long as there is current flowing in the wire coil.

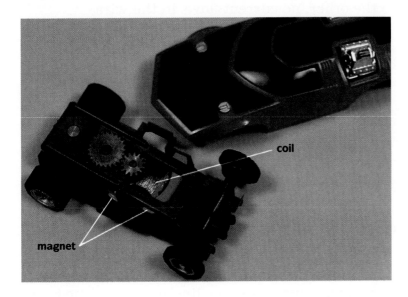

Figure 12·19
An electric motor consists of a coil of wire that turns in a magnetic field.

REVIEW

1. How does the magnetic field of a coil of wire compare with the magnetic field of a straight wire?
2. What factors affect the strength of an electromagnet?
3. How does an electric motor work?

CHALLENGE In heavy-duty electric motors, several coils of wire, each set at a different angle, are placed between the poles of permanent magnets. How does this increase the strength of motors?

12·5 Producing Electricity from Magnetism

After completing this section, you will be able to

- **describe** how an electric current can be produced by a magnetic field.
- **explain** how a generator works.
- **distinguish** between alternating current and direct current.

The key terms in this section are
alternating current
direct current
generator

PRODUCING ELECTRIC CURRENT

You have learned that an electric current can produce magnetism. But can magnetism produce an electric current? To answer this question, look at Figure 12·20. The wire is connected to a galvanometer. A *galvanometer* (gal vuh NAHM uh tuhr) is a meter used to measure tiny amounts of electric current. When the wire is moved downward between the poles of the magnet, the galvanometer needle moves. This shows that a current flows in the wire. What happens to the needle when the wire is moved upward through the magnetic field? This shows that the current flows in the opposite direction. If the wire is not moved or if it is moved from one pole to the other, no current flows in the wire.

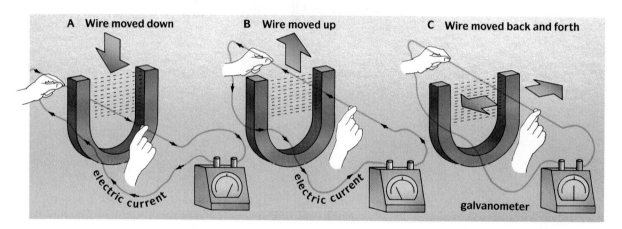

Figure 12·20
A current is induced in a wire when the wire is moved down *(A)* or up *(B)* in a magnetic field. No current is induced when the wire is moved parallel to the magnetic field *(C)*.

To produce an electric current in a wire, the wire must move across the lines of a magnetic field. Thus, current can be produced in a wire when the wire is moved through a magnetic field at right angles to that field. A current can also be produced by moving the magnet up and down while holding the wire in place.

If a wire is made into a loop and rotated in a magnetic field, a stronger current can be produced. This is how a generator (JEHN uh ray tuhr) works. A **generator** is a device that changes mechanical en-

genus (birth)

ergy into electrical energy. In a generator, many loops of wire are turned in a magnetic field to produce a current. Increasing the number of loops in the coil of wire increases the amount of current produced. Increasing the speed at which the coil rotates also increases the amount of current produced in the coil.

In a generator, mechanical energy is used to rotate the coil. This energy can come from the falling water in a waterfall. In many electric power plants, the mechanical energy comes from heat energy produced by the burning of coal. The heat boils water and creates steam. The force of moving steam is used to turn the coil in a generator.

Figure 12·21
The generator in an electric power plant changes mechanical energy into electrical energy. Where does the mechanical energy of this power plant come from?

ALTERNATING CURRENT

The electricity produced by generators in power plants is a type of current called alternating current. **Alternating current** (ac) is a type of electric current that changes direction at regular intervals in a circuit. For example, the alternating current in household circuits in North America moves back and forth 60 times each second.

Alternating current differs from the type of current produced by an electric cell or by a battery. Recall that the electric current produced by an elec-

Figure 12·22

The direction of the current induced in a coil of wire depends on the direction the coil moves in the magnetic field. A turning coil changes direction and produces alternating current.

tric cell or by a battery travels in one direction. Electric current that travels in one direction in a circuit is called **direct current** (dc).

To see how a generator produces alternating current, look at Figure 12·22 *(left)*. Notice the position of part *A* of the coil. As the coil turns through the magnetic field, part *A* moves upward through the field. One-half turn later, as shown in Figure 12·22 *(right)*, part *A* of the coil moves downward through the field. Each time the coil makes a half turn, part *A* moves in the opposite direction in the field. Notice that this is also true for part *B* of the coil. Each time the coil makes a half turn, part *B* moves in the opposite direction. These changes in direction cause the current in the coil to change direction. Thus as the coil turns, an alternating current is produced.

Power companies find that they can send electric power to households with less power loss using ac instead of dc. Recall that wires have resistance to electric current. The greater the electric current in a wire, the greater the loss of electric power. To reduce this loss, electric power is sent through power lines using a low current and a high potential difference. Before this power reaches households, the current must be increased and the potential difference lowered for household use. This is done by a device called a transformer, which works only on ac, not dc.

REVIEW

1. How can magnetism be used to produce electric current in a wire?

2. How does a generator produce electric current?

3. In what way does alternating current differ from direct current?

CHALLENGE Would a compass needle change direction when brought near a wire that carries household current? Explain why or why not.

CHAPTER SUMMARY

The main ideas in this chapter are listed below. Read these statements before you answer the Chapter Review questions.

- Objects can become electrically charged when two objects are rubbed against each other. (12·1)

- Static electricity is produced by the separation of negative and positive charges. (12·1)

- A conductor is a substance that allows electric charges to flow through it easily. An insulator does not allow electric charges to flow through it easily. (12·1)

- Induction is a process by which a charged object causes a nearby, uncharged object to become charged. (12·1)

- An electric current is a flow of charges. (12·2)

- The purpose of an electric cell is to supply energy to move electric charges in a circuit. (12·2)

- Electric current, measured in amperes, is the flow of electrons. Potential difference is a measure of the energy available to move charges in a circuit. Opposition to the flow of

charges is called resistance; it is measured in ohms. (12·2)

- A series circuit is a circuit in which there is only one path for the current to follow. A parallel circuit is a circuit in which there is more than one path for the current. (12·2)

- The magnetic properties of materials are caused by the arrangement of the atoms within the materials. (12·3)

- Certain materials, called magnetic materials, become magnets when placed in magnetic fields. (12·3)

- The strength of an electromagnet can be increased by increasing the current or the number of turns in the coil of wire. (12·4)

- When a wire is moved through a magnetic field at right angles to that field or when a magnetic field is moved at right angles to a wire, a current is produced in the wire. (12·5)

- When a coil of wire turns in a magnetic field, an alternating current is produced in the coil. (12·5)

The key terms in this chapter are listed below. Use each term in a sentence that shows the meaning of the term.

alternating current	electric motor	magnetic field
ampere	electric power	magnetism
conductor	electromagnet	potential difference
direct current	generator	resistance
electric cell	induction	static electricity
electric circuit	insulator	
electric current	magnet	

Chapter Review

VOCABULARY

Write the letter of the term that best matches the definition. Not all the terms will be used.

1. A substance that allows charges to flow through easily
2. A device that changes mechanical energy into electrical energy
3. A substance that attracts magnetic materials
4. The flow of charges
5. A measure of the energy available to move charges in a circuit
6. The area around a magnet on which magnetic force acts
7. The opposition to the flow of charges in a circuit
8. The effects of the separation of charges
9. The process of charging an object through the presence of a nearby charged object
10. A device that changes electrical energy into mechanical energy

a. conductor
b. electric current
c. electric motor
d. generator
e. induction
f. insulator
g. magnet
h. magnetic field
i. potential difference
j. resistance
k. static electricity

CONCEPTS

Identify each statement as True or False. If a statement is false, replace the underlined term or phrase with a term or phrase that makes the statement true.

1. Rubbing two objects together can cause <u>electrons</u> to move from one object to the other.
2. Copper is a good <u>insulator</u>.
3. If a string of light bulbs is connected in a <u>parallel circuit</u>, all the lights will go out if one bulb is removed.
4. Electric current will not flow in an <u>open circuit</u>.
5. The metal <u>nickel</u> is a magnetic material.

Choose the term or phrase that best answers the question or completes the statement.

6. When the south pole of a magnet is brought near the south pole of another magnet, the poles
   a. attract
   b. repel
   c. attract, then repel
   d. repel, then attract

7. As the current in an electromagnet decreases, the strength of the magnetic field it produces
   a. increases   c. remains the same
   b. decreases   d. increases, then decreases
8. Which of the following turns in an electric motor?
   a. anode   c. permanent magnets
   b. cathode   d. coil of wire
9. Which type of current is produced by an electric cell?
   a. direct current   c. series current
   b. alternating current d. parallel current
10. In which direction should a wire be moved through a magnetic field to produce the maximum amount of current?
    a. parallel to the field   c. right angles to the field
    b. 45° to the field   d. 60° to the field

Answer the following in complete sentences.

11. Why can an unmagnetized iron nail be attracted by the north pole or south pole of a magnet?
12. How does a charged comb pick up pieces of paper?
13. Two balloons are rubbed against a wool sweater. What will be the result when the balloons are brought near each other?
14. A dimmer switch in a circuit can be used to control the brightness of a light on that circuit. If a dimmer switch changes the potential difference in the circuit, how would it control the brightness of the light?
15. What happens to a battery when it "goes dead"?

1. Lightning rods are often attached to houses to keep lightning from hitting the houses. Explain how lightning rods work.
2. To save on the cost of a return wire, electric power companies use the earth as a return path for electric current. Explain how this is possible.
3. If a magnet is divided into pieces, each piece is found to be a complete magnet, having both a north pole and a south pole. How is this explained by the presence of domains?

APPLICATION/
CRITICAL
THINKING

1. Find out how to connect dry cells in series and in parallel. Then using flashlight batteries, wire, and a flashlight bulb, compare the brightnesses of the flashlight bulb when it is connected to the batteries in series and in parallel.
2. Make a poster to show how electromagnets are used in loud-speakers or in earpieces of telephones.

EXTENSION

CHAPTER 13

LIGHT

*J*ust as electricity can be sent through copper wires, light can be sent through glass wires called optical fibers. The photograph shows beams of light traveling through and leaving optical fibers. Like electricity in wires, light in optical fibers can be used to carry information. Although it is thinner than a human hair, an optical fiber can carry 50 times as many telephone conversations as an ordinary copper telephone wire.

- *What is light?*
- *How does light form reflections in mirrors?*
- *Where does color come from?*

13·1 The Nature of Light

After completing this section,
you will be able to

- **identify** the parts of the electromagnetic spectrum.
- **compare** objects that are transparent, translucent, and opaque.
- **relate** the intensity of light to distance.

The key terms in this section are
electromagnetic spectrum
intensity
radiant energy

WAVES

Through the vacuum of space, light travels at a speed of 3×10^8 m/s. It takes light from the sun about 8 minutes to travel 150 billion m to reach the earth. To understand the nature of light, you must first understand the properties of waves.

When a pebble drops into still water, ripples will spread out in all directions. If a piece of wood were floating in the water, it would bob up and down in a regular pattern. Ripples following each other at regular intervals are called waves. A *wave* is a disturbance that travels through space or matter in a regular pattern.

From the motion of the wood, you can see that water waves cause the surface of the water to rise and fall. You can also see that water does not move along with the waves. After the wave passes, the wood returns to its original position. Only the energy that produced the waves is carried by the waves.

The parts of a wave are shown in Figure 13·1. The highest point on a wave is called the *crest*. The lowest point is called the *trough*. The distance from one point on a wave to the same point on the next wave is called the *wavelength*. The number of waves that pass a given point in one second is called the *frequency*.

crest

trough

Figure 13·1
Water waves produced by a pebble dropped into water. The crest and trough of a wave *(inset)*.

298

RADIANT ENERGY

Light is a form of energy carried by electromagnetic waves. Electromagnetic waves are waves made up of electric and magnetic fields. Energy that travels by electromagnetic waves is called **radiant energy**. The different forms of radiant energy are shown in Figure 13·2. Together, the different forms of radiant energy make up the **electromagnetic spectrum**.

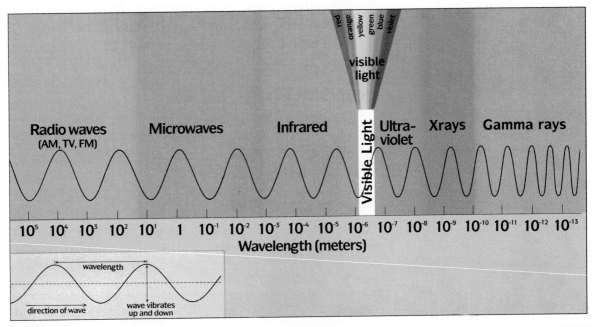

Figure 13·2

Different forms of radiant energy in the electromagnetic spectrum.

Notice in Figure 13·2 that *radio waves* have the longest wavelength in the electromagnetic spectrum. Radio waves are used in communications and broadcasting.

Microwaves are shorter in wavelength than are radio waves. Microwaves are used in communication and in cooking.

Infrared rays are invisible heat radiation. They are shorter in wavelength and higher in frequency than are microwaves. Sunlight feels warm because of the infrared rays given off by the sun. Heat lamps used to warm rooms also give off infrared rays.

Look again at Figure 13·2. Notice that visible light makes up only a small part of the electromagnetic spectrum. What is the approximate wavelength of visible light? Visible light is the only form of radiant energy that we can see.

Ultraviolet rays are a type of invisible radiation with a wavelength just shorter than that of visible light. Ultraviolet rays cause skin to tan. Too much untraviolet radiation can cause sunburn and can lead to skin cancer.

X rays and *gamma rays* are forms of radiant energy that can pass through most substances. X rays are often used by doctors and dentists to photograph inside parts of the human body. Gamma rays are more penetrating than are X rays. Gamma rays are given off by radioactive substances.

TRANSMITTING LIGHT

We see an object only when light coming from the object enters our eyes. Objects that are seen either give off their own light or reflect light. In order for light to reach your eyes, it must pass through the air. Only a small part of the light is absorbed by the air. Therefore, objects can be seen clearly through the air. A material that allows almost all light to pass through is described as *transparent*.

Figure 13·3

Which glass is transparent? Is translucent? Is opaque?

Some objects allow only some light to pass through. A material that allows only some light to pass through is described as *translucent*. An object seen through a translucent object may appear distorted. Wax paper, the frosted glass of a light bulb, and some plastics are translucent.

A material that does not allow light to pass through is called *opaque*. If an opaque object is placed in front of a light source, a shadow forms behind the object. A shadow forms because light travels in a straight line.

INTENSITY OF LIGHT

The brightness of light is called **intensity**. You know that a light source seems brighter when it is close by than when it is far away. The sun seems much brighter than the other stars because the sun is much closer to the earth than are other stars.

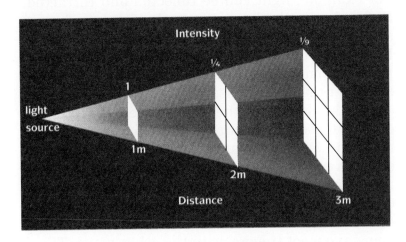

Figure 13·4
The intensity of light decreases as the distance from the light source increases.

Figure 13·4 shows what happens to light as it spreads out from its source. At a distance of 1.0 m from the source, an area of 1.0 m² is lit up. At 2.0 m from the source, the same amount of light spreads out over an area of 4.0 m². The light at 2.0 m covers four times the area it covers at 1.0 m. Thus the intensity of the light at 2.0 m is one fourth of what it is at 1.0 m. What is the intensity of light at 3 m?

REVIEW

1. What are the forms of radiant energy that make up the electromagnetic spectrum?
2. What are the differences between a transparent, translucent, and an opaque object?
3. How does intensity vary with distance?

CHALLENGE Explain why it is possible to get a tan or sunburn on a cloudy day.

13·2 The Behavior of Light

re- (back)
flectere (to bend)

WAVE MODEL OF LIGHT

You have learned that light has the wave properties of frequency and wavelength. Some scientists in the seventeenth century suggested that light is made up of waves. The idea that light is made up of waves is called the *wave model of light*.

The wave model of light is supported by the fact that light has many of the properties of waves. For example, light can be reflected and refracted. **Reflection** is the bouncing back of waves from a surface. Both a wall and a mirror can reflect light. **Refraction** is the change in direction of a wave as it passes from one medium to another. Light can be bent by prisms and lenses.

Light also shows the wave property of interference. *Interference* occurs when two or more waves meet and add to or cancel each other. Figure 13·5 shows a pattern of dark and bright areas produced by the interference of light. The wave model of light explains that light waves can add to or cancel each other. Bright lines are produced where the crests in one wave meet the crests in the other wave. These waves add to each other. Dark lines are produced where the crests in one wave meet the troughs in the other. These waves cancel each other.

Figure 13·5
The dark areas are caused by destructive interference of light.

The wave model of light also explains the diffraction of light. *Diffraction* is the spreading out of a wave as it passes through a small opening or around an object. Look at Figure 13·6. It shows close-up photographs of the edge of a shadow. Notice that the edge of a shadow is not sharp. The wave model explains that as light waves strike the edge of an object, they bend around it. The bending of the light waves produces some light where the shadow should be.

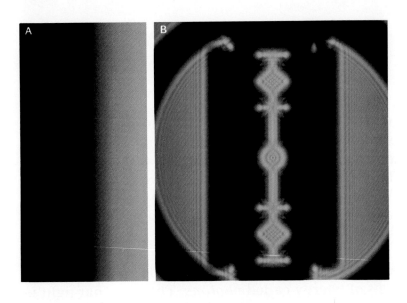

Figure 13·6
Diffraction of light around the edge of an object causes the edges of shadows to be fuzzy (*A* and *B*). The dark lines are caused by interference. *(B).* Life Science Library / LIGHT AND VISION, Photography by Ken May, © 1966 Time-Life Books, Inc.

PARTICLE NATURE OF LIGHT

The wave model of light can be used to explain many of the properties of light. However, light has some properties that do not fit the wave model.

When light strikes the knob of a negatively charged electroscope, the leaves come together. If the intensity of the light is increased, the leaves come together more quickly.

From this experiment it can be seen that light causes the metal knob to lose electrons.

The release of electrons from a metal when light strikes it is called the **photoelectric effect**. The wave model of light explains that electrons are removed from a metal by light waves in much the same way sand is removed from a beach by ocean waves. But the wave model of light cannot explain

photo (light)

Figure 13·7
A negatively charged electroscope *(A)*. It loses its charge when light strikes the knob *(B)*.

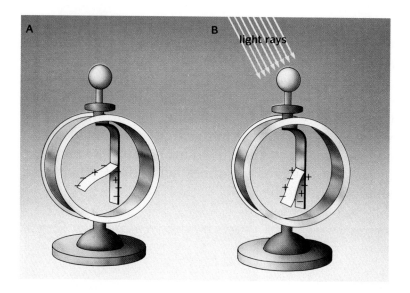

what happens when different colors of light strike some metals. When red light strikes some metals, electrons are not released. Even when red light of high intensity is used, no electrons are released. When blue light strikes the same metals, electrons are released. Electrons are released even when the blue light is faint.

In 1905, Albert Einstein came up with an explanation. He said that light was made up of tiny particles of energy called *photons*. The idea that light is made up of photons is called the *particle model of light*.

Einstein said that when a photon strikes an electron in a metal, the energy of the photon can be transferred to the electron. When it gains this energy, the electron escapes from the metal. However, the electron must gain a certain amount of energy before it can escape from the metal. If the photon does not have this amount of energy, the electron remains on the metal.

Einstein also explained that the energy of a photon depends on the frequency, or color, of light. The higher the frequency of the light, the greater the energy of the photon. Thus a photon in blue light has more energy than a photon in red light. This is because blue light has a higher frequency than red light.

According to Einstein the photons in blue light have enough energy to remove electrons from some metals, but the photons in red light do not. When the intensity of red light is increased, the number of photons is increased. But the energy of each photon is not increased.

Today the photoelectric effect is used in photocells. A photocell is an electric cell that changes light energy into electrical energy. When light strikes a photocell, electrons are released inside the cell. Thus a current can be created. The current can be used to run many electrical devices.

In the photoelectric effect, light acts as though it is made up of particles. However, light also has the wave properties of refraction, interference, and diffraction. Because light has both wave properties and particle properties, it is said to have a dual nature.

Figure 13·8

A solar cell *(inset)* can use the photoelectric effect to produce electricity, which can power a small fan *(left)*. A light meter uses the photoelectric effect to measure the intensity of light *(right)*.

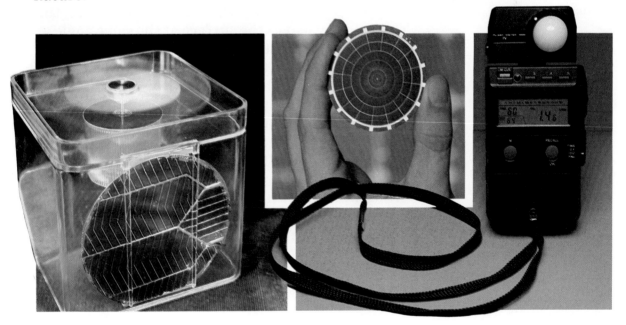

REVIEW

1. What are some examples of the wave properties of light?
2. What is the photoelectric effect?
3. Why is light said to have a dual nature?

CHALLENGE What model of light explains the bending of starlight as it passes close to the sun's surface?

13·3 Reflection and Mirrors

Both a wall and a mirror can reflect light. Recall that reflection of light is the bouncing back of waves from a surface. In addition, a mirror can reflect an image, or a copy, of an object facing it. But a wall cannot reflect an image of an object. How is the reflection from a mirror different from the reflection from a wall?

LAW OF REFLECTION

Imagine a beam of light to be made up of single, individual rays of light. To see how a ray is reflected, look at Figure 13·9. The light ray that strikes a surface is called the *incident ray*. The light ray that is reflected is called the *reflected ray*.

When a light ray strikes a smooth surface, the reflected ray leaves the surface at the same angle at which the incident ray hits the surface. The reflected ray follows the law of reflection. The *law of reflection* states that when a ray of light is reflected, the angle of reflection is equal to the angle of incidence. The angle of incidence and the angle of reflection are shown in Figure 13·9.

If you stand in front of a mirror, you will see an image of yourself. But if you stand in front of a white wall, you will not see your image. The law of reflection can be used to explain why a reflection can be seen in a mirror but not on a wall. Assume the

Figure 13·9

When a ray of light strikes a surface, the angle of reflection is equal to the angle of incidence.

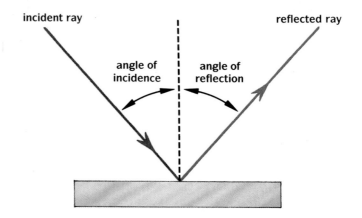

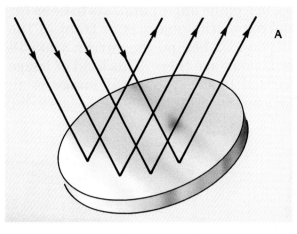
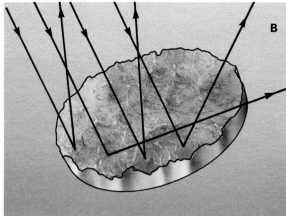

light rays that strike a mirror and wall are parallel. Because the surface of a mirror is smooth, the light rays reflected are parallel. Thus the reflected rays form a pattern, and an image can be seen.

A ceiling or wall may feel smooth to the touch, but its surface is actually rough. It is made up of millions of tiny surfaces facing in different directions. In Figure 13·10B a beam of light is being reflected from a rough surface, such as a wall. The incident light rays are parallel. When these light rays strike a rough surface, each one follows the law of reflection. But because there are many different surfaces, the light rays are reflected in many different directions. The reflected rays do not form a pattern, so no image is seen.

PLANE MIRRORS

A **plane mirror** is a mirror that has a flat surface. Parallel light rays that strike the surface of a plane mirror are reflected as parallel light rays. The mirrors used on bedroom doors and on medicine cabinets are plane mirrors.

Plane mirrors form images of objects. But the images made are not exactly like the objects. An image produced by a plane mirror is reversed from right to left. A person with a ring on the left hand would form a mirror image in which the ring appears to be on the right hand. Hold a book in your right hand and stand in front of a mirror. In which hand does the book appear to be in the mirror?

Figure 13·10

When rays of light strike a smooth surface, the reflected rays are parallel *(A)*. When rays of light strike a rough surface, the reflected rays are not parallel *(B)*.

The image in a plane mirror appears to be as far behind the mirror as the object is in front of the mirror. But if you look behind the mirror, you will see that there is no image there. This kind of image is called a virtual image. A **virtual image** is an image that does not exist in the place it seems to be.

Figure 13·11

The image seen in a plane mirror appears to be behind the surface of the mirror.

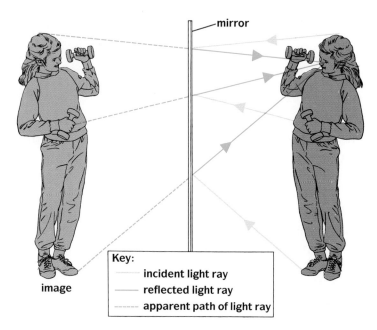

Key:
incident light ray
reflected light ray
apparent path of light ray

Figure 13·11 shows how a virtual image is formed by a plane mirror. Light rays leave the person and are reflected by the mirror. The light rays reflect at the same angle at which they strike the mirror. Although the light rays change direction when they are reflected, to the eye the light rays seem to travel in the same path. They seem to come from behind the mirror, at a distance equal to the distance between the person and the mirror. Thus the image seems to be the same distance behind the mirror as the person is in front of the mirror.

CURVED MIRRORS

Like a plane mirror, a curved mirror has a smooth, shiny surface that reflects light. If the reflecting surface curves inward, the mirror is called a **concave mirror**. If the reflecting surface curves outward, the mirror is called a **convex mirror**. Look

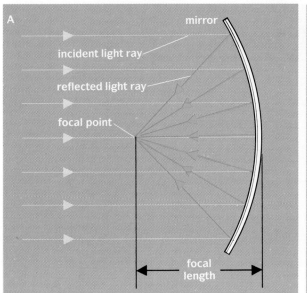

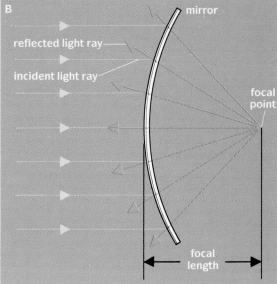

Figure 13·12

A concave mirror brings light rays together *(A)*. A convex mirror causes light rays to spread apart *(B)*.

at Figure 13·12*A*. The reflected rays of light from a concave mirror come together. Figure 13·12*B* shows that the reflected rays of light from a convex mirror spread apart.

When parallel light rays strike a concave mirror, the reflected rays come together and meet at a point. The point at which the reflected light rays meet is called the *focal point*. The distance from the mirror to the focal point is called the *focal length*.

As shown in Figure 13·12*B*, reflected light rays from a convex mirror seem to come from behind the mirror. Thus the image formed appears to be behind the mirror. The image in a convex mirror is always virtual, upright, and smaller than the actual object.

Because the images seen in convex mirrors are smaller than the objects, convex mirrors are sometimes used as outside rear-view mirrors on cars and trucks. The convex mirrors give a wider view of the road than do plane mirrors. However, because the images are reduced in size, the objects seem farther away than they really are. Why must drivers be aware of this difference? Concave mirrors have many uses. Reflecting telescopes use concave mirrors to gather and focus the light of the distant objects. Flashlights and car headlights use concave mirrors to reflect the light given off by light bulbs.

ACTIVITY   What Is the Law of Reflection?

OBJECTIVE
Demonstrate the behavior of a reflected light ray.

MATERIALS
21-cm x 28-cm sheet of white paper, metric ruler, protractor, 30-cm x 30-cm cardboard, 2 straight pins, small mirror, slit rubber stopper

PROCEDURE

A. Draw a line across the middle of a sheet of paper. Mark the midpoint as point *O*.

B. Place the vertex of a protractor on point *O*. Mark point *A* at 90°. Draw line segment *AO* by connecting point *A* and point *O*. Extend the line segment 15 cm from point *O*.

C. Using the protractor, mark point *B* at 30° to the right of line segment *AO*, as shown. Draw a line segment *BO*. Extend line segment *BO* 15 cm from point *O*. This line will represent an incident light ray.
   1. What does angle *BOA* represent?

D. Place the paper on a piece of cardboard. Insert a straight pin on line *BO*, about 10 cm from point *O*.

E. Slide a mirror into the slit of a rubber stopper. Stand the mirror so that the back of the mirror is lined up with the line

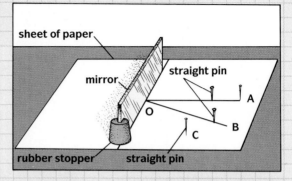

across the paper. Position the center of the mirror at point *O*.

F. Stand to the left of line *AO*, and locate the image of the pin in the mirror. Adjust your position until the image of the pin and the image of line *BO* are lined up in front of you. Place a second pin directly in front of these images, about 10 cm from point *O*. Mark this as point *C*.

G. Remove both pins and the mirror. Draw line segment *CO*.
   2. What does angle *COA* represent?

H. Using the protractor, measure angle *COA*.

RESULTS AND CONCLUSIONS
1. How do angles *COA* and *BOA* compare?
2. Compare the angle of incidence of this light ray with its angle of reflection.

REVIEW
1. How does the reflection of light from a mirror compare with that of light from a sheet of white paper?
2. What is the appearance of an image formed by a plane mirror?
3. What are the differences between a virtual image and a real image?
4. How does the way in which a concave mirror forms an image compare with the way in which a convex mirror forms an image?

CHALLENGE Convex mirrors are sometimes used as outside rear-view mirrors on cars because they give a wider view of the road than do plane mirrors. However objects seem farther away. Explain why.

13·4 Refraction and Lenses

REFRACTION

Figure 13·13*A* shows how a light ray passes through a piece of glass. Notice that the light ray changes direction. Recall that the change in direction of a wave as it passes from one medium to another is called refraction. The angle of incidence is the angle between the incident light ray and the normal line. The *angle of refraction* is the angle between the refracted light ray and the normal line.

Refraction of light can be seen when pencils are placed at an angle in water, as shown in Figure 13·13*B*. When seen from above, the pencils appear bent. The light coming from the pencils bends as it passes from the water to the air. But light from the part of the pencils above water does not bend. Above the water the light passes through only one medium, the air.

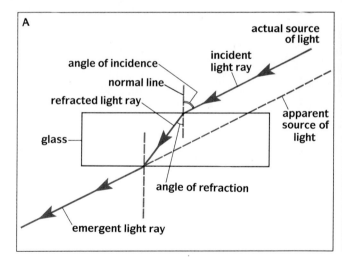

Figure 13·13
A light ray refracts when it passes from one medium to another *(A)*. Refraction causes a pencil to appear bent in water *(B)*.

INDEX OF REFRACTION

Refraction of light is caused by a change in the speed of light. The speed of light varies in different mediums. Thus the amount of refraction of light is different in different mediums. A measure of the refraction of light in a medium as the light enters from air is called the *index of refraction*.

Table 13·2 *Indexes of Refraction*

MEDIUM	INDEX OF REFRACTION
Vacuum	1.00
Air	1.00029
Ice	1.31
Water	1.333
Glass	1.52
Diamond	2.42

The indexes of refraction for different mediums are shown in Table 13·2. When entering from air, light bends more in a medium with a large index of refraction than in one with a smaller index of refraction. For example, light bends more when it passes from air into glass than when it passes from air into water. In which substance would light bend the most as the light enters from air?

Refraction also varies with the color of light. Look at Figure 13·14. When white light passes through the first prism, the white light separates into different colors. Notice that red light bends the least and violet light bends the most. What color of light forms when the different colors of light pass through the second prism?

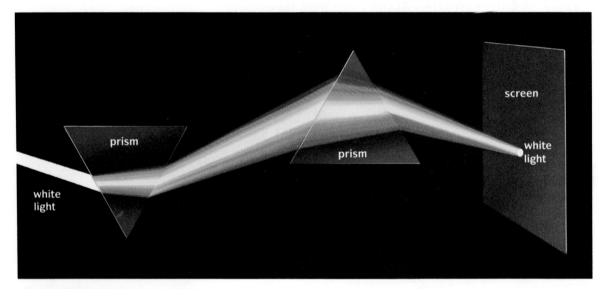

Figure 13·14
Newton's experiment showed that sunlight is made up of different colors of light.

Water drops in the air can cause sunlight to be broken up into colors. The different colors in sunlight bend in water as they bend in a prism. The colors of the rainbow are the same as the colors produced by a prism.

LENSES

A transparent object that is used to refract light from an object to form an image is called a **lens**. Lenses are used in microscopes, cameras, binoculars, and hand lenses. Lenses are also used to correct eye problems.

OBJECTIVE

Demonstrate two different types of images made by convex lenses.

MATERIALS

convex lens or hand lens, metric ruler, white paper

PROCEDURE

A. Using your eyes only, examine the print on this page.

B. Place a convex lens or hand lens directly above the print on the page. Look through the lens at the printing. As you look, slowly raise the lens from the paper to a height of about 30 cm.
   1. What happens to the appearance of the print as the lens is slowly raised?

C. Stand in front of an outside window, with your back to the window. With one hand, hold a sheet of white paper in front of you. With the other hand, hold the lens between the window and the paper.

D. Position the lens and paper so that they face some object outside. Hold the lens close to the paper. Then move the lens away from the paper until an image appears.
   2. Which is the image, erect or inverted?

RESULTS AND CONCLUSIONS

1. When the print was best in focus in step **B**, which was the image, real or virtual?

2. Compare the size of the image formed in step **D** with the size of the object. Which is the image, real or virtual?

3. How can you demonstrate whether an image is real or virtual?

Like curved mirrors, lenses are described as convex or concave, depending on their shape. A **convex lens** is a lens that is thicker in the center than at its edges. A **concave lens** is a lens that is thinner in the center than at its edges. Figure 13·15 shows examples of these types of lenses.

Figure 13·15

Convex lenses *(A)* and concave lenses *(B)*.

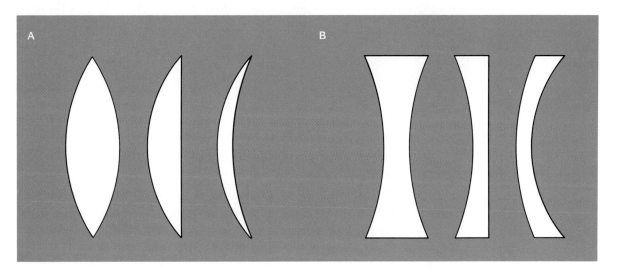

A convex lens produces an inverted, or upside-down, image when it focuses light. You can see this by looking at distant objects through a hand lens. The human eye contains a convex lens that focuses light. Why don't you see objects upside down?

Look at Figure 13·16A. Light rays passing through a convex lens come together. The point at which the light rays meet is called the focal point of the lens. The distance from the center of the lens to the focal point is the focal length.

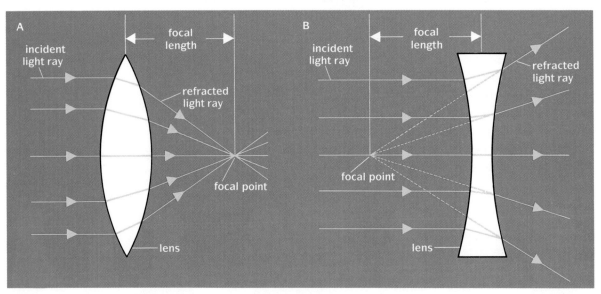

Figure 13·16

A convex lens brings light rays together (A). A concave lens spreads light rays apart (B).

As you can see in Figure 13·16B, light rays passing through a concave lens spread apart. If the refracted rays are extended back through the lens, the point where these light rays meet is the focal point of the lens. The images produced by lenses can be real or virtual. The image produced by a convex can be real or virtual and be upright or upside down.

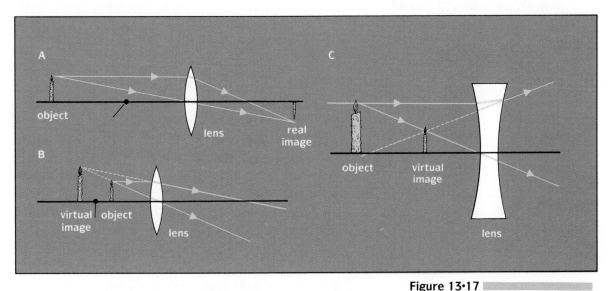

Figure 13·17

A real image produced by a convex lens *(A)*. A virtual image produced by a convex lens *(B)*. A virtual image produced by a concave lens *(C)*.

Look at Figure 13·17A. If the object is beyond the focal point of a convex lens, a real image forms. A **real image** is an image that can be projected on a screen. A real image is always upside down. The image forms on the opposite side of the lens.

Notice in Figure 13·17B that if an object is between a convex lens and its focal point, the lens causes the light rays from the object to spread apart. The image that forms is virtual. It appears to be on the same side of the lens as the object is on. The image is upright and larger than the object. A virtual image cannot be projected on a screen.

The image produced by a concave lens is always virtual. As shown in Figure 13·17C, the light rays leave the lens and spread apart. The light rays seem to come from the same side of the lens as the object is on. Thus the image appears to be on the same side of the lens. The image formed by a concave lens is always upright and smaller than the object.

REVIEW

1. What happens to the path of light as it enters glass or water?
2. What are the differences between a concave lens and a convex lens?
3. What kind of images can be produced by a concave lens?
4. What kind of images can be produced by a convex lens?

CHALLENGE Why are slides placed upside down in a slide projector?

13·5 Color

After completing this section,
you will be able to

- **explain** what causes color.
- **compare** the color of a
  transparent object with that
  of an opaque object.

The key term in this section is
filter

PRIMARY COLORS

The color of objects comes from the colors in light. Light from the sun appears white. But sunlight is made up of many colors. Three of these colors — green, red, and blue — are the *primary colors* of light. These colors can be separated from each other by the use of filters. A **filter** is a transparent or translucent substance that allows only certain colors of light to pass through.

A colored piece of glass is a kind of filter. Suppose a beam of white light enters a piece of green glass. Look at Figure 13·18*A*. The light that leaves the glass is green. Figure 13·18*B* shows what happens when a beam of white light enters a piece of blue glass. The light that leaves the glass is blue. The color of light that passes through a filter is the same color as the filter. Suppose a beam of white light enters a piece of red glass. What color of light will leave the glass?

Figure 13·18
The color of a filter is determined by the color of light that it transmits.

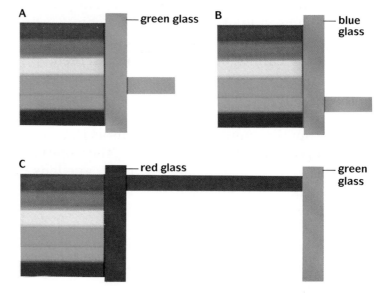

When light enters a transparent or translucent object, only the color of that object is transmitted. The other colors of light are absorbed. Look at Figure 13·18*C*. Suppose a red filter and a green filter are placed in the path of a beam of white light. A beam of red light comes through the red filter. When the red light strikes the green filter, no light passes through. The red light is absorbed by the green filter.

The color of an object that is transparent or translucent is caused by the object absorbing certain colors of light. The process of producing a color by absorbing other colors of light is called *color subtraction*. When you see a green pane of glass, the glass is absorbing all colors of light except green. Thus, green is seen because all the other colors in light are subtracted.

The color of opaque objects also is caused by the process of subtraction. When white light shines on a red rose, the rose absorbs — or subtracts — all the colors in the white light except red. The rose appears red because only red light is reflected.

Figure 13·19
The color of an object is determined by the color that it reflects.

If only blue light or green light falls on a red rose, the rose appears black. This is because the rose absorbs the blue light or green light and no light is reflected. Why is black not considered to be a color?

White objects do not subtract any colors of light. Instead these objects reflect all colors. Thus, if blue light falls on a sheet of white paper, the paper appears blue because it reflects blue light. Why does a sheet of white paper appear green under green light?

According to some researchers, color can affect human behavior. Some scientists say that when different colors are seen, the brain responds by directing the body to undergo major chemical changes. For example, a person looking at warm hues, such as yellow, orange, or red, will experience an increase in respiration and blood pressure. Blue has the opposite effect, causing some of these body functions to slow down.

You may have seen fire engines that were painted greenish-yellow rather than red. The greenish-yellow is thought to be irritating. Thus, this color should get people's attention. One study shows that greenish-yellow fire engines are involved in fewer accidents. Despite this information, fire engines in some cities have been changed back to red. Red paint lasts longer, and fire fighters prefer the traditional color.

SECONDARY COLORS

The mixing of colors of light causes the colors to combine. The process of combining colors of light to produce other colors is called *color addition*. Color addition occurs when two or more separate light sources of different colors shine on the same object. If red, green, and blue light are mixed, white-colored light is produced.

Color addition is shown in Figure 13·20. A blue beam of light mixed with a green beam of light produces cyan-colored light. Addition also occurs when a red beam of light is mixed with a blue beam of light, producing magenta-colored light. When red light and green light are mixed, yellow-colored light is produced. Cyan, magenta, and yellow are called the *secondary colors* of light.

If cyan, magenta, and yellow paints are mixed, the mixture will be black and absorb all colors of light. The process of removing colors of light is called *color subtraction*. A mixture of cyan paint and yellow paint produces green. Cyan subtracts, or absorbs, red light; yellow subtracts blue light. Thus, green is the only color light not subtracted by cyan and yellow.

The color photographs in this book were produced by color subtraction. To produce the color

Figure 13·20

Red, green, and blue lights produce white light by color addition.

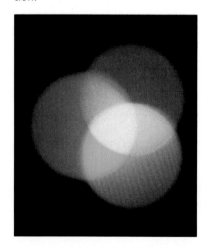

photographs, inks in the colors of cyan, magenta, yellow, and black were used. Varying proportions of the four colors were used to produce the many shades of colors.

REVIEW

1. What causes an object to have color?
2. Where does the color of transparent objects, translucent objects, and opaque objects come from?
3. How does producing color by subtraction compare with producing colors by addition?

CHALLENGE The screen in a color television set contains red, green, and blue dots. Explain how a color television screen can produce more than just these three colors.

CHAPTER SUMMARY
The main ideas in the chapter are listed below. Read these statements before you answer the Chapter Review questions.

- Light is part of the group of electromagnetic waves called the electromagnetic spectrum. (13·1)
- An object can be described as transparent, translucent, or opaque, depending on how it transmits or reflects light. (13·1)
- Evidence that light is made up of particles is the photoelectric effect. Particles of light energy are called photons. (13·2)
- Light has properties of both waves and particles. (13·2)
- Light rays obey the law of reflection. (13·3)
- The image formed by a plane mirror is upright and reversed, and it appears to be as far behind the mirror as the object is in front. (13·3)
- Concave mirrors reflect parallel light rays and bring them to a point. Convex mirrors cause the reflected light rays to spread apart. (13·3)
- When light passes from one medium to another at an angle, the direction of the light changes. This change is called refraction. (13·4)
- Convex lenses can form either real images or virtual images, depending on the distance of the objects from the lenses. Concave lenses form only virtual images. (13·4)
- Real images can be projected on a screen, whereas virtual images cannot. (13·4)
- The color of an object comes from the colors in the visible light that the object transmits or reflects. (13·5)
- Various colors are produced by subtracting or adding colors of light. (13·5)

The key terms in this chapter are listed below. Use each term in a sentence that shows the meaning of the term.

concave lens	filter	radiant energy
concave mirror	intensity	real image
convex lens	lens	reflection
convex mirror	photoelectric effect	refraction
electromagnetic spectrum	plane mirror	virtual image

Chapter Review

VOCABULARY

Use the key terms from the previous page to complete the following sentences correctly.

1. _____ is energy that is transferred by electromagnetic waves.
2. The brightness of light is called _____.
3. The change in direction of a wave as it passes from one medium to another is called _____.
4. Radio waves, microwaves, infrared rays, visible light, ultraviolet rays, X rays, and gamma rays make up the _____.
5. A transparent material that allows only certain colors to pass through is a/an _____.
6. A mirror that has a flat surface is called a/an _____.
7. An image that can be shown on a screen is a/an _____.
8. A/An _____ has a reflecting surface that curves outward.
9. A curved piece of glass that refracts light is called a/an _____.
10. The bouncing back of waves from a surface is called _____.

CONCEPTS

Identify the parts of the wave shown.

1.
2.
3.
4.
5.

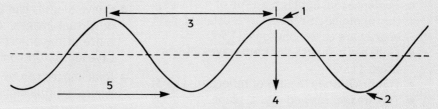

Identify each statement as True or False. If a statement is false, replace the underlined term or phrase with a term or phrase that makes the statement true.

6. Ultraviolet rays are a type of invisible radiation with a frequency <u>lower</u> than that of visible light.
7. Most objects are <u>transparent</u>, not translucent.
8. The release of electrons from a metal when light strikes it is called the <u>photoelectric effect</u>.
9. A <u>concave lens</u> is a lens that is thicker in the center than at its edges.
10. Transparent objects and opaque objects produce color by the process of <u>color addition</u>.

Write the letter of the term or phrase that best matches the statement on the left. Not all choices will be used.

11. A form of radiant energy
12. Different forms of radiant energy
13. Always forms an image that is virtual, upright, and smaller than the object
14. The change in direction of a light ray as it passes from one medium to another
15. A color that does not subtract any colors of light

a. convex mirror
b. white
c. reflection
d. X rays
e. electromagnetic spectrum
f. concave mirror
g. refraction
h. opaque object
i. black

Answer the following in complete sentences.

16. What happens to the intensity of light on a surface if the distance between the light source and the surface is increased from 1.0 m to 4.0 m?
17. What causes light to refract when it passes between two different substances?
18. Explain why a lemon appears yellow.
19. How do the images formed by curved mirrors differ from those formed by plane mirrors?
20. How can you tell if a lens is concave or convex?

APPLICATION/ CRITICAL THINKING

1. Explain why black objects become hotter in the sun than do white objects.
2. Lenses produce a rainbow of colors around images. Explain the cause of the colors.
3. If you walk toward a plane mirror at a speed of 1.0 m/s, how fast would your image approach you?
4. Why does the focal length of a convex lens depend on the color of light entering it?

EXTENSION

1. X rays are used for things other than medical purposes. Do some research to make a display that shows other uses of X rays.
2. Color photography is a subtractive color process. Find out how color photographs are made.
3. The reflectors on a bicycle will always reflect light back to the light source, regardless of the angle at which the light strikes. Examine a bicycle reflector to see how this works.
4. Study the Greek myth of Narcissus. What part did a mirror play in this myth?
5. What is a heliograph? How is it used?

CHAPTER 14

NUCLEAR ENERGY

*Y*ou are probably aware that radioactive substances are used in nuclear power plants and in nuclear-powered submarines. But did you know that these substances are also being used to detect problems in internal organs of the human body? The photograph shows a body scan of a person injected with a radioactive substance. Notice the different colors of the various parts of the body. The different colors are caused by different concentrations of the radioactive substance. The concentrations are greatest in the bones. Can you identify the person's spine, ribs, and pelvis?

● *What causes radioactivity?*

● *How are radioactive substances used to treat diseases?*

● *What are the dangers of nuclear energy?*

14·1 Radioactivity

After completing this section, you will be able to

- **define** the term *radioactivity*.
- **compare** alpha, beta, and gamma radiations.
- **describe** the decay processes of radioactive atoms.
- **explain** what the half-life of a radioisotope is.

The key terms in this section are

alpha particle	half-life
beta particle	radiation
gamma rays	radioactivity

In 1896 a French scientist named Antoine Henri Becquerel made a surprising observation. He saw that a covered photographic plate became exposed when it was placed near a uranium compound. Becquerel thought that unseen rays given off by the uranium might be the cause of the exposure. He said that the rays passed through the cover. They then reacted with the plate, just as light does. About the same time, Pierre and Marie Curie showed that covered photographic plates placed near compounds of radium also became exposed. Soon other scientists were studying the mysterious rays.

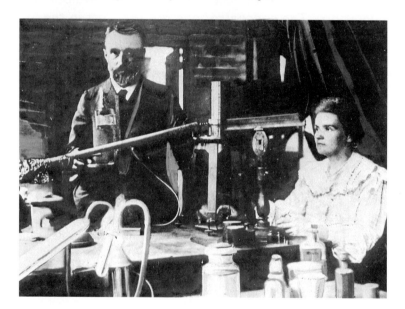

Figure 14·1
Pierre and Marie Curie made many important early discoveries about radiation.

RADIATION

Radioactivity (ray dee oh ak TIHV uh tee) is the spontaneous release of energy and particles from the nucleus of an atom. Elements that give off energy and particles are *radioactive*. As a radioactive atom releases particles from its nucleus, the atom changes into an atom of another element. This process is called *radioactive decay*. The energy and particles that are released as an atom decays are called **radiation** (ray dee AY shuhn).

radius (beam)

324

Small amounts of radiation are found in any environment. There are natural sources of radiation in the earth. Radioactive elements contain atoms whose nuclei decay spontaneously. All elements with atomic numbers greater than 82 are unstable. Some isotopes of elements with atomic numbers less than 82 are also unstable. Why are some atoms unstable? Recall that all nuclei except those of hydrogen-1 atoms contain neutrons as well as protons. In a stable nucleus there is a balance between protons and neutrons. When a nucleus has too many neutrons for its number of protons, the nucleus is unstable. It is also unstable when it has too few neutrons for its number of protons.

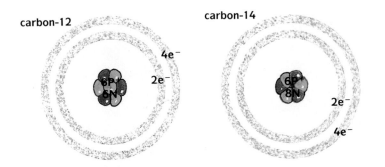

Figure 14·2
Two isotopes of carbon: carbon-12 and carbon-14.

Recall that isotopes of an element have the same number of protons but different numbers of neutrons. Small nuclei are stable when they have nearly the same number of neutrons as protons. Figure 14·2 shows two isotopes of carbon. Which of these isotopes is radioactive? Unstable isotopes, such as carbon-14, are called *radioisotopes* (ray-dee oh ɪ suh tohps).

An unstable nucleus will give off radiation in the form of alpha (AL fuh), beta (BAY tuh), or gamma (GAM uh) radiation. The alpha radiation given off by unstable nuclei is made up of alpha particles. An **alpha particle** contains two protons and two neutrons, like the nucleus of a helium atom. The symbol for an alpha particle is ^4_2He. Because it has two protons and no electrons, an alpha particle has a 2+ charge.

Beta radiation is made up of beta particles. A **beta particle** is an electron. Its symbol is $_{-1}^{0}e$. The

−1 in the symbol shows that, like other electrons, the beta particle has a negative charge.

Gamma rays are not made up of particles. **Gamma rays** are waves of energy. They do not have charges, and they do not have mass. These rays are part of the electromagnetic spectrum, shown in Figure 14·3. Notice that gamma rays are very high in energy.

Because gamma rays have a lot of energy, they can penetrate matter easily. A thick layer of lead or concrete is needed to stop them. Beta particles do not have as much energy as gamma rays. A sheet of metal 1.0 cm thick can stop beta particles. The amount of energy of Alpha particles can vary.

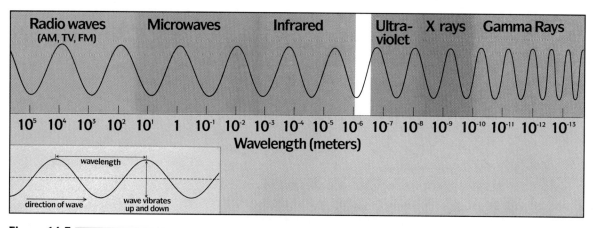

Figure 14·3

The electromagnetic spectrum.

RADIOACTIVE DECAY

When a radioactive nucleus gives off an alpha particle or a beta particle, the atom changes to a different kind of atom. Figure 14·4 shows how a nucleus of uranium-238 decays by giving off an alpha particle. This process can be written as an equation.

$$^{238}_{92}U \longrightarrow \, ^{234}_{90}Th + \, ^{4}_{2}He$$

The uranium-238 nucleus contains 92 protons and 146 neutrons. Its mass number is 238. When this nucleus gives off an alpha particle, it loses 2 protons and 2 neutrons. Its mass number is now 234. The nucleus that is left has only 90 protons. What nucleus has been formed by this alpha decay?

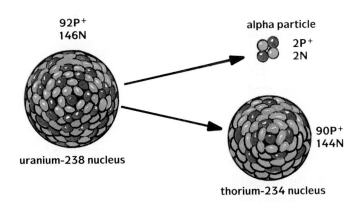

92P+
146N

alpha particle

2P+
2N

uranium-238 nucleus

90P+
144N

thorium-234 nucleus

Figure 14·4
When a uranium-238 nucleus decays, it produces a thorium-234 nucleus and an alpha particle.

Look again at the equation. A superscript represents the mass number. A subscript represents the atomic number. Recall that the charge of a proton is 1+. In this equation the total number of particles stays the same. The mass number to the left, 238, is equal to the sum of the mass numbers to the right, $234 + 4$. Also, the charge to the left, 92, is equal to the sum of the charges to the right, $90 + 2$.

The thorium-234 nucleus produced by the decay of uranium-238 is also unstable. There are many decay steps before a stable nucleus is formed. The complete set of steps that show how a radioactive nucleus changes is called a *decay series*. Look at Figure 14·5 and the Periodic Table on page 590. What stable element is formed at the end of the uranium-238 decay series?

Figure 14·5
The decay series of uranium-238 includes both alpha decays and beta decays.

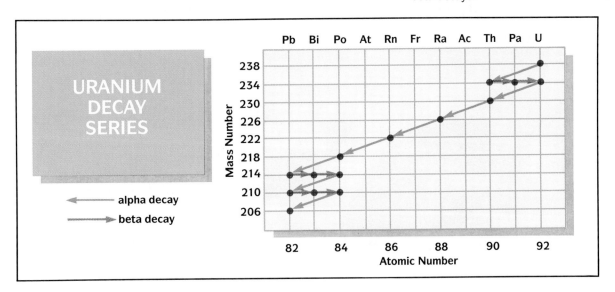

URANIUM
DECAY
SERIES

← alpha decay

→ beta decay

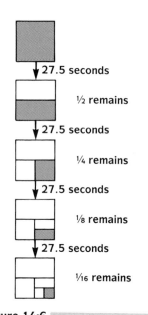

↓ 27.5 seconds

½ remains

↓ 27.5 seconds

¼ remains

↓ 27.5 seconds

⅛ remains

↓ 27.5 seconds

1/16 remains

Figure 14·6
The half-life of francium-220 is 27.5 seconds.

Figure 14·7
Some radioisotopes are used to find the age of various objects. Fossils of fish *(left)* and a type of arthropod now extinct *(right)*.

HALF-LIFE OF RADIOISOTOPES

Each radioactive substance decays at its own rate. The time it takes a single atom to decay cannot be predicted. However, the time it takes for many decays to take place is known. The time that it takes for one half of a sample of radioactive nuclei to decay is called the **half-life** of that substance. For example, the half-life of francium-220 is 27.5 seconds. Figure 14·6 shows that in 27.5 seconds, one half of the nuclei in a sample of francium-220 will decay. In another 27.5 seconds, one half of the remaining nuclei will decay, leaving only one fourth of the original nuclei unchanged. Thus, three fourths of the nuclei will decay in 55 seconds. After 110 seconds, what fraction of francium-220 will remain in the sample shown in Figure 14·6?

Some substances have long half-lives. The half-life of uranium-238 is 4.5 billion years. The age of the earth is estimated to be 4.5 billion years. Thus, one half of the uranium nuclei on the earth have decayed to other nuclei since the earth formed.

A knowledge of half-lives can be useful in finding the age of fossils. Figure 14·7 shows some radio-

ISOTOPE	HALF-LIFE	OBJECTS TO BE DATED	USEFUL RANGE (YEARS)
Carbon-14	5730	Organic materials	500–50,000
Potassium-40	1.3×10^9	Earth's crust; moon's crust	10,000,000 and more
Rhenium-187	4.3×10^{10}	Meteorites	40,000,000 and more
Uranium-238	4.5×10^9	Earth's crust	10,000,000 and more

How Can You Make a Model of Half-life?

OBJECTIVE
Demonstrate the decay of a radioisotope.

MATERIALS
shoebox with lid, 200 pennies

PROCEDURE
A. Draw a data table with headings like the one shown. Allow space for 10 trials.
B. Place 200 pennies tails up in a shoe box. Place the lid securely on the box.
C. Shake the box with one quick up-and-down motion.
D. Open the box, and remove all pennies that are heads up. In the data table, record the number of pennies removed and the number of pennies remaining.
E. Repeat steps C and D nine more times.

TRIAL	NUMBER OF PENNIES REMOVED	NUMBER OF PENNIES REMAINING
1		
2		
3		

RESULTS AND CONCLUSIONS
1. What do the coins in the model represent?
2. What do the coins with heads up represent?
3. How does the model demonstrate the concept of half-life?
4. Prepare a graph of your data. Put the trial numbers on the x-axis and the number of pennies remaining on the y-axis.

isotopes used to find the ages of different materials. Notice that the half-life of carbon-14 is 5730 years. Living plants and animals take in carbon at all times. They contain a constant percentage of carbon-14. When plants and animals die, they stop taking in carbon. Thus when the carbon-14 atoms decay, they are not replaced. The percentage of carbon-14 in a plant or animal decreases. Suppose a fossil has only one-eighth the carbon-14 that a living organism has. This indicates three half-lives have passed. Thus the fossil is estimated to be 17,190 years old.

REVIEW
1. What is radioactivity?
2. How do alpha, beta, and gamma radiations differ?
3. An atom of radium-226, $^{226}_{88}Ra$, undergoes alpha decay. What is the atomic number and mass number of the nucleus that is formed?
4. What is half-life?

CHALLENGE If one eighth of a sample of a radioisotope remains after 108 minutes, what is the half-life of the radioisotope?

14·2 Isotopes and Their Uses

ISOTOPES AS TRACERS

Some radioisotopes are used as tracers. A **tracer** is a radioactive atom or molecule that is used to study processes in living things and in nonliving things. The radioactive isotopes are easy to detect, so it is easy to trace their movements. Suppose there is a leak in a pipe buried deep in the ground. A small amount of radioactive material can be added to the liquid moving through the pipe. This material can be traced with a device that detects radiation. Thus, workers can find the leak without digging all along the pipe.

Biologists can use tracers to follow the path of substances in living things. For example, food made in the leaves of a plant can be traced through the plant. The tracer used for this is radioactive CO_2, which contains carbon-14. Such molecules used as tracers are sometimes called tagged molecules.

The leaves of the plant will absorb the tagged CO_2. The food molecules made from the tagged CO_2 will contain the radioactive carbon. When one of the leaves is placed on a piece of photographic film, the radiation from the tracer will expose the film. The greater the number of radioactive molecules in the leaf, the darker the film.

Figure 14·8

The dark areas on the film were caused by beta radiation given off by phosphorus-32 in a leaf.

Phosphorus-32 has been used as a tracer to find out how well plants absorb fertilizer. The leaf in Figure 14·8 absorbed fertilizer containing phosphorus-32. The rate at which this tracer entered the plant was measured. Through this and other tests, scientists have discovered that some nutrients can be absorbed directly by leaves.

Table 14·1 *Some Radioisotopes Used in Medicine*

ISOTOPE	HALF-LIFE	USES
Arsenic-74	17.9 days	Locate brain tumors
Barium-131	11.6 days	Detect bone tumors
Chromium-51	27.8 days	Determine blood volume
Gold-198	64.8 hours	Test kidney activity
Iodine-131	8.07 days	Detect and treat thyroid problems; find blood clots
Iron-59	54.0 days	Find rate of red blood cell production
Mercury-197	65.0 hours	Find brain tumors; test spleen function
Radium-225	14.3 days	Detect skin cancer
Sodium-24	15.0 hours	Find blockage in circulatory system
Technetium-99	6.0 hours	Detect brain tumors; detect blood clots

In medicine, tracers can be used to detect problems with internal organs. Look at Table 14·1. It lists some radioisotopes and their medical uses. Iodine-131, for example, can be used as a tracer to detect thyroid gland disorders. The thyroid gland releases a hormone that affects the rate at which the body uses energy. Iodine is used in making this hormone. So iodine is absorbed by the thyroid gland. When iodine-131 is injected into the body, this tracer is absorbed by the thyroid gland. Radiation scanners can detect the tracer to produce an image, like the one shown in Figure 14·9. Thus a doctor can tell if the gland is normal or enlarged. What radioisotope might be used to find out if the rate of red blood cell production is normal?

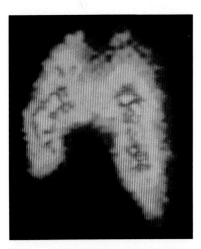

Figure 14·9
A scan of a normal thyroid gland produces an image like this.

Look back at Table 14·1. Notice that the isotopes listed have short half-lives. Radiation can be harmful to living tissues. Therefore, doctors try to use isotopes that will last long enough to help find the problem, but not long enough to harm the patient. Radiation can kill cells. It can also damage some of the chemicals that are needed by the cells. Radiation can cause genetic damage and can cause cancer.

TREATING DISORDERS

Sometimes the effects of radiation can be put to good use. Radiation is used to treat some kinds of tumors. Radioactive iodine can be used to treat thyroid tumors. Cobalt-60 is used to treat some kinds of cancer.

Figure 14·10
This person is being treated with cobalt-60.

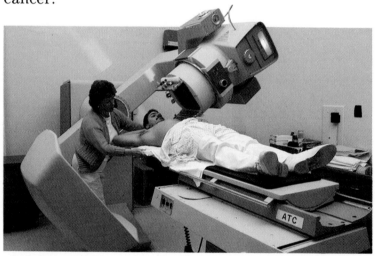

Figure 14·10 shows cobalt-60 being used in radiation therapy. This substance is a good source of gamma rays. The cobalt-60 source can be outside the patient's body or it can be placed inside the body. Because cobalt-60 has a half-life of 5.26 years, it is a long-lasting source of radiation.

SAFETY AND RADIOISOTOPES

Because radiation can be harmful, radioisotopes must be handled carefully. Radioactive substances are stored in thick containers that absorb radiation. The substances are also marked with a special label. This label is used in hospitals and laboratories all over the world to mark radioactive substances.

People who work with radioactive substances must be able to keep track of the amount of radiation around them. Many instruments are used to detect and measure radiation.

One radiation monitor is the Geiger counter, shown in Figure 14·11A. When radiation enters the tube, a gas in the tube is ionized. The ions create a small electric current. The current is recorded by the counter. Some Geiger counters make a clicking sound each time a current is created in the tube. The more clicks, the more radioactive decays counted and the more radiation in the area.

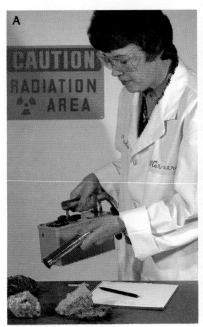
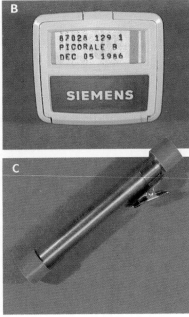

Figure 14·11
Radiation monitors include the Geiger counter (A), film badge (B), and the pocket radiation monitor (C).

Photographic film is another tool used to detect radiation. The badge shown in Figure 14·11B contains a piece of film. How would the film be a radiation detector? This is an inexpensive radiation detector. However, the film has to be developed for the effects of radiation to be seen.

A pocket radiation monitor is shown in Figure 14·11C. This monitor contains a gas that is ionized by radiation. Inside the tube is a scale that shows the total amount of radiation received.

ACTIVITY   How Can Radioactivity Be Measured?

OBJECTIVE
Determine the effect of distance on the amount of radioactivity detected by a Geiger counter.

MATERIALS
forceps, ring stand, radioactive source, Geiger counter, clamp, metric ruler, graph paper

PROCEDURE ☢

A. Prepare a data table like the one shown.
B. Using forceps, place a radioactive source on a ring stand as shown in the figure. **Caution:** Do not pick up the source with your hands.
C. Clamp a Geiger counter tube 10 cm above the source.
D. Record the number of counts registered by the Geiger counter in 1 minute.
E. Raising the Geiger counter tube, repeat step **D** for distances of 20, 30, and 40 cm.
F. Prepare a graph of your data, showing distance on the x-axis and counts per minute on the y-axis.

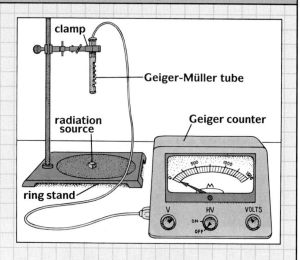

DISTANCE (cm)	COUNTS PER MINUTE
10	
20	
30	
40	

RESULTS AND CONCLUSIONS
1. Describe your graph.
2. What do the data tell you about the effect of distance on the amount of radioactivity reaching a Geiger counter?

EXTENSION
Place the Geiger counter tube 10 cm from the source, and record the number of counts in 1 minute. Then place a sheet of paper over the source, and repeat the count. Continue to add paper and record the number of counts. Graph your data, showing sheets of paper on the x-axis and counts per minute on the y-axis. Can you reduce the counts to zero?

REVIEW
1. Give an example of how a tracer is used.
2. How is carbon-14 used in plant research?
3. Give an example of how radioisotopes are used to treat disorders.
4. What are three safety measures used in handling radioactive substances?

CHALLENGE The isotope of technetium that is used as a tracer is made in the laboratory where it will be used. Why can this isotope not be purchased and stored until it is used?

14·3 Nuclear Fission

FISSION REACTIONS

In 1912, Albert Einstein said that energy and mass are different forms of the same thing. He also said that each may be changed into the other. Einstein wrote an equation, $E = mc^2$, to show how energy and mass are related. In this equation, E stands for energy, m stands for mass, and c stands for the speed of light. According to the equation, 1.0 g of mass is equal to 9×10^{13} J of energy. This is enough energy to heat a house for 1000 years. Thus, a small amount of mass can be changed into a large amount of energy.

After completing this section, you will be able to

* **describe** fission reactions.
* **identify** fission fragments.
* **explain** how a chain reaction occurs.

The key terms in this section are
chain reaction
nuclear fission

Figure 14·12
Albert Einstein made many predictions that were based on calculations and were later proven true.

Einstein's equation was based on thought and calculations. When he published the equation, no one knew how to change mass into energy. But in 1939, scientists experimenting with neutrons caused such a change. The scientists shot neutrons at a sample of uranium and produced lighter elements. Some of the uranium atoms split into smaller atoms. This change released large amounts of energy. The energy came from small amounts of mass lost from the nuclei as they split. Thus, evidence for Einstein's theory was obtained in the laboratory.

Figure 14·13
Lise Meitner was the first scientist to publish an explanation of nuclear fission.

The splitting of a nucleus into two smaller nuclei is called **nuclear fission** (FIHSH uhn). Fission releases large amounts of energy. The nuclear fission reaction can be written as an equation. The symbol for a neutron is $_0^1n$. The subscript 0 shows that the neutron has no charge. The superscript 1 shows that the mass of one neutron is about 1 amu. The fission reaction for one isotope of uranium is as follows.

$$_{92}^{235}U + _0^1n \longrightarrow _{56}^{141}Ba + _{36}^{92}Kr + 3(_0^1n) + energy$$

The energy released is a result of the fission of uranium. The total mass of the products is slightly less than the mass of the uranium and the total mass of the reactants. The "missing" mass has been changed into energy. Fission reactions, and other reactions involving the nuclei of atoms, are called *nuclear reactions*.

CHAIN REACTION

fissio (to split)

Figure 14·14 shows the fission of uranium-235. The uranium nucleus has split into a barium-141 nucleus and a krypton-92 nucleus. Fission reactions also release neutrons. Isotopes of more than 35 elements can be formed from the fission of uranium-235. As a result, the fission of a sample of uranium-235 produces a mixture of elements. The elements produced by fission are called fission fragments. Some of the fragments resulting from the fission of uranium are radioactive.

Figure 14·14
The fission of uranium.

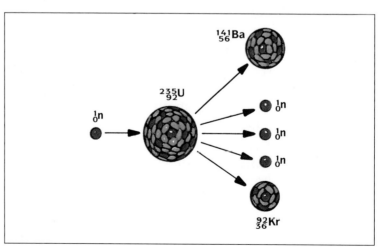

336

What happens to the neutrons released during fission? These neutrons can strike other nuclei, producing more fissions. This type of reaction is called a chain reaction. A **chain reaction** is one in which a product of a reaction causes the reaction to continue.

Figure 14·15 shows a chain reaction. Notice that each neutron produced splits another uranium atom. This can take place only in a large sample of uranium. In a small sample the neutrons can escape

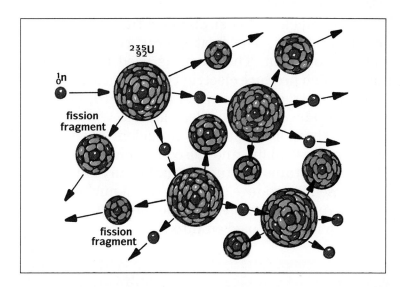

Figure 14·15
Neutrons released during fission cause a chain reaction.

from the sample without causing another fission. The fission chain reaction might start but then quickly die out. The smallest amount of uranium that can keep a chain reaction going is called the *critical mass*. If the critical mass of uranium is present, the released neutrons will have a good chance of striking other uranium-235 nuclei. A critical mass of uranium is a source of great amounts of energy. The use of chain reactions and critical mass are put to use in nuclear power plants.

REVIEW

1. What happens in a fission reaction?
2. What are fission fragments?
3. What happens in a chain reaction?

CHALLENGE Identify x, y, and Z in the following fission reaction.

$$^{235}_{92}U + ^{1}_{0}n \longrightarrow ^{x}_{y}Z + ^{137}_{52}Te + 2(^{1}_{0}n) + energy$$

14·4 Nuclear Power

Recall that fission reactions release energy. Much of this energy is in the form of heat and radiation. A **nuclear reactor** is a device that controls nuclear reactions and makes use of the energy, usually used to produce electricity.

NUCLEAR FUEL

In nonnuclear power plants, a fuel such as coal or oil is burned. The heat energy released turns water into steam. The steam is used to turn turbines, which produce electricity. In a nuclear power plant, like the one shown in Figure 14·16, heat energy is produced from nuclear fission.

The three main parts of a nuclear reactor are the core, the coolant, and the containment building. The core contains the fuel. A **fuel** is any substance that is used to produce energy. In most nuclear reactors the fuel is uranium-235. The fuel is shaped into pellets, which are packed into rods.

Figure 14·16
A nuclear power plant.

Recall that the fission of a uranium-235 nucleus releases neutrons. These neutrons can cause more fissions to take place. Thus a chain reaction can be produced. However, many of these neutrons move so quickly that they cannot cause any more fissions. Thus a substance called a *moderator* is used to slow down the neutrons. As a result, they are more likely to cause fissions. Water is commonly used as a moderator.

NUCLEAR REACTOR

Figure 14·17 is a diagram of a nuclear power plant. Notice that the core contains control rods. The *control rods* are used to absorb neutrons and slow or stop the chain reaction. The control rods are made of boron, steel, or cadmium, materials that absorb neutrons easily. As the control rods are pushed into the core, neutrons are absorbed and the fission reaction slows. The reaction stops completely when the control rods are pushed all the way into the core.

Figure 14·17

The structure of a nuclear power plant.

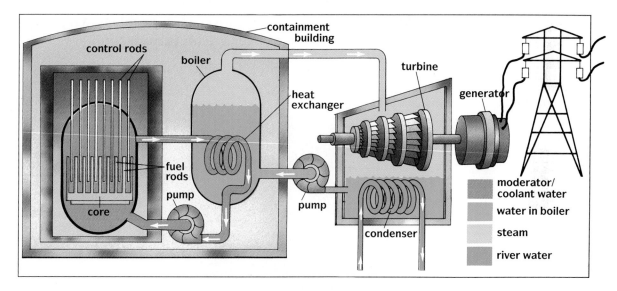

The chain reaction produces large amounts of heat energy. A substance called a *coolant* flows through the core and absorbs heat. If this heat were not carried away from the core, the core could be damaged. It could even melt. Water is the most commonly used coolant.

As it leaves the core, the coolant flows through a device called a *heat exchanger*. There heat from a coolant boils water. The steam that is produced turns a turbine, which generates electricity. Notice in Figure 14·17 that the coolant does not mix with the water that produces the steam used to power the generator. Heat is transferred, but the fluids are kept apart.

The steam that leaves the turbine must be condensed to a liquid before it can be pumped back to the boiler. Thus, nuclear power plants are usually built near rivers or other large bodies of water. Water from the river or other body is pumped through a *condenser*. This cool water causes the steam to condense. The cooling water is then returned to the river or other source. Is radioactivity released into the water?

When the cooling water is returned to its source, it contains more heat than it originally had. Thus the temperature of the water in the source can be raised. Because the added heat can harm living things in the water, this heat is called *thermal pollution*. Thermal pollution is a problem with any power plant that uses steam turbines.

Figure 14·18

Cooling towers used in many nuclear power plants.

The problem of thermal pollution can be solved by using cooling towers like those shown in Figure 14·18. Water passing through a cooling tower gives off excess heat to the air. The water can then be returned at a safe temperature to its source.

The core of a nuclear reactor is housed in a structure called a *containment building*. This building is designed to prevent radiation from

The coolant in most nuclear reactors is water. As shown in Figure 14·17, the coolant flows through a heat exchanger and causes water in the boiler to turn into steam. However, the coolant water itself does not boil. How can the coolant water cause boiling when the coolant is not boiling?

escaping. Its thick concrete walls absorb radiation. But problems with the coolant system could cause a dangerous build-up of heat energy in the core. If the core were allowed to overheat, it could melt down into the earth and could contaminate the soil and the ground water. Therefore, nuclear reactors have many safety systems that provide emergency cooling if the reactor must be shut down quickly.

In April 1986 there was an accident at a nuclear reactor in Chernobyl, in the Soviet Union. The reactor was shut down, but heat continued to build up in the core. The core overheated, and the graphite used as a moderator began to burn. The reactor lacked a containment building. So radioactive materials were released into the atmosphere.

NUCLEAR WASTES

Recall that fission reactions produce many different fission products. Many of these products are radioactive. These products cannot be used as fuel for more fission reactions. They are waste products that must be removed from the reactor.

Nuclear wastes contain a mixture of radioisotopes. Some decay very quickly. Others may take hundreds or thousands of years to decay. When wastes are removed from a reactor, they must be stored in a place where they will not leak into the environment.

Research is being carried out to find ways to dispose of nuclear wastes. In one method being tested, wastes are changed into solid form and are stored deep in the earth. Figure 14·19 (*right*) shows how the wastes are buried in underground containers. Another method involves adding glass-forming materials to the wastes. Such mixtures produce stable, insoluble wastes. These wastes can be buried in formations such as salt beds, salt domes, basalt, or granite. These formations are stable. Thus the land will not shift and will not allow radioactive materials to escape.

Figure 14·19
Underground storage of nuclear wastes *(left)*. Containers holding nuclear wastes are buried in underground tunnels *(right)*.

Because of the danger that radioactive wastes present, they are stored in remote areas. Nuclear reactors are not located near these remote areas, so the wastes must be transported over long distances. Safety precautions must be taken when nuclear wastes are moved to storage areas.

REVIEW

1. List the major parts of a nuclear reactor.
2. How does a nuclear power plant produce electricity?
3. Identify some safety features of nuclear power plants.
4. Explain why waste products from a nuclear power plant are dangerous.

CHALLENGE In many reactors the control rods are inserted into the core from above. The control rods are held in place by electromagnets, which can release the control rods quickly. Why is this a useful safety feature?

14·5 Nuclear Fusion

After completing this section, you will be able to

- **describe** a fusion reaction.
- **describe** the conditions necessary for fusion reactions.

The key term in this section is **nuclear fusion**

As you have seen, fission is the splitting of a nucleus to form smaller nuclei. **Nuclear fusion** (FYOO zhuhn) is the joining of light nuclei to form heavier nuclei. Fusion takes place in the sun and in other stars. Like fission, fusion releases large amounts of energy.

fusio (to melt)

The simplest fusion reaction is the combining of hydrogen nuclei to form a helium nucleus. One kind of fusion reaction involves two isotopes of hydrogen. Figure 14·20 shows this reaction. The equation for the reaction is as follows.

$$^{2}_{1}H + ^{3}_{1}H \longrightarrow ^{4}_{2}He + ^{1}_{0}n + \text{energy}$$

As in a fission reaction, in a fusion reaction a small amount of mass is changed into energy.

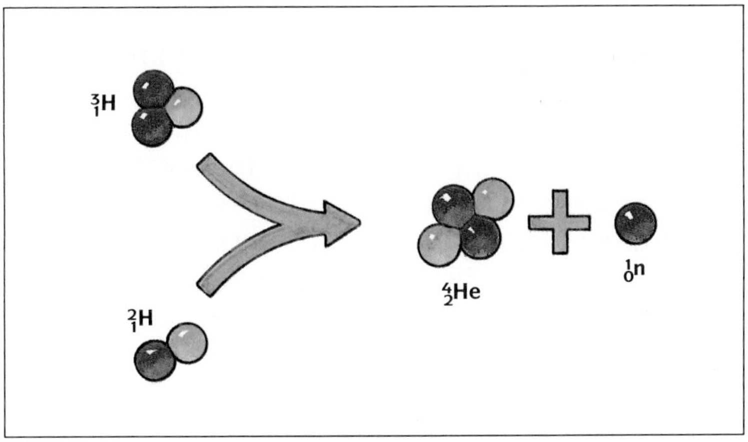

Figure 14·20
In this example of nuclear fusion, two isotopes of hydrogen are combined to form a helium nucleus.

In the sun, ordinary hydrogen nuclei combine to form helium nuclei. The process involves many steps. But fusion takes place only if the hydrogen nuclei are moving at very high speeds. Such high speeds are possible only in the plasma state, at temperatures in the tens of millions of degrees. Thus, fusion reactions are difficult to produce in the laboratory. However, the temperature at the center of the sun is high enough to allow fusion to take place. The energy released by fusion reactions keeps the

Controlling fusion is like trying to bottle the sun. The two biggest problems are creating plasma at very high temperatures and then holding the plasma long enough for it to react. In a container with ordinary walls, the highly charged plasma particles would lose their energy as they touched the walls. The plasma would cool.

The solution to these problems might be a tokamak, like the one shown here. A tokamak is a device that produces a powerful magnetic field around plasma. The magnetic field confines the plasma without absorbing energy from the plasma.

In experiments with tokamaks, only a few fusion reactions have been created. Right now much more energy is put into making the reactions occur than is being produced by the fusion reactions themselves.

Scientists and engineers are designing new tokamaks. New models are expected to release power greater than the amount of energy put into the reacting particles.

temperature high enough for more fusion reactions to take place.

At even higher temperatures, helium nuclei can fuse into carbon nuclei. At still higher temperatures, carbon nuclei can fuse into even heavier nuclei. Thus as fusion in a star continues, the fusion of light elements into heavier ones continues. It is believed that all the naturally occurring elements were made through the process of fusion at the center of very hot stars.

Fusion reactions could provide large amounts of energy for generating electricity. Today, fusion reactors are only in experimental use. These reactors use more energy than they produce.

When in commercial use, fusion reactors will have some advantages over fission reactors. Hydrogen fuel is not radioactive. It is much more abundant on the earth than is uranium. And the products of fusion reactions are not as dangerous as those of fission reactions.

There are some problems with fusion reactors. The biggest problem is the high temperature needed for fusion reactions to occur. It takes a large amount of energy to set up the temperature and pressure conditions that make fusion possible. So fusion is not yet a practical energy source.

REVIEW

1. What is fusion?

2. Diagram a fusion reaction.

3. What conditions are necessary for fusion to take place?

CHALLENGE Write a possible fusion reaction for the formation of carbon-12 from helium-4.

CHAPTER SUMMARY

The main ideas in this chapter are listed below. Read these statements before you answer the Chapter Review questions.

- Elements that spontaneously release energy and particles from their nuclei are said to be radioactive. (14·1)
- An unstable nucleus will give off radiation in the form of alpha particles, beta particles, or gamma rays. (14·1)
- Both alpha radiation and beta radiation are made of particles. Gamma rays are waves of energy and are not made of particles. (14·1)
- The time that it takes for one half of a radioactive sample to decay is called the half-life of that substance. (14·1)
- Radioisotopes are used as tracers in research. Radiation is used medically to treat disorders such as tumors. (14·2)
- Fission reactions occur when a nucleus is split into smaller pieces. The products of a fission reaction are called fission fragments. (14·3)

- Neutrons released from a fission reaction hit other nuclei, causing them to split. This type of reaction is called a chain reaction. (14·3)
- A nuclear reactor has three main parts: the core, the coolant, and the containment building. (14·4)
- The fuel in a nuclear reactor produces heat energy. This heat is used to produce steam, which turns a turbine to generate electricity. (14·4)
- Fusion reactions occur when light nuclei are joined to create heavier nuclei. This type of reaction can occur only at very high temperatures, like those that occur on the sun and other stars. (14·5)
- At present, fusion reactions are impractical to use as an energy source on the earth because of the tremendous heat necessary for the reactions to take place. (14·5)

The key terms in this chapter are listed below. Use each term in a sentence that shows the meaning of the term.

alpha particle	gamma rays	nuclear reactor
beta particle	half-life	radiation
chain reaction	nuclear fission	radioactivity
fuel	nuclear fusion	tracer

Chapter Review

VOCABULARY

Use the key terms from the previous page to complete the following sentences correctly.

1. A radioactive atom or molecule used by scientists to study processes in living and nonliving things is called a/an _____.
2. _____ are waves of energy that do not have charge and do not have mass.
3. Any substance used to produce some type of energy is called a/an _____.
4. Light nuclei are joined to form heavy nuclei during the process of _____.
5. _____ is the spontaneous release of energy and particles from the nucleus of an atom.
6. A nuclear reaction that causes a nucleus to split into smaller pieces is called _____.
7. A/An _____ is one in which the product of a reaction causes the reaction to continue.
8. A type of radiation that contains two protons and two neutrons is called a/an _____.
9. A device that is capable of controlling nuclear reactions and using the energy produced is called a/an _____.
10. A/An _____ is an electron released from a radioisotope.

CONCEPTS

Write the correct term for each numbered structure shown in the diagram.

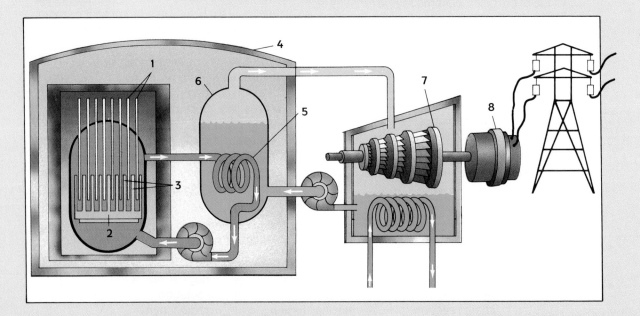

Choose the term or phrase that best answers the question or completes the statement.

9. A nucleus that releases an alpha particle will
   a. increase in atomic number by 1.
   b. increase in mass number by 2.
   c. decrease in atomic number by 2.
   d. decrease in mass number by 2.
10. Partially removing the control rods from the core of a nuclear reactor will
   a. cause fewer neutrons to be available.
   b. increase the rate of fission.
   c. decrease the rate of fission.
   d. lower the temperature of the reaction.
11. Radioisotopes can be used as tracers because
   a. they undergo fission easily.
   b. they produce detectable radiation.
   c. their chemical properties are different from those of non-radioactive isotopes.
   d. they are not absorbed by the body.

Answer the following in complete sentences.

12. How do gamma rays differ from alpha particles and beta particles?
13. Why is the carbon-12 nucleus stable and the carbon-14 nucleus unstable?
14. Why is it so important to package and store nuclear waste materials properly for long periods?

---

1. Tritium ($^3_1$H) is a radioisotope. Can it emit an alpha particle?
2. Friction in moving metallic parts is a major source of machine wear and breakdown. How might iron-59 be used as a tracer to improve petroleum products that are used to reduce friction?
3. Can fusion be called a chain reaction? Why or why not?

APPLICATION/ CRITICAL THINKING

---

1. Report on the advantages and disadvantages of producing electric power by using coal, nuclear fusion, and nuclear fission.
2. Find out about breeder reactors. What are they used for?
3. Do library research on the ''mass defect''.

EXTENSION

Science in Careers

You may think of your neighborhood drugstore as the place in which to buy school supplies or magazines. But the most important function of a pharmacy, or drugstore, is to sell medicine.

Pharmacists provide the medicine specified in a doctor's prescription. Usually the medicine is measured and put into a labeled container. The label includes directions and cautions to the patient. Pharmacists must keep an accurate record of each prescription. Pharmacists working in drugstores also help customers select medicines that do not require a prescription.

In addition to working in drugstores, pharmacists may work in hospitals or clinics. Pharmicists earn a 5- or 6-year college degree in pharmacy. They must then pass a test to be licensed. If you are interested in this career, you should take courses in biology and chemistry in high school.

PHARMACIST

In the past, most of the products that people used were made by the people themselves or by craftworkers. Each product was checked for flaws as it was made.

Today, most products are factory-made. Often there are too many products to check that each one is without flaws. However, by checking a portion of the products, it is possible to find and correct defects.

Testing products is the job of a quality-control technician. A quality-control technician must have a high school diploma. If you are interested in being a quality-control technician, you should take courses in shop in high school.

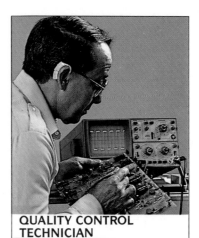
QUALITY CONTROL
TECHNICIAN

People in Science

Dr. Franklin Chang-Diaz
ASTRONAUT

Dr. Franklin Chang-Diaz is both a physicist and an astronaut. When he was a small boy, he dreamed about traveling in space. Today, he is one of the first Hispanic Americans to have flown on a space mission. Dr. Chang-Diaz also designs new types of rocket engines for future space exploration.

Dr. Chang-Diaz worked toward his goal by studying physics. This background has enabled him to design an ion engine. An ion engine may someday be used to travel the great distances between the earth and the outer planets.

The chemical engines now in use require a great amount of fuel. To save fuel, spacecraft using chemical engines coast over long distances. In contrast the ion engine would continue to propel a spacecraft throughout its course, reducing travel time. The heavy fuel tanks needed for chemical engines would be unnecessary in ion engine rockets. Dr. Chang-Diaz hopes to one day travel in spacecraft using the type of engine he designs.

Issues and Technology

What Can Be Done with Nuclear Wastes?

Nuclear power is a controversial subject, and one of the biggest issues is the problem of nuclear wastes. Using nuclear power to make electricity or nuclear weapons produces radioactive wastes. All radioactive substances—including radioactive wastes—decay, or break down into other substances. In the process, energy and particles known as radiation are given off.

Radioactive wastes can be dangerous. Exposure to radioactive substances can damage body tissues. It can lead to cancer or genetic damage. Exposure to large amounts of radiation can be fatal.

Radioactive wastes can remain dangerous for thousands of years. Right now there is no simple way to safely get rid of the wastes. Does using nuclear power make sense when there is no safe way to dispose of its by-products?

Different radioactive substances emit radiation for different lengths of time. The length of time depends on the half-life of the substance. The half-life is the amount of time it takes for one half of the radioactive nuclei in a sample to decay.

Some radioactive substances have short half-lives. Their radioactivity disappears in a few days. Others have long half-lives. Plutonium-239 has a half-life of 240,000 years. Uranium-238 has a half-life of 4.5 million years. Radioactive wastes containing these substances have to be kept away from living things for hundreds of thousands or even in millions of years. The radiation level of one element found in nuclear wastes is shown in Figure 1.

APPLYING CRITICAL THINKING SKILLS

1. How long does it take for one half of this radioactive substance to decay? How long does it take for three fourths to decay?
2. Do you see any problem with creating wastes that remain dangerous for so long? Why or why not?
3. Wastes that are produced today must be safely contained for hundreds or, sometimes, thousands of years. Do you think that it is all right to produce wastes that must be safeguarded by future generations? Explain your answer.

Figure 1

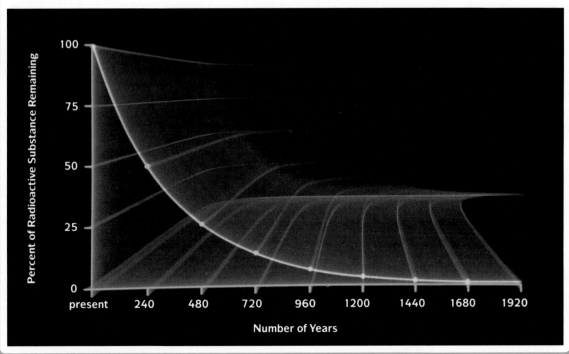

349

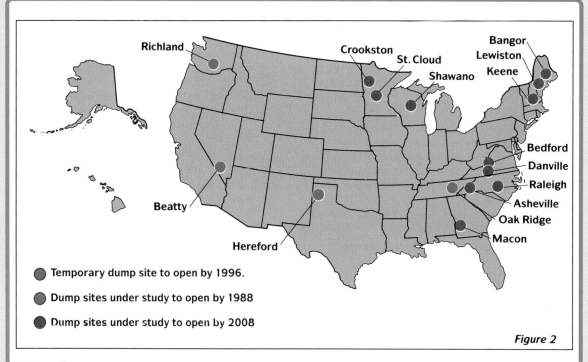

Temporary dump site to open by 1996.

Dump sites under study to open by 1988

Dump sites under study to open by 2008

Figure 2

Figure 2

4. No one has yet found a satisfactory way to permanently and safely deal with radioactive wastes. Should that fact be taken into account when deciding to use nuclear power? Why or why not?

The United States has 100 licensed nuclear power plants. These plants produce from 3 million to 4 million kg of radioactive wastes each year. Millions of kilograms of wastes also result from the military's production of nuclear weapons. Additional wastes are produced by research laboratories and hospitals that use radioisotopes for medical treatment.

Facilities that produce nuclear wastes are located in all parts of the nation. But there are few places where these wastes can legally be stored. Therefore, highly radioactive wastes must be moved thousands of kilometers across the country, from the places where they are produced to the places where they can be buried.

So far there have been no transport-related accidents in which radioactive materials have been released. Nuclear materials are shipped in special containers. The containers are made to withstand impacts, falls, fire, and submersion in water without breaking open and releasing their contents. However, some people worry that no system is fool-proof. Just because there have been no accidents to date does not mean that there will be no accidents in the future.

The spent fuel from nuclear reactors is a high-level waste. Currently this fuel is stored in pools of water at the site of nuclear power plants. Such wastes cannot be moved because there is no permanent storage facility for high-level nuclear wastes in the United States. There is no such storage anywhere in the world.

There are plans for the United States to have a permanent site ready to accept these wastes by 1998. Figure 2 shows the locations of several possible nuclear waste dumps.

APPLYING CRITICAL THINKING SKILLS

1. In what part of the country are most of the proposed dump sites located?

2. In 1986 the Department of Energy withdrew from consideration all of the dump sites shown in red on the map. Where are these formerly proposed dump sites located? Many people in the West were upset about this change. What do you think about eliminating these possible dump sites?

3. Most of the nation's nuclear reactors are located in the East. This area of the country is also the most densely populated. Taking both of these facts into consideration, how would you choose a site for the storage of nuclear wastes?

4. When the decision about a permanent dump for all of the nation's nuclear wastes is made, the government will pick the site. Should the people in the proposed area have the right to refuse? If every place chosen votes against the dump, how will the site of the nuclear waste facility be decided?

The final decision on the location of the permanent high-level nuclear waste storage facility will not be made until 1991. However, people living near the three most likely sites are getting ready to fight the decision.

There are some people in each location who would like the nuclear waste facility to be located in their community. The facility would bring jobs. With guarantees that it will be safe, these people see no reason why they should turn down such a large employer.

People in the nuclear industry say that there is no need to worry. The wastes would be placed in huge leakproof steel canisters. These canisters would be monitored and guarded; no one could be able to disturb their contents.

People on the other side of the argument point out that there have already been problems with leakage at waste storage sites now in use. Almost 2 million L of radioactive wastes have seeped into the soil near the government's temporary site in Hanford, Washington. Some people are worried that the wastes could get into the ground water there and travel to the nearby Columbia River. This river is used by millions for shipping, fishing, and recreation.

What can happen when an unsuitable storage site is chosen? Figure 3 is a diagram of a waste site that had leakage problems.

APPLYING CRITICAL THINKING SKILLS

1. A special seepage basin was constructed to catch possible leakage from the waste containers. Into what other areas did the radioactive wastes spread?

2. The clay layer below the soil was thought to be a barrier that would trap water or toxins. However, the clay was not an effective barrier. What has happened here?

3. What is the probable effect of the leakage on the nearby well?

4. Do you think the leakage could affect areas in addition to those places close to the storage site? Explain your answer.

Figure 3

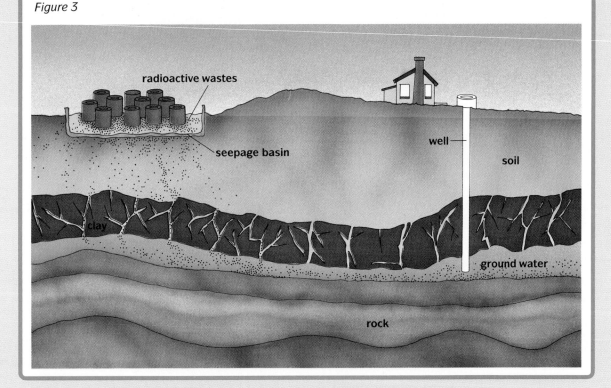

INVESTIGATING
THE EARTH
AND SPACE

*T*hroughout history, people have studied the earth and the planets and stars that surround the earth. Modern equipment can detect the presence of galaxies at the distant reaches of the universe or determine the composition of the interior of the earth. In this unit you will learn more about the exploration of the universe and the nature of the earth.

▲ *The Lick Observatory in California is used to study space.*

Scuba divers can directly explore the oceans. ▶

A weather vane shows the direction of the wind.

An active volcano in Hawaii.

The layers of the ▶ earth can be seen in the Grand Canyon.

CHAPTER 15

EXPLORING THE UNIVERSE

If you were to look at the constellation Orion through a powerful telescope, you would see a dark shape like the one shown in the photograph. This dark mass is a nebula, a dense cloud of gas and dust. This particular nebula is about 1200 times larger than the solar system and is located nearly 1000 light-years from the earth.

The shape of the dark mass gives the nebula its name, the Horsehead Nebula. Notice the clouds of glowing gas and dust that surround the nebula. These clouds block the light of many background stars.

Nebulas are sometimes referred to as the birth-place of stars. It is believed that our solar system was formed from the gas and dust in a nebula.

- *How do scientists learn about the life cycle of stars?*
- *What changes will the sun undergo as it ages?*
- *How old is the universe?*

15·1 Observing the Stars

After completing this section, you will be able to

- **identify** some common constellations in the night sky.
- **explain** why different constellations appear during different seasons.
- **describe** several instruments used to study stars.

The key terms in this section are
constellation
reflecting telescope
refracting telescope

CONSTELLATIONS

A **constellation** is a group of stars that forms a pattern or picture in the sky. Many constellations were named and described thousands of years ago. Ancient peoples imagined that groups of stars formed pictures in the sky. But the star groups seldom look like the creatures, people, and objects that their names describe. You must use your imagination to see the pictures in the sky.

The Big Dipper is part of the constellation Ursa Major, or the Great Bear. Locate the Big Dipper in Figure 15·1. The shape of the Big Dipper is easy to recognize. But you have to use your imagination to see the Great Bear. The Big Dipper can be used to find the North Star. As shown in Figure 15·1, a line extended from the two stars at the front of the cup reaches the North Star, or Polaris (poh LAIR ihs). What constellation does Polaris belong to?

Figure 15·1
The two stars at the outer edge of the bowl of the Big Dipper point to Polaris, the North Star.

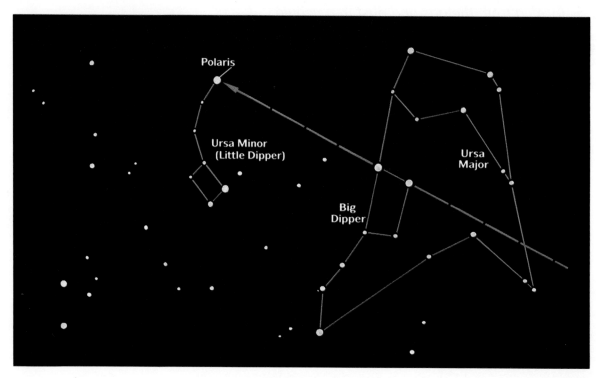

Why is Polaris called the North Star? Figure 15·2 shows the position of Polaris with respect to the earth. Notice that the earth's North Pole points toward Polaris. In the northern hemisphere, stars appear to move from east to west across the sky, just as the sun moves. But because the North Pole points toward Polaris, Polaris does not move across the sky. In fact, all other stars seem to circle Polaris. Stars that appear close to Polaris remain above the horizon all the time. Other stars rise and set as the earth rotates.

Ursa Major, Ursa Minor, and other constellations near Polaris can be seen in the night sky throughout the year. However, many constellations are mainly seen in certain seasons. For example, the constellation Orion is most visible in the winter.

Why does the night sky change from season to season? As you know, the earth orbits the sun. You can see in Figure 15·3 that the night side of the earth faces different directions in different seasons. Notice that in winter, Orion is visible in the night sky, but Sagittarius is not. In which season is Sagittarius visible?

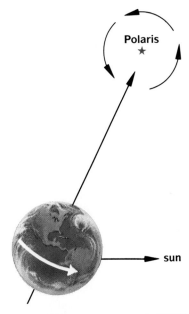

Figure 15·2
Because the earth rotates, the stars appear to circle counterclockwise around Polaris.

Figure 15·3
Different constellations are visible during different seasons of the year.

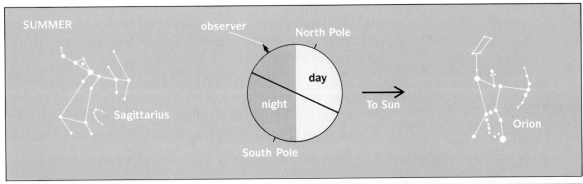

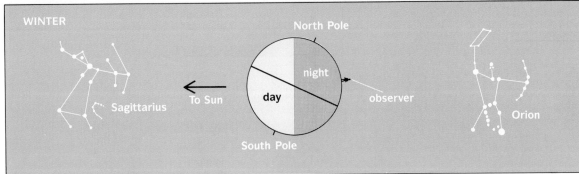

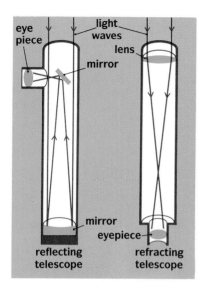

Figure 15·4

A reflecting telescope and a refracting telescope. How do they differ in the way they gather light?

Figure 15·5

Spectral lines produced by different gases in a star.

INSTRUMENTS USED TO STUDY THE STARS

By studying the energy that a star produces, astronomers learn about the star's makeup, temperature, age, and motion. To study this energy, astronomers use many kinds of instruments. These instruments include light telescopes, the spectroscope, and the radio telescope.

One type of light telescope is the refracting telescope. A **refracting telescope** uses a lens to gather light and produce an image. Figure 15·4 shows what happens to light rays that enter a refracting telescope.

Another type of light telescope is the reflecting telescope. A **reflecting telescope** uses a concave mirror to gather light rays and produce an image. Figure 15·4 shows what happens to light rays that strike the mirror.

Light gathered by a telescope can be analyzed by a spectroscope. A *spectroscope* can separate light into a pattern of colored lines. These colored lines are called *spectral lines*. Spectral lines are shown in Figure 15·5.

The spectral lines of a star are produced by the different elements in it. Each element has a unique pattern of spectral lines. Thus the spectral lines give information about the makeup of a star.

Much of what astronomers have learned about stars in recent years has come from the use of *radio telescopes*. Notice in Figure 15·6 that a radio telescope contains a giant antenna and dish. Unlike

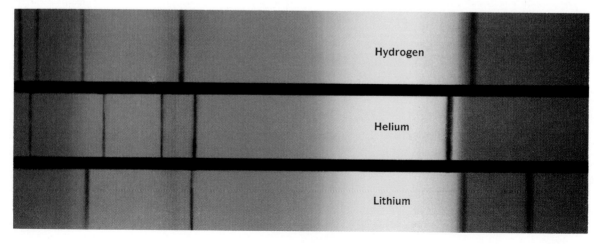

Hydrogen

Helium

Lithium

ACTIVITY   Observing Spectrums

OBJECTIVES

Observe the types of spectrums produced by different materials.

Deduce the way in which spectrums can be used to analyze stars.

MATERIALS

safety goggles; spectroscope; lamp; Bunsen burner; matches; long-handled spoon; small quantities of the salts of sodium, copper, calcium, potassium

PROCEDURE

A. A glowing solid produces a continuous spectrum. Wear safety goggles throughout this activity. Use the spectroscope to observe the glowing filament of a light bulb.
   1. Describe what you see.
B. A glowing gas produces a bright-line spectrum. Light the Bunsen burner. Have your partner place a small amount of the sodium salt on the tip of the spoon. **Caution: Do not taste any salt.**

C. Have your partner hold the tip of the spoon in the flame. **Caution: Hold the spoon in the flame for a short time only, as it will get hot.** Observe the glowing color with the spectroscope.
   2. Describe what you see.
D. Repeat steps **B** and **C**, using samples of the other salts.
   3. Describe what you see in each case.

RESULTS AND CONCLUSIONS

1. Based on your results, explain what a continuous spectrum is.
2. Based on your results, explain what a bright-line spectrum is.
3. Each element has a unique bright-line spectrum. The sun and other stars produce dark-line spectrums. The dark lines indicate that wavelengths of light are being absorbed by elements. An element's bright-line and absorption patterns are the same. How can scientists determine a star's composition from its spectrum?

---

light telescopes, which gather light, radio telescopes gather radio waves given off by stars. Radio waves are not absorbed by the earth's clouds or atmosphere as light waves are. Thus, unlike light telescopes, radio telescopes can be used on cloudy nights. Radio telescopes can even be used in daylight.

REVIEW

1. Name four constellations seen from the Northern Hemisphere.
2. Why do different constellations appear during different seasons of the year?
3. How are three different instruments used to help astronomers study stars?

CHALLENGE Suppose a solar eclipse occurred around noon on a winter day. What season's constellations would be visible in the darkened sky? Explain your answer.

Figure 15·6
A radio telescope gathers radio waves from space.

15·2 Distances to Stars

About 2000 stars are visible on a dark, clear night. It is easy to imagine that these stars are all the same distance away from the earth. However, all stars are not at the same distance from the earth.

Figure 15·7 shows the stars of the constellation Cassiopeia. The screen to the left shows the pattern these stars form as seen from the earth. The screen to the right shows how far three of the stars are from the earth. Notice that the stars are not equally distant from the earth. Some are much farther than others.

Because the distances between stars are so great, the distances are measured in light-years (ly). The light-year is a unit of distance based on the speed of light: 300,000 km/s. A **light-year** is the distance light travels in one year: 9,460,000,000,000 km. The distance to Proxima Centauri, the closest star, is about 40,605,000,000,000 km. Measured in light-years this distance is 4.3 ly.

PARALLAX

How do astronomers find the distances to stars? One method is based on the apparent shift, or change in position, of stars. The apparent shift is

Figure 15·7

When viewed from the earth, the stars in the constellation Cassiopeia appear to be the same distance away. In reality the stars are located at different distances from the earth.

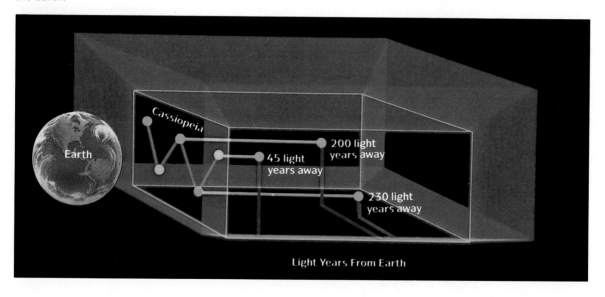

Earth — Cassiopeia — 45 light years away — 200 light years away — 230 light years away

Light Years From Earth

seen in nearby stars when they are observed from different parts of the earth's orbit. The apparent shift of an object when it is seen from different places is called **parallax** (PAR uh laks).

parallaxis (change)

You can observe the effect of parallax by doing the following experiment. Close your left eye, extend one arm, and hold your index finger vertically in front of you. Line your finger up in front of a distant object. Then, without moving your finger, close your right eye and view the object with your left eye. Notice that your finger is no longer lined up in front of the object. Your finger appears to have shifted. Next repeat the experiment, holding your finger closer to you. You should notice that your finger appears to shift more when it is closer. The farther away your finger is held, the less the shift appears to be. Thus the amount of shift is an indication of the distance to your finger.

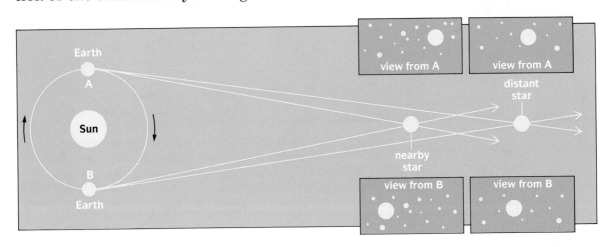

In a similar way the apparent shift of a star is an indication of its distance from the earth. Figure 15·8 shows how this apparent shift can be observed. First the position of a nearby star is compared with the positions of more distant stars. Six months later the position of the star is again compared with the positions of the distant stars. By this time, the earth has moved to the other side of its orbit. Notice in Figure 15·8 that the star is now in front of a different group of distant stars. The star seems to have moved. The greater the change in the position of the star, the closer the star is to the earth.

Figure 15·8
When viewed from position *A* in the earth's orbit, a nearby star appears to be in front of a group of background stars. When viewed from position *B*, the nearby star appears to have moved. How does this movement compare with the apparent movement of a distant star?

What Is Parallax?

OBJECTIVES

Observe the effect of parallax.
Predict the effect of distance on parallax.

MATERIALS

unlined paper, metric ruler, clay, toothpick

PROCEDURE

A. Place a piece of paper on the table in front of you. Draw a line across the paper 2 cm from the top, as shown in the drawing. Using a metric ruler, mark a centimeter scale along the line and number it from 0 to 20.

B. Draw a second line across the paper 5 cm from the top, as shown. Draw a third line down the center of the paper and mark off 5 cm, 10 cm, 15 cm, and 20 cm, as shown.

C. Fold the paper along the second line so that the scale stands up on the table.

D. Place the paper in front of you along the edge of the table. Stand the toothpick in a piece of clay and place it on the 5-cm mark, as shown.

E. Crouch down so that when you look at the tip of the toothpick, you see the scale behind it. Close your left eye. While looking with the right eye, find the closest mark that the toothpick aligns with on the scale. Have your partner record the number of that mark in a data table.

F. Without moving your head, open your left eye and close your right eye. Read the number that the toothpick now lines

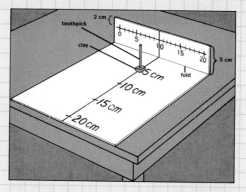

up with on the scale. Have your partner record that number.

G. Subtract the first number from the second to measure how much the apparent position has shifted. Record the difference in a table.
  1. Predict how the parallax shift will change as the distance increases.

H. Repeat steps **D** through **G**, using the toothpick placed at 10 cm, 15 cm, and 20 cm. Record your data.
  2. Predict how the parallax shift would change if you moved back.

I. Leave the toothpick 20 cm from the scale, and move 2 m back from the table. Repeat steps **E** through **G**. Record your data.

RESULTS AND CONCLUSIONS

1. When you moved away from the table, did the toothpick appear to move more or less than it did when you were close?
2. Why is it difficult to use this method for measuring the distances to stars when the stars are very far away?

MAGNITUDES

One method uses the brightnesses of stars and other objects in the sky. The method is based on a system of brightnesses or magnitudes, created by early astronomers. The system was based on a scale numbered from one to six. The brighter a star ap-

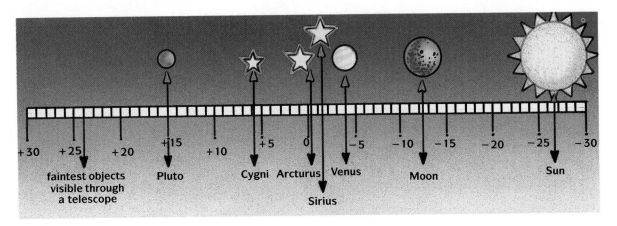

Figure 15·9
The apparent magnitudes of some stars, objects, and the sun.

peared to be, the lower the number it was given. The brightest stars were called first-magnitude stars. The dimmest stars were called sixth-magnitude stars.

The system of magnitudes used by astronomers today is shown in Figure 15·9. Notice that the scale has been extended to include the sun, planets, and objects visible through telescopes. The magnitudes shown on the scale are called apparent magnitudes. The *apparent magnitude* is the brightness of an object as seen from the earth. Notice that the brightest objects in the sky have negative magnitudes. What is the magnitude of the sun?

The sun appears to be billions of times brighter than any other star in the sky. But the sun only appears to be so bright because it is close to the earth. Locate the star Sirius on the scale in Figure 15·9. Sirius is the brightest-looking star in the night sky. If the sun were located at the same distance from the earth as Sirius is, the sun would appear to be only one-twentieth as bright as Sirius.

To compare the true brightnesses of stars, a measure of brightness called absolute magnitude is used. The *absolute magnitude* is a measure of a star's true brightness. It is equal to the apparent magnitude a star would have if it were placed 32.6 ly from the earth. Table 15·1 shows that the sun's absolute magnitude is +5. This means that if the sun were placed 32.6 ly from the earth, its apparent magnitude would be +5. Which star in Table 15·1 has the greatest actual brightness?

Table 15·1
Absolute Magnitudes of Various Stars

STAR	ABSOLUTE MAGNITUDE
Arcturus	−0.04
Sirius	+1
Alpha Centauri	+4
Sun	+5
Barnard's Star	+13

CEPHEID VARIABLES

Ordinarily, the true brightness, or absolute magnitude, of a star is difficult to measure. A star may appear bright because it is close to the earth. Or a star may appear dim because it is far from the earth. But astronomers have been able to measure the absolute magnitude of one special type of star. This type of star, called a *Cepheid* (SEHF ee ihd) *variable*, changes in brightness over a regular period of time. The periods can vary from 1 to 50 days. For example, the Cepheid variable Delta Cephei, shown in Figure 15·10, goes through a period of brightening and dimming about every 5 days. Between what apparent magnitudes does the brightness change?

Astronomers have found that brighter Cepheid variables have longer periods of change than do dimmer ones. Thus the period of a Cepheid variable can be used to find its absolute magnitude. For example, suppose different wattages of light bulbs brighten and dim over regular periods of time. Suppose a 50-W light bulb brightens and dims every 5 minutes, a 100-W light bulb every 10 minutes, and a 150-W light bulb every 15 minutes. If a light bulb of unknown brightness is observed to change over a period of 10 minutes, it is probably a 100-W bulb. Similarly, by observing the period of change of a Cepheid variable, astronomers can determine the star's absolute magnitude.

Figure 15·10

The apparent magnitude of the star Delta Cephei varies.

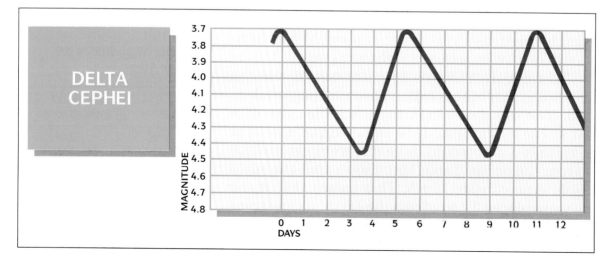

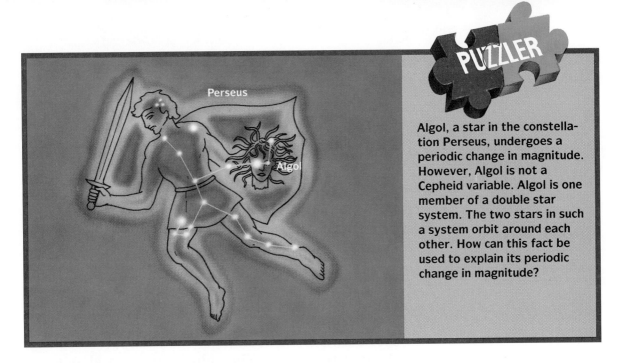

PUZZLER

Perseus

Algol

Algol, a star in the constellation Perseus, undergoes a periodic change in magnitude. However, Algol is not a Cepheid variable. Algol is one member of a double star system. The two stars in such a system orbit around each other. How can this fact be used to explain its periodic change in magnitude?

Once the absolute magnitude of a Cepheid variable is known, astronomers can determine the distance to the star. The distance is found by comparing the star's absolute magnitude with its apparent magnitude. For example, if a star is known to be bright but appears dim, you could conclude that the star is distant. Suppose a star is known to be dim but appears bright. What could you conclude about its distance from the earth?

The use of Cepheid variables is one of the most important methods for measuring distances to stars. When astronomers want to measure the distance to a group of stars, they search for a Cepheid variable in the group. By determining the distance to the Cepheid variable, astronomers can estimate the distance to any other star in the group.

REVIEW

1. What is the meaning of the term *light-year*?
2. What is the difference between apparent magnitude and absolute magnitude?
3. What are two methods used to determine the distances to stars?

CHALLENGE Polaris is a Cepheid variable that has a period of change of about 4 days. Compare its absolute magnitude with that of the Cepheid variable Delta Cephei.

15·3 Types of Stars

After completing this section, you will be able to

- **explain** the relationship between a star's color and its temperature.
- **describe** three groups of stars.

The key terms in this section are
main sequence stars
red giant
white dwarfs

COLOR OF STARS

Stars are not all the same color. Figure 15·11 *(left)* shows the constellation Orion, the Hunter. The bright star at Orion's shoulder is a red star called Betelgeuse (BEE tuhl jooz). The bright star in Orion's leg is a blue-white star called Rigel (RI juhl). Stars can appear blue, white, yellow, orange, or red in color.

The color of a star is related to its surface temperature. Perhaps you have watched the heating element of a toaster as it warms up. As it warms up, the heating element changes color. First the heating element turns red. The color may then change to orange. If the temperature continued to increase, the color would change to yellow and then to white.

Figure 15·11 *(right)* shows how a star's color is related to its surface temperature. Notice that a star with a surface temperature of 3250°C appears red. What is the color and surface temperature of the sun?

Figure 15·11

The constellation Orion. Betelgeuse is a red star. Rigel is a blue-white star *(left)*. A star's color is determined by its temperature *(right)*.

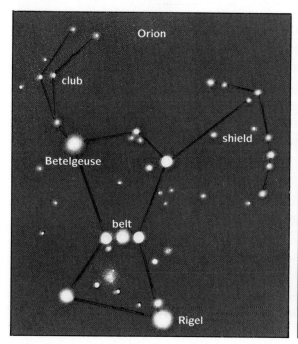

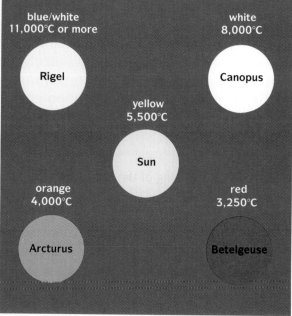

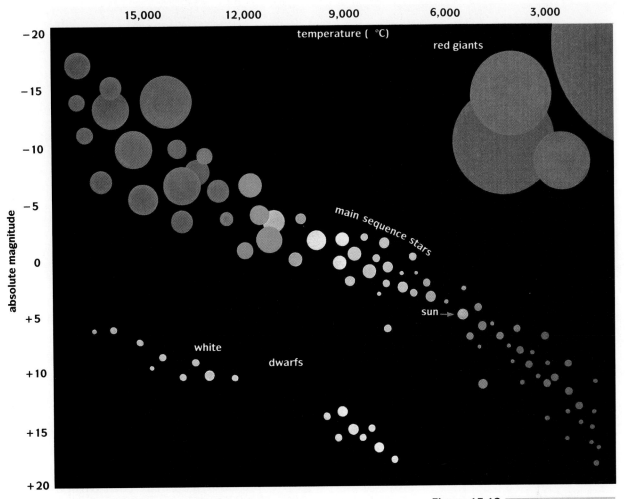

temperature (°C)

15,000   12,000   9,000   6,000   3,000

red giants

main sequence stars

sun →

white

dwarfs

absolute magnitude

−20
−15
−10
−5
0
+5
+10
+15
+20

H-R DIAGRAM

In the early 1900s, two astronomers made a graph showing the relationship between absolute magnitudes and temperatures of stars. This graph, shown in Figure 15·12, is called the *Hertzsprung-Russell diagram,* or the H-R diagram. As you read from left to right, the surface temperature decreases. From the bottom to the top, the absolute magnitude decreases. As the absolute magnitude decreases, what happens to the actual brightness of a star?

The H-R diagram shows that stars fall into three main groups. One group of stars falls in a band that starts in the upper left corner and continues to the lower right of the diagram. This portion of the graph is called the main sequence. **Main sequence**

Figure 15·13

Pleiades is an open cluster of relatively young main sequence stars.

stars are stars that appear on the main sequence of the H-R diagram. About 90 percent of the stars that have been observed are main sequence stars. The stars of the main sequence show a relationship between a star's brightness and its surface temperature. The higher the surface temperature of a star, the brighter the star.

A second group of stars is in the upper right of the H-R diagram. These stars have low surface temperatures but are bright. These stars are called red giants. A **red giant** is a cool, red star that appears very bright because of its large size. Red giants are usually about 20 times the diameter of the sun. Very large red giants, called supergiants, can be 500 to 1000 times the diameter of the sun.

In the lower left is another group of stars that does not fit into the main sequence. These stars are called white dwarfs. **White dwarfs** are hot stars that do not appear bright because they are very small. White dwarfs are usually about one-hundredth the diameter of the sun.

REVIEW

1. How is a star's color related to its surface temperature?

2. What are three groups of stars? Describe each group.

CHALLENGE The star Rigel is a *blue giant*. Antares is a red giant. If both stars have about the same apparent magnitude, which star is larger?

15·4 Life of Stars

BEGINNING OF STARS

Astronomers think that stars begin in a large cloud of gas and dust called a *nebula*. One such nebula is shown in Figure 15·14. Under the force of gravity, the nebula comes together, or contracts. Notice in Figure 15·14 that matter within the nebula is not spread evenly. Regions of dense matter may contract further into spinning balls of gas and dust that are called **protostars.**

The force of gravity in the protostar causes it to contract. As it contracts, its temperature rises. Eventually the protostar becomes so hot that nuclear fusion reactions begin. The fuel of this reaction is hydrogen atoms, and a large amount of energy starts to radiate outward. This energy slows the contracting of the protostar's matter and begins the life of a main sequence star.

MAIN SEQUENCE STAGE

The length of time a star spends on the main sequence depends on the star's mass. The most massive stars may remain only a few million years on

proto- (first)

Figure 15·14
Nebulas are star-forming areas. These nebulas are in the constellation Monoceros.

369

On the morning of February 24, 1987, an astronomer observed what many consider to be the event of a lifetime—the explosion of a star. Called 1987A, it was the nearest and brightest supernova to be observed in almost 400 years.

Although the name *nova* comes from the Latin word meaning ''new,'' a supernova actually occurs at the end of a massive star's life. When the nuclear fuel in the star's core is used up, the core collapses.

This triggers a violent explosion. The explosion releases a tremendous amount of energy.

Astronomers are studying the material left after the explosion. For one thing, they are looking for the heavier elements predicted by one theory. The theory states that hydrogen and helium were the only elements created when the universe began. It also says that some of the heavier elements may have been created in super-

novas. Perhaps the most exciting discoveries are still to come.

the main sequence. A star the size of the sun may spend about 10 billion years. The smallest, least-massive stars may spend many billions of years on the main sequence.

When a star begins to run out of hydrogen, the star goes through many changes. When the hydrogen fuel is used up in the core, the core contracts. The contraction causes a burst of energy to be released. This burst of energy causes the outer layers of gases in the star to be pushed outward. The star expands to hundreds of times its original size.

With expansion, the star cools and becomes a red giant. Helium replaces hydrogen as the fuel. When the sun becomes a red giant, it will expand beyond the orbits of Mercury and Venus.

FINAL STAGE

Although most stars go through the red giant stage, the final stage in the life of a star depends on its mass. The final stages of stars of different masses are shown in Figure 15·15. A star of small mass begins a series of changes that lead from the red giant stage to the white dwarf stage. The expanding shell of gases spreads into space and does not return. The remaining matter contracts and heats up. This star produces little light but has a high surface temperature. Its gravity may be

500,000 times the gravity of the earth. A white dwarf slowly cools until its heat is gone. It then becomes a cold piece of matter called a black dwarf. This may be the future of our sun.

Stars larger than eight times the sun's mass go through different changes after the red giant stage. These stars may expand and contract several times, and then explode. The violent explosion of such a star near the end of its life is called a **supernova**. A supernova may produce as much light as billions of stars. Much of the matter from a supernova is shot through space at tremendous speed, forming a spreading cloud. In 1987 a supernova was observed in the Large Magellanic Cloud galaxy. The remains

novus (new)

Figure 15·15

The life cycle of a star is determined by its original mass.

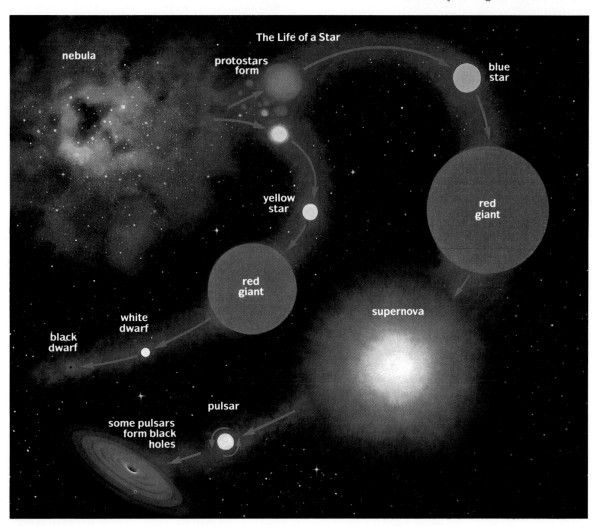

371

Figure 15·16

The Crab Nebula is the remains of a supernova that occurred in 1054 A.D.

of a supernova that was observed in 1054 A.D. is shown in Figure 15·16.

One result of a supernova can be a type of neutron star called a pulsar. A neutron star is a star made up mostly of neutrons. A neutron star is so dense that a teaspoon of its matter would weigh 100 million metric tons.

pulsus (beating)

A **pulsar** is a spinning neutron star. One form of energy that pulsars give off is radio waves. As a result of their rapid spin, the energy from pulsars is detected as rapid bursts of radio waves.

Another result of a supernova can be an object much denser than a neutron star. The object is called a black hole. A **black hole** is an object that is so dense that its gravity can keep light from escaping. It is believed that stars with masses of 30 to 100 times the mass of the sun will end as black holes. Astronomers estimate that there may be many black holes in the Milky Way galaxy.

REVIEW

1. How do stars form?
2. What changes do astronomers predict the sun will go through?
3. How does the mass of a star relate to its life cycle?

CHALLENGE The Crab Nebula is the result of a supernova that was observed in 1054 A.D. The Crab Nebula is about 6500 ly from the earth. In what year did the supernova actually occur?

15·5 Galaxies

In 1924 an American astronomer, Edwin Hubble, used a telescope to study faint patches of light. He observed that they were actually large systems of stars. A large system of stars is called a **galaxy**.

TYPES OF GALAXIES

Hubble spent many years studying galaxies. He found that they can be organized into three basic types. The three basic types are shown in Figure 15·17 *(right)*. One type of galaxy shown is the *elliptical galaxy*. This galaxy may be nearly round but most often resembles a flattened sphere. The largest galaxies that have been found are elliptical. Elliptical galaxies are the most common type of galaxy.

galaxias (milk)

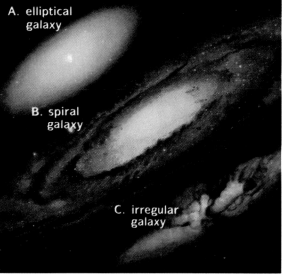

Figure 15·17
The Andromeda galaxy *(left)* is very much like our galaxy, the Milky Way. The three types of galaxies *(right)*.

The second most common type of galaxy is the *spiral galaxy*. Notice in part *B* of Figure 15·17 *(right)* that this galaxy looks like a pinwheel. A small number of galaxies have no regular shape. This type of galaxy is called an *irregular galaxy*. Part *C* of the figure shows an irregular galaxy.

Astronomers believe that more than half of the stars seen with the naked eye are actually multiple star systems. A *multiple star* system may contain two, three, or more stars. For example, a globular cluster is a dense system of 1000 or more stars found within a galaxy.

MOTION OF GALAXIES

One of Hubble's most important discoveries was the relationship between the motion and the spectrums of galaxies. He observed that the spectral lines of the light from galaxies were often shifted toward the red end of the spectrum. The shifting of spectral lines toward the red end of the spectrum is called a *red shift*. Part A of Figure 15·18 shows a spectrum with a red shift. Part B shows the same spectrum with no shift. Part C shows a blue shift, that is, a shift of spectral lines toward the blue end of the spectrum.

Hubble explained that shifts in spectral lines occur as galaxies move toward or away from the earth. He explained that a red shift is caused by a galaxy moving away from the earth. A blue shift is caused by a galaxy moving toward the earth. Hubble also explained that the larger the shift, the greater the speed at which the galaxy moves toward or away from the earth. Hubble observed that light from nearly all galaxies shows a red shift.

Figure 15·18

A star's spectral lines shift toward the red end of the spectrum if the star is moving away from the earth *(A)*. No shift is observed if the star is not moving toward or away from the earth *(B)*. A star's spectral lines shift toward the blue end of the spectrum if the star is moving toward the earth *(C)*.

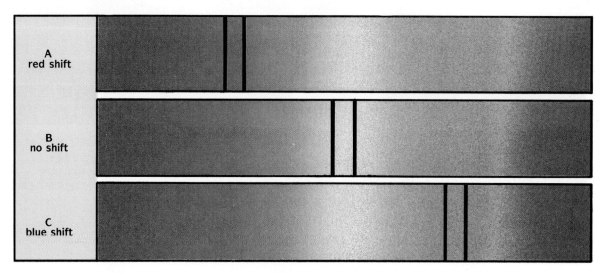

A
red shift

B
no shift

C
blue shift

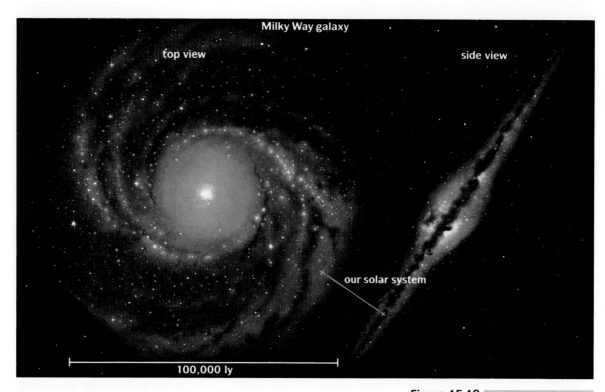

top view

Milky Way galaxy

side view

our solar system

100,000 ly

Figure 15·19
The solar system is located in the Milky Way galaxy.

This means that nearly all galaxies are moving away from the earth.

The largest red shifts have been observed in objects called quasars (KWAY sahrz). They are objects believed to be the most distant from the earth. *Quasars* are thought to be galaxies that are powerful sources of radiant energy.

THE MILKY WAY

Almost all of the stars that you can see in the sky without a telescope belong to the Milky Way galaxy. The **Milky Way galaxy,** which contains billions of stars, is the home of our solar system. The galaxy is a spiral galaxy. Its disk, which is about 100,000 ly across and 5000 ly thick, is surrounded by many small clusters of stars.

The Milky Way galaxy spins around an axis that passes through its center. The solar system completes one revolution in about 250 million years. Notice in Figure 15·19 that the Milky Way galaxy resembles a pinwheel. Where in the galaxy is the solar system located?

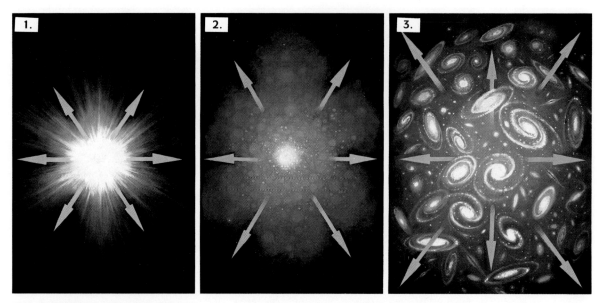

Figure 15·20

The big bang theory explains that the universe began with an explosion.

THE ORIGIN OF THE UNIVERSE

The earth, solar system, stars, and galaxies, and everything between them, make up the universe. How did the universe begin? Scientists believe that the universe is between 15 billion and 20 billion years old. The idea that the universe began with a tremendous explosion is called the **big bang theory**. It is based on the fact galaxies appear to be moving away from each other. According to this theory, all of the energy and matter in the universe was once together. Mass, energy, and the forces of nature were all one. The universe, with its matter, energy, and forces, was formed when the explosion occurred. And the universe began to expand with the explosion. The big bang theory is the most widely accepted theory on the origin of the universe.

The *oscillating universe theory* is similar to the big bang theory, in that it also states that the universe started with an explosion. But the oscillating universe theory adds that, in time, everything will come back together, or collapse. This change from a spreading universe to a collapsing universe could occur if the total mass of the universe were enough for gravity to pull everything back together. After the material collapsed, another big explosion would start the universe expanding again. Many astronomers feel that there is not enough matter, and therefore not enough gravity, to cause the collapse. Other astronomers believe that estimates for the amount of matter in the universe are too small.

REVIEW

1. What are the three kinds of galaxies shown in Figure 15•17?
2. What is the shape of the Milky Way galaxy?
3. What are two theories for the origin of the universe?

CHALLENGE Almost all galaxies show a red shift. Does this mean that the earth is the center of the universe? Explain your answer.

CHAPTER SUMMARY

The main ideas in this chapter are listed below. Read these statements before you answer the Chapter Review questions.

- A constellation is a group of stars that forms a pattern. Constellations are useful in locating other objects in the sky. (15•1)
- Astronomers use different instruments to study energy from stars. Light telescopes, radio telescopes, and spectroscopes are examples of instruments used by astronomers. (15•1)
- The light-year—the distance light travels in one year—is used to measure distances in space. (15•2)
- Several methods are used to determine the distances to stars. These methods include observing parallax and measuring the periods of change of special stars called Cepheid variables. (15•2)
- Stars are classified according to their temperatures and brightnesses. The H-R diagram is a graph of these two properties. (15•3)

- A star begins within a nebula—a cloud of gas and dust. The gas and dust condense into spheres of matter called protostars. A nuclear fusion reaction produces energy within the star. (15•4)
- Small stars become white dwarfs, and eventually, black dwarfs. Large stars may become supernovas and, possibly, pulsars or black holes. (15•4)
- A galaxy is a large system of stars. The galaxies all seem to have formed at about the same time and are all moving away from one another. (15•5)
- The big bang theory states that the universe began as a tremendous explosion. The oscillating universe theory states that the universe will expand and contract periodically. (15•5)

The key terms in this chapter are listed below. Use each term in a sentence that shows the meaning of the term.

big bang theory	main sequence stars	red giant
black hole	Milky Way galaxy	reflecting telescope
constellation	parallax	refracting telescope
galaxy	protostars	supernova
light-year	pulsar	white dwarfs

Chapter Review

VOCABULARY

Use the key terms from the previous page to complete the following sentences correctly.

1. The apparent shift of an object after a change in the position from which the object is viewed is _____.
2. The violent explosion of a large star that is near the end of its life is a/an _____.
3. A large, cool star that can shine brightly in the sky is a/an _____.
4. A group of stars that forms a pattern in the sky is a/an _____.
5. A theory that says the universe began with a tremendous explosion and that it will probably continue to expand is the _____.
6. Dense spheres of dust and gas that will become stars are called _____.
7. Hot, dense stars that do not shine brightly in the sky are _____.
8. A large system of stars is a/an _____.
9. A unit of measure used to describe the distance to a star or galaxy is the _____.
10. A telescope that uses a concave mirror to focus light is called a/an _____.

CONCEPTS

Choose the term or phrase that best answers the question or completes the statement.

1. Which of the following constellations is visible mainly in the summer in the Northern Hemisphere?
   a. Big Dipper
   b. Little Dipper
   c. Sagittarius
   d. Orion
2. Which of the following uses a lens to collect light?
   a. refracting telescope
   b. reflecting telescope
   c. spectroscope
   d. radio telescope
3. What type of information about a star would parallax be most useful in obtaining?
   a. temperature
   b. composition
   c. distance from the earth
   d. mass
4. What property of a Cepheid variable is its period of change related to?
   a. color
   b. mass
   c. apparent magnitude
   d. absolute magnitude
5. Which of the following stars would have the highest temperature?
   a. white
   b. yellow
   c. blue
   d. red
6. An example of a main sequence star is
   a. the sun.
   b. a red giant.
   c. a white dwarf.
   d. a black hole.

7. Which of the following determines the life span of a star?
   a. color
   b. temperature
   c. mass
   d. composition
8. An exploding star is called a
   a. pulsar.
   b. black hole.
   c. nebula.
   d. supernova.
9. What is the basic shape of the Milky Way galaxy?
   a. elliptical
   b. spiral
   c. irregular
   d. round
10. Most scientists believe that the universe began with a/an
   a. nebula.
   b. black hole.
   c. explosion.
   d. protostar.

Answer the following in complete sentences.

11. What information about stars can be obtained by using a spectroscope?
12. How are Cepheid variable stars used by astronomers to measure distances in space?
13. Compare a red giant, a white dwarf, and a main sequence star.
14. Compare the life cycle of a star having a mass equal to or smaller than the mass of the sun with that of a star having a mass that is considerably larger.
15. Why would an accurate measurement of the mass of the universe either support or refute the oscillating universe theory?

---

1. The relative positions of stars in the sky do not change from night to night. Will the patterns of constellations change over thousands of years? Explain your answer.
2. The height, in degrees, of Polaris over the horizon is equal to the latitude from which it is viewed. Where would Polaris appear if you were at the equator? At the North Pole?
3. Why is life unlikely to exist on planets that circle very hot stars?

APPLICATION/ CRITICAL THINKING

---

1. Use a guidebook to the constellations to make your own investigation of the night sky. Identify the first magnitude stars that are visible. Identify several constellations.
2. Using a telescope and sky charts, locate prominent nebulas and galaxies. For example, in winter and spring the nebula in Orion's sword is visible.

EXTENSION

CHAPTER 16

THE EARTH'S STRUCTURE

The photograph shows a volcanic eruption. You might think of a volcanic eruption as a destructive force. But the lava released during volcanic eruptions has formed much of the earth's surface. And the gases released are believed to have been the source of the earth's oceans and atmosphere. Volcanic eruptions are also helpful to scientists. The materials given off during eruptions provide important information about the interior of the earth. What does lava indicate about the temperature inside the earth?

- *What is the structure of the earth?*
- *What is the composition of the earth's interior?*
- *What processes form the earth's rocks?*

16·1 The Structure of the Earth

When Mount Kilauea (kee low AY uh) erupted in Hawaii in 1986, hot molten, or melted, rock poured onto the earth's surface. Where did this molten rock come from? What is the inside of the earth like?

EARTH'S INTERIOR

Geologists cannot study the inner structure of the earth directly. The deepest holes drilled for oil, about 8 km deep, do not penetrate very far below the earth's surface. The distance to the earth's center is about 6400 km. What fraction is 8 km of this distance? But by studying events such as volcanic eruptions and earthquakes at the earth's surface, geologists have learned about the inner structure of the earth.

Geologists have learned that the earth is made up of three main layers. These layers are called the *core, mantle,* and *crust.* The innermost region of the earth is called the core. The core, which has a radius of 3500 km, is thought to be mainly iron with a small amount of nickel. The average density of the core is about 11.7 g/cm³. This is more than twice the average density of the earth, which is about 5.5 g/cm³.

Figure 16·1

Eruption of Mt. Kilauea *(left)*. The three main layers of the earth: the crust, the mantle, and the core *(right)*.

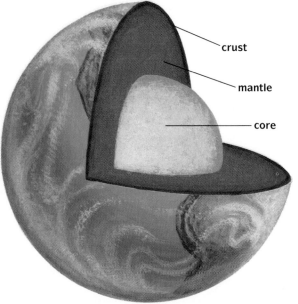

crust

mantle

core

Evidence for the existence of an iron core is the earth's magnetic field. The earth behaves as if it contains a magnet. Because iron is a magnetic substance, it could explain the magnetic field of the earth.

Notice in Figure 16·2 that the core is divided into two smaller layers: the inner core and the outer core. How do the thicknesses of these two layers compare? The **inner core** is believed to be mostly iron, nickel, and cobalt. The temperature of the inner core is estimated to be 4300°C. Because of the great pressure at this depth, the inner core is solid. The **outer core** is about 2200 km thick and is probably composed mostly of iron. The temperature of the molten outer core is 3800°C.

Figure 16·2
The layers of the earth vary in thickness and density. Which layer has the highest density?

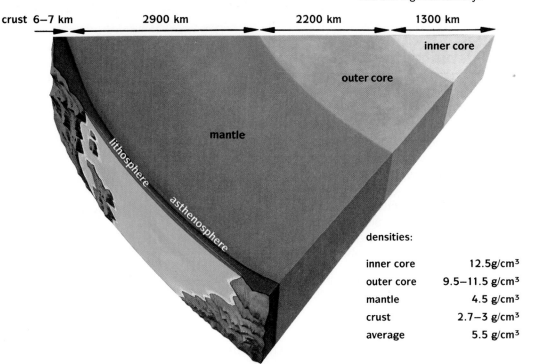

crust 6–7 km   2900 km   2200 km   1300 km

inner core

outer core

mantle

lithosphere

asthenosphere

densities:

inner core	12.5g/cm³
outer core	9.5–11.5 g/cm³
mantle	4.5 g/cm³
crust	2.7–3 g/cm³
average	5.5 g/cm³

The layer between the core and the crust is the **mantle**. Unlike the core, the mantle is composed mainly of rock. What is the density of the mantle? Hot temperatures within the earth's mantle can cause rock to melt. However, geologists believe the mantle is solid. They have found that earthquake waves that do not travel through liquid can travel through the mantle.

ACTIVITY

How Would You Determine the Average Density of the Earth?

OBJECTIVES

Determine the density of rocks and iron.
Propose an average density of the earth.

MATERIALS

balance; samples of basalt, granite, and slate; plastic graduate; water; sample of iron

PROCEDURE

A. Make a data table like the one shown below.

	MASS	VOLUME	DENSITY
Basalt			
Granite			
Slate			
Average	—	—	
Iron			

B. Determine the mass of each of your rock samples. Record the data in your table.

C. Determine the volume of each rock sample by the water-displacement method. Follow the steps in the figure. Record the data in the table.

D. Using the same procedures you used for the rocks, determine the mass and volume of an iron sample. Record the mass and volume in your table.

E. Density is the mass of an object divided by its volume.

$$density = \frac{mass}{volume}$$

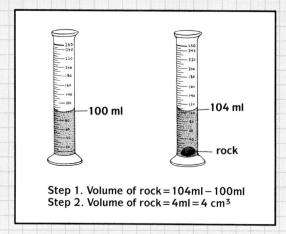

Step 1. Volume of rock = 104ml − 100ml
Step 2. Volume of rock = 4ml = 4 cm³

Determine the density of basalt, granite, and slate. Add the three densities and divide by 3 to get the average rock density. Record your results in the table.

F. Determine the density of the iron. Record the density of iron in the table.

RESULTS AND CONCLUSIONS

1. How does the density of the rocks compare with the density of iron?
2. What layer of the earth do the rocks represent?
3. What layer of the earth does the iron represent?
4. The known density of the earth is 5.5 g/cm³. How does this compare with your proposal of the average density of the earth?

In the upper region of the mantle the rock seems to flow. If you have handled plastic putty, you know that even though it is a solid, the putty flows. The ability of a solid material to flow is called *plasticity* (plas TIHS uh tee). Within the upper mantle the *asthenosphere* (as THEHN uh sfihr) is a region that has the property of plasticity.

The outermost layer of the earth is called the **crust**. The thickness of the crust of the earth can be compared to that of the apple skin of an apple.

PUZZLER

Many of the world's mountains were formed when sections of the earth's crust were pushed together. The crust folded and was pushed upward. However, the Catskill Mountains in New York, shown here, are not folded mountains. In fact, it is thought that the Catskill Mountains are an old plateau. How might a plateau come to look like mountains?

HEAT IN THE EARTH

Geologists believe that the earth became molten in its early history. When the earth became molten, the heavy metals, iron and nickel, sank toward the earth's center. These metals are believed to have formed the core. Lighter rock materials formed the mantle. The lightest rock materials floated to the top and formed the crust.

Many geologists believe that radioactive elements caused the earth to melt. *Radioactive elements* are elements that change into other elements, giving off heat in the process. Large amounts of radioactive elements, such as uranium, were probably found in the interior of the earth. The heat produced by the breakdown of these buried elements melted much of the rock that formed the earth.

The melting of the earth probably took place more than 4 billion years ago. Even today, much heat is generated within the earth. But since the earth is no longer completely molten, radioactive heating has decreased.

REVIEW

1. What is the structure of the earth's interior?
2. What are three properties of each layer of the earth?
3. How does the structure of the earth's interior relate to the way it formed?

CHALLENGE How would the earth's properties differ if it were composed entirely of rock, without any layers?

16·2 The Earth's Surface

You have probably noticed different landscapes in pictures or when you have traveled. The features that make up landscapes include mountains, plateaus, and plains.

EARTH'S LAND

Mountains are found on all continents on the earth. *Mountains* are elevated sections of the earth's surface. They can occur in chains on the land or on the ocean floor. To be classified as mountains, land must be at least 600 m higher than the surrounding surface. Elevated sections under 600 m are called hills.

Mountains and other high land separate the surrounding sections of low land. An area of high land between sections of low land is called a *divide*. The rivers and streams on either side of a divide are usually kept separated by the divide.

A *plateau* is an area of high elevation made up of horizontal rock layers. Plateaus may have steep slopes where rivers have cut valleys. An example of such a plateau is the Colorado Plateau. Locate the

Figure 16·3

Landscape regions of the United States.

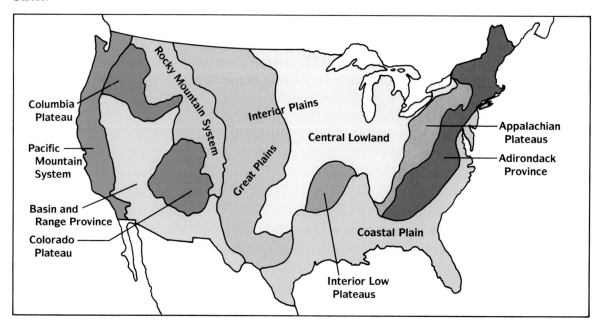

386

Colorado Plateau in Figure 16·3. Rivers have cut into the rock layers of the plateau, forming the Grand Canyon.

Plains are areas of land with low elevation and little change in slope. Plains usually are made up of horizontal rock layers. The region between the Rocky Mountains and the Appalachian Plateau is called the Interior Plains. On the Interior Plains a region called the Great Plains is an area of much agricultural activity. What is the location of the Great Plains?

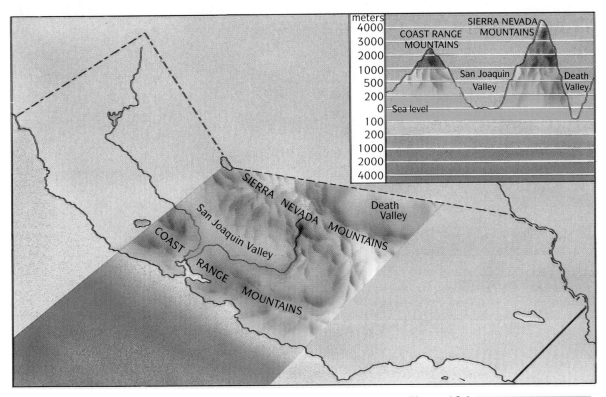

Figure 16·4

A relief map of the San Joaquin Valley.

Variation in elevations of areas on the earth's surface is called *relief*. A map that shows mountains, valleys, plains, and their elevations is called a *relief map*. Such a map may use color to indicate the altitude, or height, of the land above sea level. *Sea level* is the average level of the sea where it meets the land. Figure 16·4 shows a relief map. Notice that the shading changes as the elevation of the land changes. How is color used to show the depth of water?

TOPOGRAPHIC MAP

Another type of map shows the shape of the land at various heights. This map is called a topographic map. A **topographic map** shows the shape and height of land by using lines that connect points of the same elevation. A line that connects points of the same elevation on a topographic map is called a **contour line**.

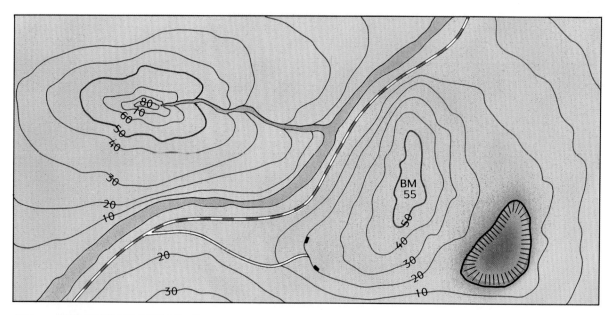

Figure 16·5

A topographic map shows land features.

Contour lines are drawn at regular intervals. For example, a contour line may be drawn every 5 m, every 20 m, or every 100 m. The **contour interval** is the difference in height between two adjacent contour lines. The elevations shown in Figure 16·5 are in meters. What is the contour interval?

Bench marks are shown on a map by **X** or **BM**, and the exact elevation is printed in brown or black ink near the mark on the map. What is the elevation of the bench mark in Figure 16·5? The United States Geological Survey (USGS) measures exact elevations at many locations across the United States.

A depression is shown by a closed contour line with short lines on the inside. In Figure 16·5 a depression is located between the 10-m and 20-m contour lines. These short lines, called hachures (ha-SHURZ) point in the direction that the land slopes.

A map is smaller than the region it shows. Thus it is important to know the relationship between the distance shown on a map and the actual distance on the ground. The ratio used to compare the distance on a map with the actual distance on the earth's surface is called the *map scale*. The USGS produces maps in which the map scale is approximately one inch to one mile.

Elevation of the land is only one of the features that might be shown on a topographic map. Lakes, rivers, cities, bridges, and railroads might also be shown. Symbols for these and any other features are listed in the map's legend, or key.

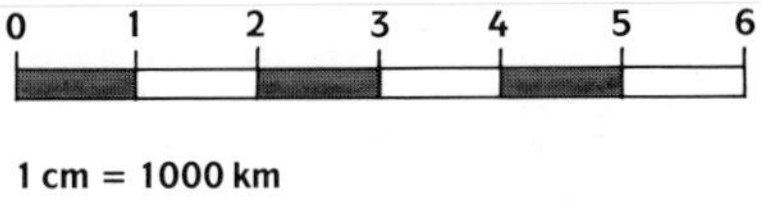

1 cm = 1000 km

Figure 16·6
The scale of a map.

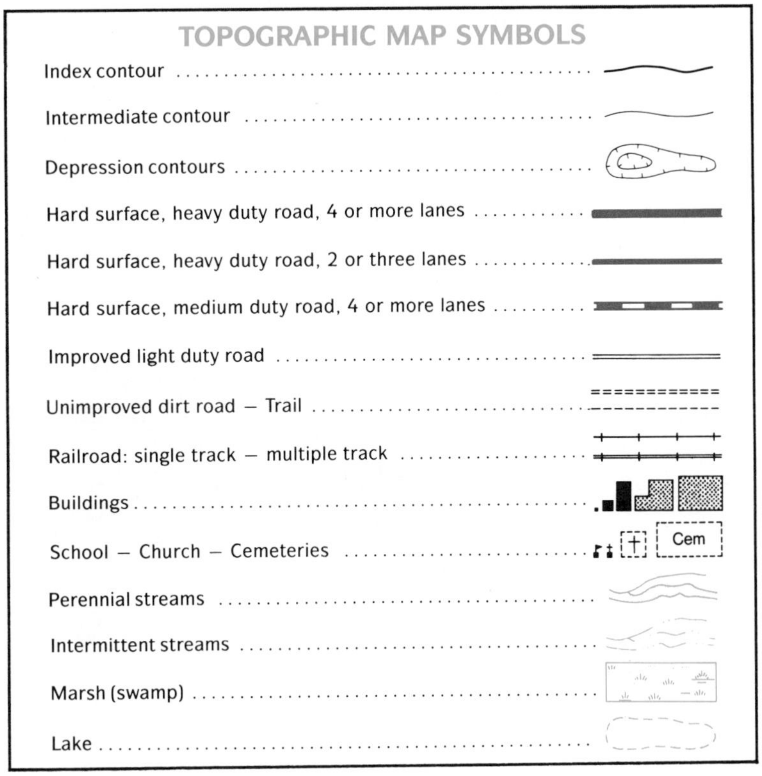

Figure 16·7
The legend of a topographic map.

TOPOGRAPHIC MAP SYMBOLS

Index contour

Intermediate contour

Depression contours

Hard surface, heavy duty road, 4 or more lanes

Hard surface, heavy duty road, 2 or three lanes

Hard surface, medium duty road, 4 or more lanes

Improved light duty road

Unimproved dirt road — Trail

Railroad: single track — multiple track

Buildings

School — Church — Cemeteries

Perennial streams

Intermittent streams

Marsh (swamp)

Lake

REVIEW

1. Give a brief description of three landscape features of the earth.

2. How are relief maps and topographic maps similar? How are they different?

3. What features are shown on a topographic map?

CHALLENGE What features would you look for on a topographic map to find a stream that is surrounded by steep slopes?

16·3 Rocks

On the evening of November 8, 1982, a rock crashed through the roof of a home in Wethersfield, Connecticut. This rock was not an ordinary rock. It was a meteorite—a rock from outer space.

The way geologists looked at this "alien" rock was similar to the way they would look at an earth rock. They studied its texture, or the size of its mineral crystals, and its composition. From this study they learned about the conditions that existed when the meteorite formed. These same characteristics can be studied in earth rocks.

ROCKS AND MINERALS

Geologists have found that all rocks have one thing in common: they are made of one or more minerals. Minerals are the solid materials that make up rocks. Minerals are each composed of a single substance. Most rocks are made up of many minerals.

Figure 16·8

Granite, and the minerals that form it.

quartz

granite

orthoclase feldspar

biotite mica

hornblende

Look at the rock shown in Figure 16·8, page 390. This rock is called granite (GRAN iht) and is made up of the four minerals shown. What are the names of these minerals?

The lines in Figure 16·8 show places where each of the four minerals can be found. Because granite is a mixture, the amount of each mineral can vary from sample to sample. Also, the color of the minerals can vary from one sample to another.

A few rocks are formed from only one mineral. Look at the rock shown in Figure 16·9. This rock, called limestone, forms from a single mineral, calcite. How does the appearance of the limestone differ from the appearance of the granite?

Figure 16·9
Limestone *(left)* is made up of one mineral, calcite *(right)*.

TYPES OF ROCKS

Rocks form in three main ways. Based on how rocks form, they can be classified into three groups. The first group of rocks is igneous (IHG nee uhs) rocks. **Igneous rocks** form from molten rock material as it cools and hardens. The word *igneous* means "from fire." The second group of rocks is sedimentary (sehd uh MEHN tuh ree) rocks. **Sedimentary rocks** form from sediments (SEHD uh-muhnts) that have been pressed together. Sediment may come from plant or animal remains. It may come from minerals that dissolved in water. Sediment may also come from large rocks that have been broken into smaller pieces by water, wind, or ice. The third group of rocks is metamorphic (meht uh-MAWR fihk) rocks. **Metamorphic rocks** are rocks changed by heat or pressure.

ignis (fire)

sedere (to settle)

meta (change)
morphe (form)

A Florida company called Microgravity Research Associates wants to grow crystals in outer space for use in electronics. Research has shown that crystals grow better under conditions with little gravity and without other earthly disturbances. This is because gravity prevents crystals from growing past a certain size. Also, since crystals grow by adding layer upon layer of only atom-thick material, any disturbance, such as moving air, causes a flaw in the finished product. When flawed crystals are used in circuits, not as much electricity will flow through the circuits. Thus the entire electrical system's performance and reliability are affected. But in space, without gravity or air currents, crystals grow quickly and freely in all directions. They also have fewer flaws.

Microgravity Research Associates wants to use the mineral gallium arsenide for the crystals. Gallium arsenide crystals would be used in sophisticated devices that demand utmost performance and durability. These devices might include supercomputers that perform billions of computations every second. The crystals would also be suitable for strategic defense systems and satellite communications.

Other companies are taking advantage of the ease with which crystals can be grown in space. Microgravity Technologies, Inc., in California, wants to grow gallium arsenide and other compounds in space to use in producing lasers and optical fibers.

The changes that form metamorphic rocks are only part of a never-ending process. This process is called the rock cycle. The *rock cycle* shows how the different types of rocks are related and how rock material is used and reused. The rock cycle has no beginning and no end.

The rock cycle diagram, Figure 16·10 (*left*), page 393, shows that igneous rock forms from molten rock. When igneous rock is exposed to water, wind, or ice, it is broken down into sediments. The sediments can be carried away and deposited in layers. The layers may be pressed together by the weight of materials above them or the sediments may become cemented together by minerals in water. The sediments turn into sedimentary rock. This rock may become buried by other layers. Below the surface of the earth, heat and pressure can change the sedimentary rock into metamorphic rock.

If the metamorphic rock melts, the melted material may once again form new igneous rock, and the rock cycle will continue. However, the metamorphic rock may follow other paths. For example, the metamorphic rock may be brought to the surface of the earth during mountain building. There it can be exposed to the process of weathering. The rock can be broken down into sediments which can then form sedimentary rock. What other paths can you identify in the rock cycle? In Figure 16·10 (*right*), identify the processes that form quartzite.

The study of rocks can provide information about their past. For example, the mineral composition of rocks can often be used to tell where they formed. If a mineral that usually forms in oceans is found in a rock, that rock probably formed in an ocean. Some rocks also provide clues about the conditions that existed when they formed. For example, some rocks form only at high temperatures. If such rocks are found in the crust, that part of the crust was probably once hot.

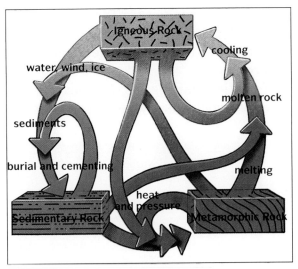
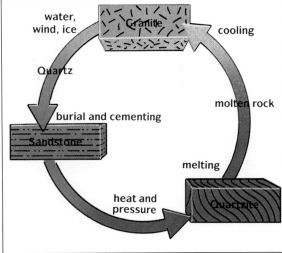

Figure 16·10
The different paths that a rock can take in the rock cycle *(left)*. The different paths that granite may take in the rock cycle *(right)*.

REVIEW

1. Describe igneous, sedimentary, and metamorphic rocks.
2. Explain the path a rock might follow as it moves through the rock cycle.

CHALLENGE Is it possible to tell what paths a certain rock will take in the rock cycle? Explain your answer.

16·4 Igneous Rocks

The diver in Figure 16·11 (*right*) is watching molten rock erupt from the ocean floor. When the molten rock hardens, it will become part of the ocean floor. Molten rock indicates to geologists that the inside of the earth must be very hot. By studying molten rock, geologists can find clues about how rocks form inside the earth.

Molten rock is formed when heat inside the earth causes rock to melt. Molten rock below the surface of the earth is called *magma*. The temperature of magma is usually between 550°C and 1200°C. Magma is lighter than the solid rock around it and therefore tends to rise toward the earth's surface. Molten rock that comes out onto the earth's surface is called *lava* (LAH vuh).

TEXTURE

All igneous rocks are formed either from lava or from magma. Igneous rocks that form from lava are called **extrusive** (ek STROO sihv) **rocks**. Igneous rocks that form from magma are called **intrusive** (ihn TROO sihv) **rocks**.

ex- (out)
trudere (thrust)

One way of distinguishing between extrusive rocks and intrusive rocks is by texture. *Texture*

Figure 16·11
Lava on the earth's surface *(left)* and underwater *(right)*.

refers to the size, shape, or arrangement of the mineral crystals, or grains, in a rock. A rock's texture depends on how quickly or slowly the molten material cools and hardens. The longer it takes molten rock to cool and harden, the larger the crystals will be. This is because mineral crystals in the molten rock require time to grow.

An igneous rock with large crystals probably formed from magma that cooled and hardened slowly, below the earth's surface. An igneous rock with small crystals probably formed from lava that cooled quickly, at the earth's surface. An igneous rock with both large crystals and small crystals probably began as magma cooling below the earth's surface and then was pushed up to the surface before cooling and hardening completely.

Extrusive rocks usually have small mineral crystals and are called fine-grained rocks. A microscope is often needed to see the mineral crystals. A common fine-grained igneous rock is *basalt*.

Some types of extrusive rocks do not have mineral crystals. These rocks are formed when lava cools so quickly that crystals do not have time to form. One example of such a rock is called *obsidian*

Figure 16·12
Basalt can sometimes form in columns when magma cools.

ACTIVITY   Growing Crystals

OBJECTIVE
Identify the effect of rate of cooling on crystal size.

MATERIALS
safety goggles, 8 g of alum, graduate, water, 100-mL beaker, hot plate, spoon, 2 petri dishes, bowl of ice cubes, paper towel

PROCEDURE
A. Wear safety goggles. Place 8 g of alum in a beaker containing 60 mL of water.
B. Heat the beaker on a hot plate, and stir until the alum dissolves.
C. Pour the liquid into two petri dishes, covering the bottom of each dish.
D. Set one petri dish on a table, and set the other in a bowl of ice cubes. Observe the liquid in each dish for 5 to 7 minutes.
E. Make a sketch of a crystal from each dish. Try to show the actual size of the crystals. One way to make a sketch is by tracing around the alum crystals. To do this, remove a crystal from the liquid, pat it with a paper towel, and then lay the crystal on your paper and trace around it.

RESULTS AND CONCLUSIONS
1. What effect did the rate of cooling have on the size of the alum crystals? Why?
2. Why are there differences in the sizes of mineral crystals in igneous rocks?

Figure 16·13
Obsidian *(left)*, scoria *(middle)*, and pumice *(right)*.

and is shown in Figure 16·13 *(left)*. Why is obsidian also called volcanic glass?

Another kind of extrusive rock that does not have crystals comes from the top of a lava flow. Sometimes the lava at the surface cools so quickly that the hot gases mixed with the lava do not have time to escape. The gases become trapped inside the hardened lava, resulting in a rock called *scoria*, shown in Figure 16·13 *(middle)*. Another extrusive rock that cools quickly is *pumice*. Pumice, shown in Figure 16·13 *(right)*, forms from lava thrown out of volcanoes during explosions. Pumice contains so many holes that it floats when placed in water.

Intrusive rocks usually have large mineral crystals and are called coarse-grained rocks. The mineral crystals in coarse-grained rocks are usually large enough to be seen without magnification. Granite is an example of a coarse-grained rock.

FORMING IGNEOUS ROCKS

Geologists believe that different igneous rock can form from the same magma. These scientists have found that as magma cools, some minerals crystallize before others. These mineral crystals

Table 16·1

Common Igneous Rocks

	DARK ←	COLOR	→ LIGHT	
Coarse-grained	Periodotite	Gabbro	Diorite	Granite
Fine-grained	None	Basalt	Andesite	Rhyolite
Main minerals	Olivine, augite	Plagioclase feldspar, augite, olivine	Plagioclase feldspar, hornblende, biotite	Orthoclase feldspar, quartz, biotite, muscovite

Figure 16·14
Common igneous rocks.

may sink in the magma. The sinking causes the amount of each mineral to change from one place to another. Then, as minerals crystallize in different parts of magma, different igneous rocks form. Thus many kinds of igneous rocks can form from one kind of magma.

Table 16·1 organizes some common igneous rocks according to their texture and color and the minerals they contain. Notice that the rocks vary in color. Dark-colored igneous rocks usually contain dark-colored minerals, such as olivine and augite. Light-colored igneous rocks usually contain light-colored minerals, such as quartz and feldspars.

Table 16·1 shows information about the rocks in Figure 16·14. What are the minerals in basalt and gabbro? How are basalt and gabbro different? Why are andesite (AN duh zīt) and diorite (DI uh rīt) lighter in color than basalt and gabbro?

REVIEW

1. How do igneous rocks form?
2. Why do intrusive rocks often have larger mineral crystals than do extrusive rocks?
3. What are some examples of common igneous rocks?

CHALLENGE Under what conditions could an extrusive rock have larger crystals than an intrusive rock?

397

16·5 Sedimentary Rocks

Sedimentary rocks have not always existed on the earth. About 4 billion years ago, the earth's surface was covered with igneous rocks. The earth's surface at that time probably resembled the moon's surface today. Even now, sedimentary rocks make up less than 10 percent of the earth's rocks. At the surface, however, they make up 75 percent of the rocks.

Since igneous rocks first formed on the earth's surface, they have been exposed to water, wind, and ice. Rocks that come into contact with water, wind, and ice are broken down into smaller pieces. This process is called *weathering*. Figure 16·15 shows the effects of weathering on old sidewalks.

Figure 16·15
Cracked sidewalks show the effects of weathering.

After large rocks are broken down into sediments, running water may pick up the sediments. They are carried by the running water until the running water slows down or stops. The water may slow down as it nears a lake or an ocean. When running water slows down, it can carry fewer sediments than when it was moving faster. As a result, some of the sediments fall to the bottom of the water. Over time the sediments collect on the bottom. Materials that have been deposited in water form most sedimentary rock. Materials deposited by wind and ice can also form sedimentary rock.

FORMING SEDIMENTARY ROCKS

Sediments usually build up very slowly. It may take a thousand years for sediments to build up a layer one centimeter thick. A layer grows in thickness until the environment changes. For example, a layer of sand might form where a river enters an ocean. If the river dries up, the layer of sand stops growing. When the river starts flowing again, a new layer of sand is started. Over many thousands of years, layers of sediment become covered by many other layers of sediment.

Figure 16·16
Layers of rock in the Grand Canyon.

To form sedimentary rock from sediments, the sediments must be held together. One way in which pieces of rock are held together is through a squeezing process called *compaction* (kuhm PAK shuhn). Pieces of rock become compacted as the weight of the sediments deposited above squeezes out air and water from between the pieces of rock. This process can cause sediments to stick together.

Another way in which sediments are held together is through minerals acting like cement, in a process called *cementation* (see muhn TAY shuhn). Sediments can be "cemented" together when the spaces between the pieces are filled with minerals, usually left behind by ground water.

CLASSIFYING SEDIMENTARY ROCKS

Sedimentary rocks that form from pieces of other rocks are called **clastic rocks**. Pieces of rocks, or sediments, can vary in size. Clastic rocks are classified according to the size of the pieces of sediments that they contain.

Conglomerates (kuhn GLAHM uhr ihts) and *breccias* (BREHCH ee uhz) are clastic rocks that contain large sediments. These rocks contain pebbles of many different sizes. Conglomerates contain pebbles that are rounded; breccias contain pebbles that are angular, or sharp-cornered. *Sandstone, siltstone,* and *shale* are clastic rocks made from smaller pieces of sediments.

Sedimentary rocks that form from dissolved minerals in water or from the remains of once-living things are called **nonclastic rocks**. Nonclastic rocks are classified by their composition. Nonclastic rocks may contain calcite, halite, gypsum, or quartz.

siltstone

shale

conglomerate

breccia

sandstone

Figure 16·17
Common sedimentary rocks.

Limestone is a nonclastic rock formed from dissolved calcite in seawater or from pieces of seashells. *Coquina* (koh KEE nuh) is a kind of limestone that contains seashells.

REVIEW

1. How do sedimentary rocks form?
2. What is the difference between clastic rocks and nonclastic rocks?
3. List five examples of common sedimentary rocks.

CHALLENGE Explain why conglomerates might be found farther downstream than breccias.

16·6 Metamorphic Rocks

It may seem that solid rocks never change. Over long periods of time, however, all rocks change. A rock can change if it is put under great pressure or heat. A rock changed by great pressure or heat is called a metamorphic rock. *Metamorphic* means "changed in form." Both igneous and sedimentary rocks can be changed into metamorphic rocks.

FORMING METAMORPHIC ROCKS

Metamorphic rocks may form at great depths within the earth's crust. Great pressure is put on rocks when they are buried by many layers of sediment. The weight of the layers compresses the rocks, causing their minerals to change shape or to line up in layers. How can you tell this rock was once under great pressure?

Rocks are also changed when they come into contact with or are near magma. The high temperature of the magma "bakes" the rocks. Although the heat is not great enough to melt them, it can change their structure. The heat can cause the minerals to recrystallize into larger or different minerals.

Figure 16·18
Great pressure caused these sedimentary rock layers to bend.

401

TYPES OF METAMORPHIC ROCKS

The minerals in some metamorphic rocks are arranged in bands or layers. Metamorphic rocks that have minerals arranged in bands or layers are called **foliated** (FOH lee ay tihd) **rocks**.

Some foliated rocks contain bands of minerals that appear as bands of different colors. For example, alternating bands of dark-colored and light-colored minerals can be seen in the rock shown in Figure 16·19 (*left*). This rock is called gneiss (nīs). *Gneiss* is formed from granite, an igneous rock, under great pressure and heat.

Another foliated rock that shows banding of minerals is schist (shihst). *Schist* is one of the most common metamorphic rocks and is usually formed from shale, a sedimentary rock. As you can see in Figure 16·19 (*right*), schist does not have the well-defined bands that are seen in gneiss.

Nonfoliated rocks are metamorphic rocks that do not have bands or layers of minerals. Rocks in this group are usually composed of one mineral that recrystallizes. A nonfoliated rock does not show banding of minerals, because all of its mineral crystals look the same.

An example of a nonfoliated rock is marble. *Marble* is formed by the recrystallization of the mineral calcite in limestone. Sometimes, colorful

Figure 16·19
Gneiss *(left)* and schist *(right)* are foliated rocks.

veins can be seen in marble. Look at Figure 16·20 Why is marble used to make tabletops?

Quartzite and *hornfels* are also nonfoliated rocks. Quartzite is formed from sandstone, a sedimentary rock. Hornfels can be formed from basalt, an igneous rock.

REVIEW

1. How do metamorphic rocks form?
2. What is the difference between foliated rocks and nonfoliated rocks?
3. List five examples of common metamorphic rocks.

CHALLENGE A layer of basalt is found between two layers of sedimentary rock. How can knowledge of metamorphism be used to tell whether the basalt formed from a lava flow or pushed its way between the two layers?

Figure 16·20
Marble is a nonfoliated rock.

CHAPTER SUMMARY

The main ideas in this chapter are listed below. Read these statements before you answer the Chapter Review questions.

- The earth is composed of the core, the mantle, and the crust. (16·1)
- The inner core probably consists of iron and nickel. The outer core is molten and is probably composed mostly of iron. (16·1)
- The mantle and the crust are made mostly of rock. (16·1)
- Mountains, plateaus, and plains are major landscape features of the earth. (16·2)
- A topographic map uses contour lines to show elevations.(16·2)
- Rocks are classified according to how they form. The three main groups of rocks are igneous, sedimentary, and metamorphic. (16·3)
- The rock cycle shows how rock material is used and reused. (16·3)
- Igneous rocks form from molten rock material. Igneous rocks can be put into two

groups: extrusive rocks, which form at the earth's surface, and intrusive rocks, which form deep in the earth. (16·4)
- Igneous rocks can differ in their mineral composition and texture. (16·4)
- Sedimentary rocks can be put into two groups: clastic rocks and nonclastic rocks. Clastic rocks form from pieces of rocks, and nonclastic rocks form either from minerals dissolved in water or from the remains of once-living things. (16·5)
- Metamorphic rocks are rocks changed by great pressure or heat. (16·6)
- Metamorphic rocks can be put into two groups: foliated rocks, which have bands or layers of minerals, and nonfoliated rocks, which are composed mainly of one mineral. (16·6)

The key terms in this chapter are listed below. Use each term in a sentence that shows the meaning of the term.

clastic rocks	extrusive rocks	intrusive rocks	nonfoliated rocks
contour interval	foliated rocks	mantle	outer core
contour line	igneous rocks	metamorphic rocks	sedimentary rocks
crust	inner core	nonclastic rocks	topographic map

Chapter Review

VOCABULARY

Use the key terms from the previous page to complete the following sentences correctly.

1. The earth's outer layer is called the _____.
2. The layer within the earth that is solid and composed of iron and nickel is the _____.
3. The earth's middle layer is the _____.
4. A/an _____ shows the height and shape of land by using lines to connect points having the same elevations.
5. Rocks formed under great pressure and heat are _____.
6. Rocks formed from sediments pressed or cemented together are _____.
7. Rocks formed from the hardening of molten rock material are _____.
8. Sedimentary rocks formed from weathered pieces of rocks are _____.
9. Metamorphic rocks that have bands or layers within them are _____.
10. Igneous rocks that form deep within the earth are _____.

CONCEPTS

Write the correct term for each number in the diagram.

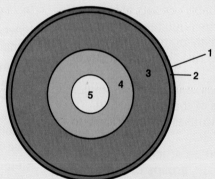

Choose the term or phrase that best answers the question or completes the statement.

6. Which layer of the earth has the highest density?
   - a. crust
   - b. mantle
   - c. asthenosphere
   - d. core
7. Which landscape feature has the highest elevation?
   - a. plain
   - b. plateau
   - c. mountain
   - d. valley
8. Minerals make up which type of rock?
   - a. igneous
   - b. sedimentary
   - c. metamorphic
   - d. all of the above

9. An igneous rock with large crystals is called
   a. intrusive.
   b. extrusive.
   c. foliated.
   d. nonfoliated.
10. A rock that melts under great heat and pressure will form which type of rock?
   a. igneous
   b. sedimentary
   c. metamorphic
   d. all of the above

Answer the following in complete sentences.

11. Compare the densities of the core, mantle, and crust.
12. How might rivers cause an old plateau to appear to be mountains?
13. Why is the rock cycle called a never-ending process?
14. Explain how the rate of cooling affects crystal size in igneous rocks.
15. What are some ways in which sediments can form?

APPLICATION/
CRITICAL
THINKING

1. Predict the shape and direction of contour lines across streams.
2. Identify any rocks used to construct your school building. Why, do you think, were these particular kinds of rocks used?
3. Explain each of the following observations.
   a. In a cemetery the writing is more worn on some gravestones than on other gravestones.
   b. Most rocks found at the earth's surface are sedimentary rocks.
   c. Shale is the most common kind of sedimentary rock found on the earth's surface.
   d. The most common feature seen in sedimentary rocks is layers.
   e. Granite is used as a building material in many buildings.
   f. Fossils are rarely found in metamorphic rocks.

EXTENSION

1. Find out what areas outside the United States have been mapped by the USGS.
2. Add gravel, sand, and soil to a jar of water, and mix them together with a spoon. Pour this mixture into another jar. When all the particles have settled, use rubber tubing to siphon off the water. How does this demonstration explain how sediments settle in water to form layers? What must happen to the layers in order for them to become rock?
3. Hold a piece of obsidian rock up to a light. Try to look at the light through a thin edge of the obsidian. The edge should appear to be a lighter color than the rest of the rock. Find out what gives obsidian its dark color.

CHAPTER 17

WEATHERING AND EROSION

When you pick up a handful of soil, you may be picking up what was once part of a mountain. Mountains may seem to never change. But when exposed to water, ice, and wind, the hard, solid rock of mountains slowly crumbles. The rock structure shown in the photograph is evidence that the earth's surface is carved and changed. Over time, even the highest mountains are leveled.

- *What caused the pile of rocks at the base of this rock structure?*
- *Under what conditions does rock change the most?*
- *How do the forces of water, ice, and wind produce soil?*

17·1 Weathering

You have learned that rocks are not as permanent as they seem to be. New rocks are being formed while others are being broken apart and changed. When rocks are exposed to air, water, and temperature changes, they slowly crumble into smaller pieces. The breakup and change of rocks and minerals is called **weathering**.

There are two main types of weathering: physical weathering and chemical weathering. **Physical weathering** is a process that breaks large rocks into smaller rocks. Each smaller rock has the same mineral composition as the original rock. **Chemical weathering** is a process that changes the minerals in rocks into new substances. Physical and chemical weathering usually work together to break up and change rocks on or near the earth's surface.

PHYSICAL WEATHERING

Several forces in the environment can cause physical weathering. Large temperature changes from forest fires, volcanic activity, or hot springs can heat a rock. A surface of the rock may then

Figure 17·1

The rocks at the base of this mountain fell down from the cliff. What kind of weathering is this?

expand and break off. Sometimes the heat from forest fires is so intense that rocks completely split apart.

Changes in pressure can also cause rocks to break. Rocks under the earth's surface are under great pressure. When a rock that has been buried becomes exposed at the surface, the pressure decreases. The outer layers of the rock may expand and peel off. The dome-shaped structure of Liberty Cap is shown in Figure 17·2. The dome formed when layers of the rock peeled off.

Figure 17·2
Liberty Cap, found in Yosemite National Park, was formed by exfoliation *(left)*. Exfoliation occurs when slabs of rock peel off in sheets *(right)*.

Frost action, or the freezing and thawing action of water, plays a major role in physical weathering. The weathering process begins when water seeps into a crack in a rock. At night the water may freeze as the temperature drops. When the water freezes, it expands. The expansion enlarges the crack. During the day, the temperature may rise enough for the frozen water to melt. The water may then freeze and melt again. Over time, this freezing and melting process can occur many times. Each time the water freezes, the force of the expanding ice widens the crack. Eventually the rock will break apart.

Animals and plants also contribute to physical weathering. Earthworms and insects burrow in the soil and open up holes to the rock below. Water

OBJECTIVES

Compare the effects of physical weathering on rocks.

Graph the change in mass as rocks undergo physical weathering.

MATERIALS

samples of each of three types of rocks, such as granite, shale, and sandstone; balance; container with a tight-fitting lid; water; filter paper; funnel; hand lens; paper towel; graph paper; different colored pencils

PROCEDURE 👐

A. Examine the rock samples that you have.
   1. Which type of rocks do you think would weather the fastest? Why?
B. Place all the samples of one type of rock on a balance, and find their mass. Record the mass in a table like the one shown.
C. After you have recorded the mass of the rock samples, place all the rocks of one type in a container with a lid. Add water to cover the rocks, and put the lid on tightly.

D. Shake the rocks vigorously for 100 shakes.
E. Pour off the water through filter paper that has been placed in a funnel. Look at the filter paper under a hand lens.
   2. What do you see?
F. Remove the wet rock samples, dry them, and determine their mass. Record their mass in your data table.
G. Repeat this procedure with the other two rock types. Record the data in your table.

	MASS		
	GRANITE	SHALE	SANDSTONE
Before shaking			
100 shakes			

RESULTS AND CONCLUSIONS

1. Which rock decreased in mass the most?
2. Which rock disintegrated the fastest?
3. What kind of weathering did you imitate?
4. What specific force in nature would cause rocks to weather in this way?

Figure 17·3

The roots of trees can cause physical weathering.

then seeps through these holes, causing weathering. Plant and tree roots grow into rock cracks. How is the tree in Figure 17·3 causing weathering?

CHEMICAL WEATHERING

Chemical weathering can occur in a number of ways. Both water and oxygen can cause chemical weathering. Some minerals, such as feldspar, combine with water in a process called *hydration*. Eventually the feldspar is changed into clay. Other minerals combine with oxygen in a process called *oxidation*. For example, oxygen combines easily with the minerals pyrite and magnetite. Both minerals have iron in them. This reaction produces iron oxide, or rust. When water is present, the reaction occurs more rapidly.

Rain water can cause chemical weathering. Falling raindrops dissolve tiny amounts of carbon dioxide, CO_2, from the air. When CO_2 combines with water, it forms carbonic acid. This is the same weak acid that is found in carbonated drinks. The reaction of carbonic acid with other substances is called *carbonation*. Although carbonation is harmless to humans, rocks can be weathered by it. Minerals such as calcite, gypsum, and halite are dissolved by the carbonic acid in rain water. The effects of carbonic acid on rock are shown in Figure 17·4.

There are other acids in the environment that contribute to chemical weathering. The decay of plant and animal materials produces acids. Some organisms, such as lichens, produce acids. As lichens grow on rocks, the acids they produce dissolve some of the minerals in the rocks.

RATE OF WEATHERING

Weathering is usually a slow process, but the rate of weathering varies. The type of rock being weathered, for example, affects the rate of weathering. Rocks that contain quartz weather very slowly. Quartz is one of the hardest common minerals found on the earth. Why is granite, a rock that contains quartz, often used as a building material? Rocks such as limestone usually weather rapidly.

Figure 17·4
This limestone cave was formed by water dissolving limestone.

PUZZLER

The unusual rock formation shown is Natural Bridge in Kentucky. Natural Bridge is believed to have formed from the action of ground water. How could ground water have produced such a formation? What is probably the nature of the rock material in the bridge? Give reasons for your answers.

411

Figure 17·5

The writing on Cleopatra's Needle remained clear in a dry climate *(left)*. In a humid climate the writing has been worn away *(right)*.

Limestone contains the mineral calcite. Calcite is dissolved by carbonic acid in rain water.

Climate also affects the rate of weathering. Generally, rocks weather faster in warm, humid climates than in hot, dry climates. The history of Cleopatra's Needle demonstrates the effect of climate. The Egyptians built this monument about 3500 years ago. This giant structure stood in the desert, so the rate of weathering was slow. After many centuries, the writing on the stone structure was still clear. But in 1880, Cleopatra's Needle was moved to New York City, where moist air and air pollution increased the rate of weathering. In less than 100 years, the lettering on the windward side was nearly worn away.

REVIEW

1. What are two ways in which rocks weather?
2. What factors affect the rate of weathering?

CHALLENGE Where would you expect weathering to occur more rapidly, in Boston or in Phoenix? Explain your answer.

17·2 Soil

WHAT IS SOIL?

Physical weathering and chemical weathering produce rock fragments of different sizes. These pieces of rock gradually break into even smaller pieces. By breaking down rocks and minerals, weathering eventually produces soil. **Soil** is the loose material on the earth's surface in which plants with roots can grow. All life depends on soil.

Generally, soil includes four ingredients: weathered minerals, organic materials, water, and air. Quartz, feldspar, and calcite are common minerals in soil. Organic materials are materials formed from the decay of plants and animals. These materials make up humus, the dark-colored part of soil.

The diameter of the particles that make up soil determine soil *texture*. There are three types of soil texture: sand, clay, and loam. *Sand* is made up of particles that are larger than those in clay. Sand is produced through physical weathering. It is usually composed of gypsum, calcite, or quartz grains. *Clay* is produced by the chemical weathering of feldspar and other minerals and is made up of very small particles. Soils called *loam* contain a combination of sand, clay, and pieces of sedimentary rock called silt.

Figure 17·6

Sand *(left)*, clay *(middle)*, and loam *(right)* are three types of soil textures.

413

Figure 17·7
Weathered limestone around Meteor Crater, in Arizona, produces a soil rich in calcium carbonate.

horos (limit)

Figure 17·8
A soil horizon showing layering of the soil *(left)*. Topsoil, subsoil, partly weathered rock, and unweathered rock *(right)*.

When a rock first begins to weather, a thin layer of soil may cover the unweathered rock, or *bedrock*. Over time, with the right conditions, a thicker layer of soil may develop. In time, humus may be added to the soil. The rock from which soil is formed is known as the soil's *parent rock*. Limestone parent rock produces a type of soil different from that produced by sandstone parent rock.

As soil develops, it forms layers called **horizons**. These horizons make up the *soil profile*. Notice the distinct horizons in Figure 17·8. The top layer is known as the A-horizon. This top layer is also referred to as the **topsoil**. Fertile topsoil is soil that contains the humus and weathered minerals that plants need to grow. Animals such as ants, worms, moles, and shrews also live in the topsoil.

Below the topsoil is the B-horizon. This layer is also called the **subsoil**. Minerals from the topsoil are carried downward by water and are deposited in the subsoil. The subsoil may also contain some humus and living organisms.

Beneath the subsoil lies partly weathered rock. This rock is constantly producing new soil. Plant roots may extend into this rock. What layer lies below the partly weathered rock?

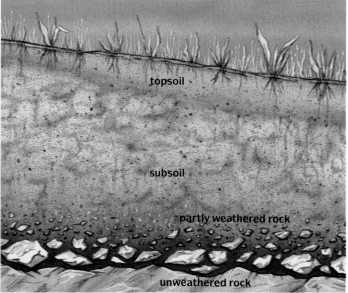

topsoil

subsoil

partly weathered rock

unweathered rock

TYPES OF SOIL

North America has a variety of soil types. Forest soil exists mostly in forests in the eastern United States and Canada. In northern areas, forest soil looks gray-brown. In southern areas, the color varies from yellow to red. Forest topsoil generally contains decayed leaves, animal matter, and particles of sand. Forest subsoil usually contains aluminum, iron, and particles of clay.

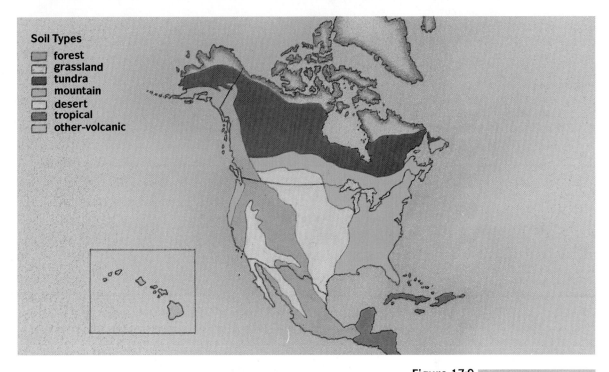

Soil Types
- forest
- grassland
- tundra
- mountain
- desert
- tropical
- other-volcanic

Figure 17·9
The various soil types of North America.

In central North America there is grassland soil, or prairie soil. Wheat, rye, and corn flourish in this soil. The grasslands and prairies form the heart of the United States agricultural area. The topsoil in this area is often thick and fertile. Grassland soil has a top layer that is dark brown. Underneath, however, the soil is often whitish because it contains calcium carbonate.

Along the mountain slopes of western North America lies mountain soil. This type of soil is produced mainly by physical weathering. The topsoil is thin, and it contains large bits of rock. Only a limited variety of plants can grow in mountain soil.

In China there are 1.1 million km² of desert. But only 61 percent of this amount represents true desert caused by lack of rain. The rest has been caused by people. The addition of desert land to China is just one example of the expansion of deserts all over the world.

In their quest for food and fuel, people have cut down forests for pastures and firewood and have allowed animals to overgraze on grasslands. With no vegetation on the land, winds can remove soil, leaving areas of deserts. In the United States, overgrazing by sheep has stripped vegetation from land in Arizona and New Mexico, transforming once-rich grassland to desert.

Some programs to reclaim deserts are underway. In China, people have covered thousands of acres in the Gobi Desert with trees. But despite attempts with new technologies, fighting the growth of deserts is an uphill battle.

North America's western deserts contain desert soil. Desert soil is made mostly of sand and minerals. The soil is extremely dry because deserts receive little rain.

Tundra soil is another type of soil found in North America. Tundra soil lies in the polar regions of Alaska and Canada. The temperature in these regions remains below freezing much of the time. The surface of the land is often covered with ice.

Tropical soil is another soil type. It is not found in Canada or the United States. Tropical soil is mainly formed in warm, humid regions of Africa, Asia, and South America. Tropical soil is red in color because it contains iron oxide. However, this soil has few other minerals and little humus. As a result, tropical soil is poor for farming.

REVIEW

1. How is soil formed?

2. Describe the layers of soil in a soil profile.

3. How do the different types of soil compare?

CHALLENGE How much is the composition of soil formed in a dry area likely to differ from the bedrock? Explain your answer.

17·3 Erosion

You have learned that a number of forces cause rocks to break into smaller pieces. For example, large rocks can be split apart by the action of freezing water. Once rocks are broken into smaller pieces, the pieces can be carried away in a process called erosion.

Erosion is the wearing away and moving of rock materials by natural forces. The main cause of erosion on the earth's suface is running water. Other causes of erosion are wind and moving ice. Along coasts, ocean waves also cause erosion.

Erosion occurs mainly in two ways. It occurs when rock materials are picked up and carried by water, wind, or ice. Erosion also occurs by abrasion. *Abrasion* is a process in which rock is worn away by pieces of rock that are carried by water, wind, or ice. The rock pieces act like grinding tools. Sand

After completing this section, you will be able to

- **name** three agents of erosion.
- **describe** two ways in which erosion can occur.
- **explain** how deposition occurs.

The key terms in this section are
deposition
erosion

erodere (to eat away)

Figure 17·10

The ability of sand to abrade can be used to clean the outside of a building *(left)*. Wind-blown sand created this natural land bridge *(right)*.

How Do Rock Materials Settle?

OBJECTIVE

Predict what will happen to rock particles of different sizes when they are deposited by water.

MATERIALS

sand, gravel, pebbles, large glass jar with a tight-fitting lid, water

PROCEDURE

A. Mix together equal amounts of sand, gravel, and pebbles. Place some of the mixture in a jar. Add water until the jar is about three-fourths full of water.

B. Put a lid on the jar. Carefully shake the jar until its contents are thoroughly mixed.

C. Allow the contents to settle.

RESULTS AND CONCLUSIONS

1. What happened to the contents of the jar when you set the jar down? Explain your observations.

2. Describe the contents of the jar at the end of the activity.

3. How do you think materials settle in a river or stream?

that is picked up by wind can abrade, or wear away, rocks in its path. How can sand be used to clean the outside of stone or brick buildings?

Rock pieces that are carried by agents of erosion — water, wind, or ice — eventually settle. If the agent is running water or wind, settling occurs when the water or wind slows down or stops. With glaciers, rock materials settle as the ice melts. The settling of materials is called **deposition**.

deposer (to put down)

Each agent of erosion produces different effects on the rock materials it moves. Running water rounds and smooths the rocks it carries. Wind-blown materials are rounded and have pitted surfaces. Rocks moved by ice tend to have irregular shapes. These different effects are important to a scientist. They are clues to the processes that carried materials to where they are found.

REVIEW

1. What are three agents of erosion?

2. What are two ways in which erosion can occur?

3. How does deposition occur?

CHALLENGE Explain why many more craters exist on the moon's surface than on the earth's surface.

17·4 Running Water

Running water is water that flows over the earth's surface. It usually begins as runoff. *Runoff* is rain water that moves over land. Runoff often forms as a thin sheet, or layer, of water. The sheet can be broken into narrow streams of water by rocks. The water carves out narrow channels called rills. With each new rainfall, more water collects in the rills. In time, running water deepens and widens the rills to form larger channels called gullies.

As gullies are enlarged more water can collect and flow there. Eventually, running water will be present all of the time. The water becomes a stream. A *stream* is a natural body of flowing water.

Small streams may come together to form larger streams. All the streams in an area join to form one large body of flowing water called a **river**. A stream that flows into a larger stream or a river is called a **tributary** (TRIHB yuh tehr ee). What are the tributaries of the Mississippi River, shown in Figure 17·11 *(right)?* The land area that supplies water for a river is called a **watershed**.

Figure 17·11

Running water from rainfall formed these gullies *(left)*. The watershed of the Mississippi River *(right)*.

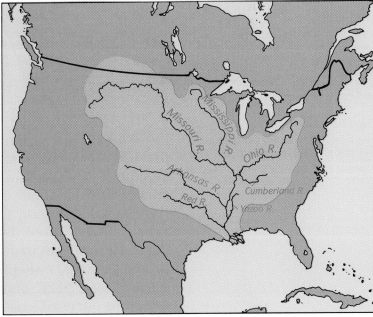

THE DEVELOPMENT OF A RIVER

A river can pass through various stages of development. Depending on the properties the river develops, it can be classified as young, mature, or old. A young river flows rapidly along a steep, rugged course. As the river flows, it erodes its channel. A young river mainly cuts its channel lower, not wider. The river threads its way through steep-sided, narrow valleys, like those shown in Figure 17·12*A*. This type of valley is typical of young rivers.

Eventually the river is unable to easily cut its channel lower. It passes into the mature stage. At this stage a river mainly erodes its banks. Its path begins to wind back and forth. Gradually the river valley expands, producing a broad valley called a flood plain. A flood plain is the area that a river fills when it overflows its banks during a flood. As it flows onto the flood plain, the river loses speed. It deposits its sediments, making the plain smooth and flat. The sediments enrich the soil, making it more productive for agriculture.

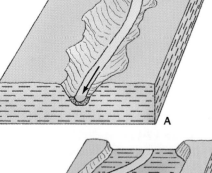

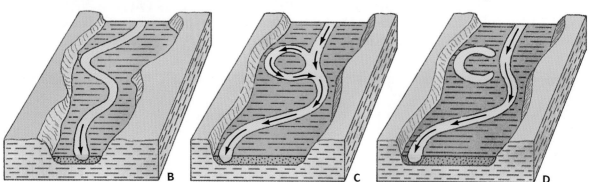

Figure 17·12

The development of a river: young (A), mature (B), and old (C, D).

An example of a mature river is shown in Figure 17·12*B*. Mature rivers have curves along their channels. A river flows faster on the outside of a curve. More channel erosion occurs there. As the river slows down on the inside of the curve, sediments are deposited. The combination of erosion on the outside of the curve and deposition on the inside produces large, sweeping curves called meanders.

Figure 17·12*C* shows a river in old age. The sweeping curve of a meander may form a loop at one

Figure 17·13

Notice the rapid flow of water in this river *(left)*. Notice the wide flood plain and oxbow lakes *(right)*. How do the stages of development of the two rivers compare?

end. Figure 17·12*D* shows how a river can break away from this loop and form a straight channel. Then the river deposits material across the meander until it is cut off. If the cutoff meander fills with water, an *oxbow lake* is formed. Old rivers usually have numerous meanders and oxbow lakes, as well as wide flood plains.

At its end, or mouth, a river may enter a larger body of water, such as an ocean, a gulf, or a lake. If the river enters quiet waters, its speed slows suddenly. The river then deposits its sediments, producing a large triangular formation called a *delta*.

THE WORK OF RUNNING WATER

Erosion by running water begins with raindrops falling on soil. Each drop loosens soil particles. The raindrops from a single rainstorm hitting an area of land the size of a football field can loosen almost 100 metric tons of soil. Then rushing water from runoff can carve rills and gullies into the loosened soil.

Running water in streams and rivers causes most of the erosion of the earth's surface. The water can wear away rocks in three ways. One way is by dissolving the rocks. For example, limestone can be dissolved by acids that are present in running water. A second way uses the force of the running water. This force can widen cracks and re-

Figure 17·14
The force of rushing water can break rocks apart.

move pieces of rocks from the channel. The third way running water can wear away rocks is by abrasion. Sand and gravel carried by the water scrape against the rocks of the channel, abrading it like sandpaper abrades wood. Larger materials, such as pebbles, roll, slide, and bounce along the stream bottom and chip away the rock.

Many factors affect how quickly a river can erode its channel. One factor is the speed at which the water is flowing. A fast-flowing river can carry more materials than can a slow-moving river. The greater the amount of materials a river carries, the faster it can abrade the channel. A second factor is how much water is flowing. A river with a large volume of water can carry more material and erode the channel faster than can a river with a small volume.

A third factor that affects channel erosion is the type of material a river carries. A river carrying a hard material, such as quartz, will erode the channel quickly. The fourth factor is the type of rock that makes up the channel. A river channel made of soft rock, such as limestone, will erode quickly.

REVIEW

1. How does a river form?
2. What are three stages in the development of a river?
3. How does a river cause erosion?

CHALLENGE Rivers that enter the ocean along the Atlantic coast do not form deltas. Explain why.

17·5 The Work of Wind and Glaciers

WIND EROSION

Travelers through deserts in the southwestern United States might find their cars stripped of paint and their cars' windshields pitted after a sandstorm. When wind picks up sand, it can sandblast objects in its path.

Like water, wind can force rock pieces to move and to abrade a surface. In dry areas where there is little plant life, wind can pick up lightweight particles, such as clay, silt, and sand. Heavier objects, such as pebbles and small rocks, are not picked up. What eventually remains is a layer of pebbles and small rocks called a *desert pavement*. As you can see in Figure 17·15, a desert pavement forms a cover that can protect the surface from the effects of further wind erosion.

Figure 17·15
A desert pavement forms when wind blows away the lighter particles and leaves the larger, heavier stones *(left)*. A desert pavement *(right)*.

WIND DEPOSITS

Materials carried by wind are deposited when the wind slows down or stops. The lightest materials, such as sand, silt, and clay, can be carried great distances. However, the speed of the wind can be slowed down by an object like a rock, fence, bush, or even a mound of sand. Objects that slow down the speed of wind are called *windbreaks*.

Figure 17·16

Sand dunes begin to form when sand collects around windbreaks, such as clumps of grass.

When wind-blown sand reaches a windbreak, the sand is deposited in a mound in front of the windbreak. As the mound of sand grows, it blocks more wind, causing more sand to accumulate. Eventually a hill of sand called a **dune** forms. Notice that one side of the dune has a gentle slope. This side of the dune faces the wind. Sand is blown up the gentle slope and over the top of the dune. The sand then drops down the steep slope.

glacies (ice)

GLACIERS

Imagine that your town received so much snow one winter that the snow had not completely melted by the end of the next summer. This occurs on mountains where there is enough winter snowfall and low enough summer temperatures for snow to remain year-round. As more and more snow collects, air is squeezed out of the snow by the weight of the new snow. The snow becomes compacted, and it changes into ice. When the mass of snow and ice becomes thick enough, its weight causes them to move. A large mass of moving snow and ice is called a **glacier**.

As a glacier moves around curves or over uneven surfaces, the ice near the surface of the glacier breaks. Large cracks called crevasses (kruh VAS-ihz) form. Crevasses also form when some parts of a glacier move faster than other parts.

Figure 17·17

As a valley glacier moves over a hill, the ice bends and cracks, forming crevasses.

Formation of crevasses

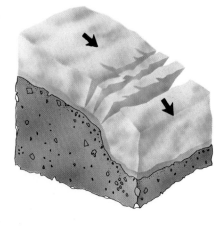

There are two types of glaciers: valley glaciers and continental glaciers. Both are masses of moving snow and ice; they differ in where they form. *Valley glaciers* are glaciers that form in mountain valleys. Valley glaciers often look like dirty rivers of ice, as shown in Figure 17·18. A *continental glacier* is a huge ice sheet that forms over a large area of the earth's surface. The weight of the ice causes the ice to spread outward. Today, continental glaciers are found only in Greenland and Antarctica.

GLACIAL EROSION

Some of the most spectacular erosional features on the earth are found in mountains where valley glaciers form. Valley glaciers begin forming when snow collects in small hollows on a mountain. As the glacier moves down the mountain, the glacier picks up large blocks of rocks from the steep slope. The rocks are carried along, carving away more rocks as they move. Rocks are scooped away from the hollow, forming a bowl-shaped basin called a cirque (serk). A cirque lake is formed if water fills the basin after the glacier has left the cirque.

Figure 17·18
A valley glacier erodes the mountainside as the glacier flows down.

Figure 17·19
Before glacial erosion, a mountain has smooth, rounded surfaces *(left)*. Snow and ice collect in hollows on the mountain *(middle)*. The mountain is rough and sharp after glacial erosion *(right)*.

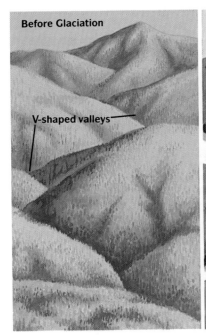

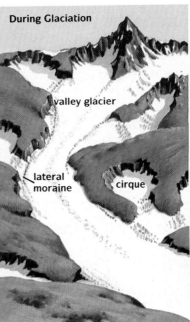

As a glacier moves down a mountain, the glacier may enter a V-shaped river valley that is narrower than the glacier. As the glacier squeezes through, it erodes both the floor and the sides of the valley, changing the shape of the valley from a V shape to a broad U shape.

The landscape left behind by a valley glacier is rugged and filled with sharp peaks. A continental glacier, however, levels the land by eroding everything except the tallest mountains. The landscape it forms is smooth.

GLACIAL DEPOSITS

Glacial deposits form when the ice in a glacier melts and rock materials are released. Deposits from glaciers are called *drift*. There are two types of drift: till and outwash. *Till* is rock materials deposited directly by a glacier. Till is made of a mixture of all kinds and sizes of rock particles. *Outwash* is rock materials deposited by water produced from the melting of a glacier. Unlike till, the materials in outwash form distinct layers, like those produced when sediment settles to the bottom of a lake or stream. When till or outwash piles up, it forms various features on the land.

Figure 17·20
The features formed by glacial deposits.

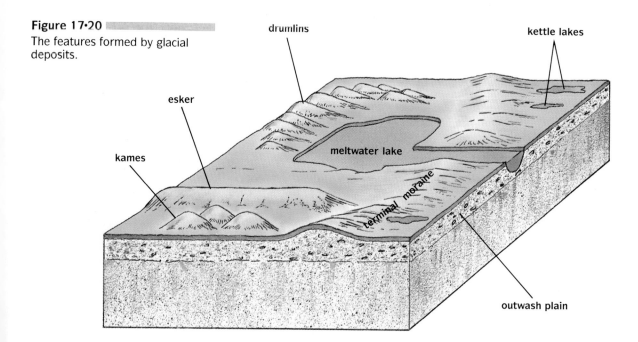

kames · esker · drumlins · kettle lakes · meltwater lake · terminal moraine · outwash plain

Probably the most common feature made of till is a moraine. A **moraine** is a layer or ridge of till. When a ridge of till is deposited at the front of a glacier, it is called a *terminal moraine*. A terminal moraine marks the farthest point of a glacier's movement. Other features made of till are shown in Figure 17·20. They include ridges called *eskers*, round-shaped hills called *kames*, and oval-shaped hills called *drumlins*.

REVIEW

1. How does wind cause erosion?
2. What features are caused by wind deposits?
3. How does a glacier form?
4. How do glaciers cause erosion?

CHALLENGE Explain why piles of rocks are placed around the base of telephone poles in deserts.

CHAPTER SUMMARY

The main ideas in this chapter are listed below. Read these statements before you answer the Chapter Review questions.

- Weathering is caused by the action of water, wind, and ice. The two types of weathering are physical weathering and chemical weathering. (17·1)
- The rate of weathering is affected by the type of rock being weathered, the climate, and the amount of air pollution present. (17·1)
- Soil forms from weathered rocks and generally includes organic materials, weathered minerals, air, and water. (17·2)
- Soil may be described as sand, clay, or loam, based on its texture. (17·2)
- Different types of soil are found in different parts of North America. (17·2)

- The earth's land surface is worn away in a process called erosion. (17·3)
- The main causes of erosion are wind, water, and moving ice. (17·3)
- Depending on the properties a river develops, it can be classified as young, mature, or old. (17·4)
- Running water causes most of the erosion that occurs on the earth's surface. (17·4)
- Wind erosion usually occurs close to the ground and causes surfaces to become polished and pitted. (17·5)
- There are two kinds of glaciers: valley glaciers, which form in mountain valleys, and continental glaciers, which form over large areas of land. (17·5)

The key terms in this chapter are listed below. Use each term in a sentence that shows the meaning of the term.

chemical weathering	glacier	river	tributary
deposition	horizons	soil	watershed
dune	moraine	subsoil	weathering
erosion	physical weathering	topsoil	

Chapter Review

VOCABULARY

Use the key terms from the previous page to complete the following sentences correctly.

1. The breakup of rocks into smaller pieces is a type of weathering called _____ .
2. Distinct layers within a soil profile are called _____ .
3. A process that forms new substances from the minerals in rocks is _____ .
4. A stream that flows into a river is called a/an _____ .
5. An area of land that supplies water for a river is the river's _____ .
6. A large mass of moving snow and ice is a/an _____ .
7. A large body of flowing water is a/an _____ .
8. The wearing away and removal of rock materials is called _____ .
9. A large mound of sand deposited by the wind is a/an _____ .
10. A ridge of till left by a melting glacier is called a/an _____ .

CONCEPTS

Identify each statement as True or False. If a statement is false, replace the underlined term or phrase with a term or phrase that makes the statement true.

1. <u>Physical weathering and chemical weathering</u> cause solid rocks to be broken into smaller pieces.
2. When parent rock weathers and humus is added, <u>bedrock</u> forms.
3. Eroded materials will be deposited when the water, wind, or ice that carries them <u>speeds up</u>.
4. An <u>old river</u> tends to wander back and forth across wide flood plains and to have oxbow lakes along its path.
5. <u>Valley glaciers</u> form high in mountains where the winter's snow does not completely melt during the summer.

Choose the term or phrase that best answers the question or completes the statement.

6. The rate at which rocks weather depends on
   a. climate.
   b. pollution.
   c. the kind of rocks.
   d. all of the above.
7. The top two horizons of a soil profile are usually
   a. topsoil and subsoil.
   b. subsoil and parent rock.
   c. parent rock and weathered rock.
   d. topsoil and weathered rock.
8. Which of the following affect the rate of water erosion?
   a. volume of the water
   b. speed of the water
   c. the kind of rock pieces carried
   d. all of the above

9. The many streams and small rivers that feed a large river are that river's
   a. watersheds.
   b. tributaries.
   c. meanders.
   d. gullies.
10. Which of these is a process in which eroded particles pile up?
   a. deposition
   b. weathering
   c. dune
   d. runoff

Answer the following in complete sentences.

11. Compare the processes of physical weathering and chemical weathering.
12. What factors affect the kind of soil that forms in an area?
13. Describe how deposits of running water, wind, and ice differ.
14. Describe the path a drop of rain water might follow from the time it falls on the ground to the time it flows into a lake or ocean.
15. How is erosion by valley glaciers different from erosion by continental glaciers?

APPLICATION/ CRITICAL THINKING

1. How would a soil scientist determine whether the soil in a region had been produced mainly by physical weathering or by both physical weathering and chemical weathering?
2. Some scientific studies indicate that the average temperature and the average annual precipitation will increase in northeastern North America over the next 50 years. Predict the effects that such changes would have on the rate of weathering.
3. Ancient cities that are buried under soil and rocks do not age until they are excavated. Explain why this is true.
4. Why must wind have a much greater velocity than water to move the same size particles?
5. The Colorado River has eroded some places to a depth of 1800 m in the Grand Canyon over the past 10 million years. What is the average rate of erosion per year? Will this rate continue forever? Explain your answer.

EXTENSION

1. Investigate the effects of pollution on an important monument. One such monument is the Acropolis in Athens, Greece. What efforts are being made to deal with the effects of pollution?
2. In 1981, large holes suddenly appeared in various parts of Florida. Discover the reasons why these holes appeared. What role did weathering play in producing the holes?
3. Investigate the mud slides that often occur in California. Why do these mud slides happen? How are they similar to landslides? How are they different?

CHAPTER 18

THE CHANGING EARTH

*T*he peak shown in the photograph is one of the highest points in the Himalayas, a mountain chain on the Asian continent. What forces could have created this peak? The peak stands almost 8000 m above sea level. At this altitude, breathing becomes difficult because of the thinness of the air.

The knowledge of what forms mountains is relatively new. It may seem that mountains are ageless. But mountains rise and fall and eventually are worn away.

- *How do mountains form?*
- *How are mountains related to earthquakes and volcanoes?*
- *Do mountains exist under the ocean?*

18·1 Moving Continents

THEORY OF CONTINENTAL DRIFT

Figure 18·1 shows how the continents of South America and Africa would match if they were put together. Today these continents are separated by 3000 miles of ocean. Could they have once been part of the same land mass?

In 1912 a scientist named Alfred Wegener proposed a theory to explain the apparent fit of South America and Africa. His theory is called the theory of continental drift. The **theory of continental drift** states that the continents of the earth were once joined but had broken apart and moved to their present positions.

In addition to the jigsaw fit between South America and Africa, other evidence supported Wegener's theory. He found that the same types of rocks appeared on the Atlantic coasts of both continents. He also found that a mountain range in South America linked up with a similar mountain range in Africa.

Figure 18·1
The jigsaw-puzzle fit of the coastlines of South America and Africa.

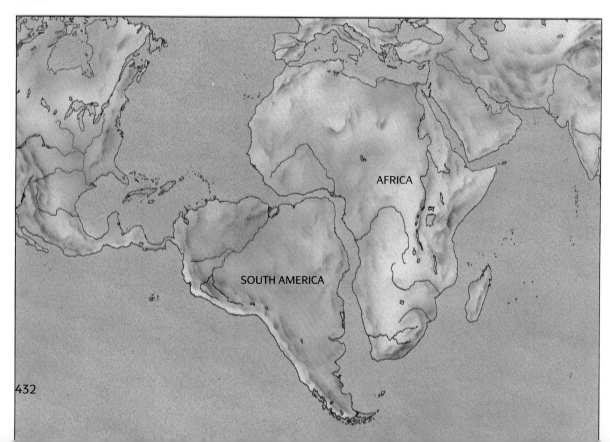

As further evidence for his theory, Wegener referred to fossils, such as the one in Figure 18·2. Fossils are the remains of once-living things. Fossils of similar plants and animals are found on different continents. Since it is unlikely that all of these plants and animals crossed the oceans, Wegener concluded that the continents must have been joined at one time.

Wegener proposed that all the continents were once joined into a single land mass. He called this large land mass Pangaea (pan JEE uh). *Pangaea* means "all lands." Wegener said that Pangaea had existed 300 million years ago. He proposed that Pangaea began to separate into a northern continent and a southern continent about 200 million years ago. Wegener called the northern land mass Laurasia (law RAY zha). He called the southern land mass Gondwana (gahnd WAH nuh). According to Figure 18·3, what continents did Laurasia break into?

Figure 18·2
Fossils of the lystrosaurus have been found in South America and Africa. How does this show that the two continents were once connected?

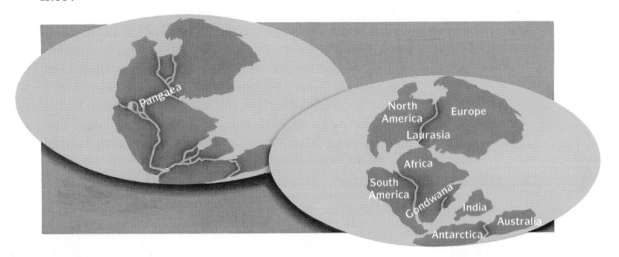

THEORY OF SEA-FLOOR SPREADING

The theory of continental drift was not accepted by most scientists when it was proposed. One reason was that the theory did not explain how the continents could move. Then during the 1960s, scientists made some surprising and important discoveries. For example, they expected to find a thick layer of sediment on the ocean floor from billions of years of settling. Instead, they found a thin layer.

Figure 18·3
The color lines show where land masses were once connected. Pangaea *(left),* Laurasia and Gondwana *(right).*

Figure 18·4
Pillow lava is a kind of rock that forms from lava that cools underwater.

While mapping the ocean floor, one discovery was made near the Mid-Atlantic Ridge, a mountain range that runs through the center of the floor of the Atlantic Ocean. There scientists found pillow lava. Pillow lava, shown in Figure 18·4, is a kind of rock that forms when lava cools underwater.

Scientists also discovered that the Mid-Atlantic Ridge is connected to other ocean ridges. These ridges form a continuous chain of underwater mountains around the earth. This chain of mountains is called the *Mid-Ocean Ridge*. The Mid-Ocean Ridge is the largest surface feature of the earth. It encircles the earth like a seam encircles a baseball.

In addition, the scientists found a deep, narrow valley running through the center of the Mid-Ocean Ridge. This type of valley is called a *rift valley* or rift. Scientists found that the rift valley is warmer than any other part of the ocean floor. They explained that the Mid-Ocean Ridge is an opening in the earth's crust through which molten rock flows out. Here, new ocean floor forms.

The idea that new ocean floor forms at the Mid-Ocean Ridge led to the theory of sea-floor spreading. The **theory of sea-floor spreading** says that the ocean floor spreads out from the Mid-Ocean Ridge. Molten rock rises out of the Mid-Ocean Ridge and fills in the space left by the spreading floor. The molten rock forms new ocean floor on each side of the Mid-Ocean Ridge.

Figure 18·5
The Mid-Ocean Ridge is a chain of underwater mountains around the earth.

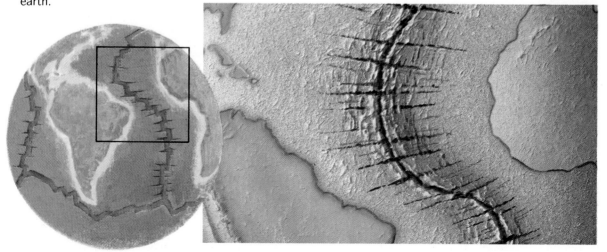

ACTIVITY   A Model of Sea-Floor Spreading

OBJECTIVE
Demonstrate the process of sea-floor spreading

MATERIALS
metric ruler, 2 sheets of notebook paper, scissors

PROCEDURE

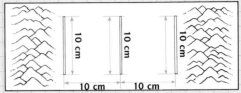

Fig. 1

A. Using a metric ruler, measure and draw three vertical 10-cm lines on a sheet of paper, as shown in Figure 1.

B. Draw mountain peaks on the outer side of each end line.

C. Use scissors to make a slit down each of the lines you have drawn.

  1. If the sheet of paper is the ocean floor, what does the middle slit represent? Label this slit.

D. Use a second sheet of paper to make two strips 9.5 cm wide and about 27 cm long. Put the two strips face-to-face, and insert them through the middle slit, as shown in Figure 2.

  2. What term do these strips represent? Write this term on each strip.

E. Pull both strips out of the slit about 6 cm. Lay the "ocean floor" on your lap so that the strips underneath are held gently in place by your knees. Above, insert each strip into the outer slit closest to it, as in the figure. Continue to pull the strips through the middle slit, and observe.

Fig. 2

  3. Which part of the strips represents young crust? Represents old crust? Write the word *old* on the part that shows the old crust on each strip.

RESULTS AND CONCLUSIONS

1. How is actual sea-floor spreading similar to your model?

2. Where would you find the oldest rocks on the ocean floor? The youngest rocks?

One of the most important contributions of the theory of sea-floor spreading is that it can explain how continents move. The theory explains that as the ocean floor moves, the continents are carried along like logs in a moving ice floe.

Possibly the most convincing evidence for sea-floor spreading is information gained from magnetism in the rocks on the ocean floor. Like tiny compass needles, iron mineral grains in magma point in the direction of the earth's magnetic north pole. When magma hardens into rock, the grains remain lined up in that direction.

It is known that the earth's magnetic poles have reversed positions many times in the past. Therefore, if new ocean floor has been constantly forming, it should contain sections of rock magnetized in opposite directions. As shown in Figure 18·6, bands of rock magnetized in opposite directions are found parallel to the Mid-Ocean Ridge.

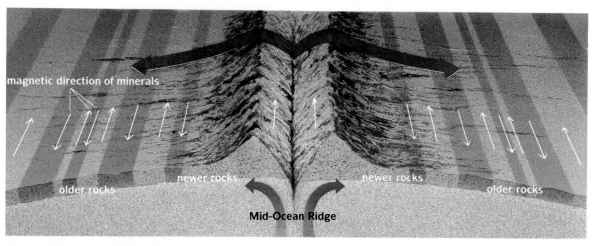

Figure 18·6

The ocean floor contains sections of rock magnetized in opposite directions.

In 1986, scientists were able to obtain direct evidence for the theory of sea-floor spreading. Using the research ship *Glomar Challenger*, scientists collected rock samples from both sides of the Mid-Ocean Ridge. Studies of these rocks showed that those found nearest to the ridge were the youngest. The rocks found farthest from the ridge were the oldest. How are these findings evidence for the formation of new ocean floor and the theory of sea-floor spreading?

REVIEW

1. What is the theory of continental drift?
2. How does sea-floor spreading influence the movement of the continents?
3. Why do scientists believe that the ocean floor is spreading?

CHALLENGE Look at Figure 18·1. Why doesn't the eastern coast of South America perfectly match the western coast of Africa?

18·2 Plate Tectonics

PLATE TECTONICS

The discovery of sea-floor spreading showed that some sections of the earth's crust move. But do other sections of the earth's crust move? What force could move them?

One answer to these questions came from the study of earthquakes. When the locations of many earthquakes were plotted on a world map, they formed a pattern that divided the earth's surface into different sections. This pattern led scientists to believe that the earth's crust is broken into sections. Based on this idea, and the ideas of continental drift and sea-floor spreading, scientists proposed the theory of plate tectonics (tehk TAHN ihks).

The **theory of plate tectonics** states that the earth's crust is broken into moving plates. The **plates** are rigid blocks of the earth's outer crust that are about 50–150 km thick. Scientists have identified about 7 major plates and 18 minor plates.

After completing this section, you will be able to

- **describe** the theory of plate tectonics.
- **compare** three kinds of plate boundaries.
- **describe** features caused when plates collide.

The key terms in this section are
plate boundaries
plates
subduction
subduction zone
theory of plate tectonics
trench

Figure 18·7
The earth's surface is broken into many plates.

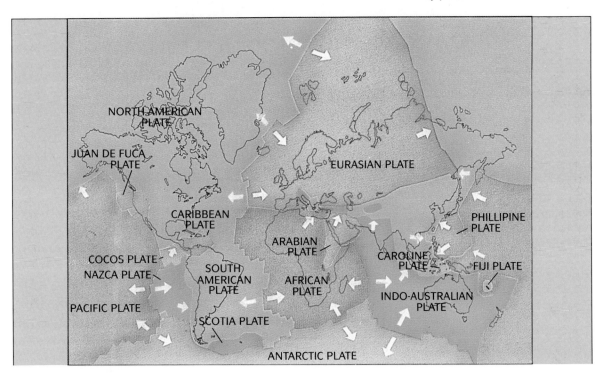

PLATE BOUNDARIES

The plates that make up the earth's crust fit together like pieces of a jigsaw puzzle. No one plate can move without affecting another plate. The areas where the plates meet are called **plate boundaries**. There are three types of plate boundaries. One type of plate boundary occurs where plates move apart, leaving a space between them. The Mid-Ocean Ridge is an example of this type of boundary. The space between the plates is filled with molten rock from the asthenosphere as the plates separate.

When two plates separate, there must be a place where other plates come together. A second type of plate boundary forms when two plates collide. As shown in Figure 18·8 *(left)*, two continental plates that collide crumple, forming mountain ranges. The Himalayas *(right)* were formed when two continental plates, the Indo-Australian Plate and the Eurasian Plate, collided.

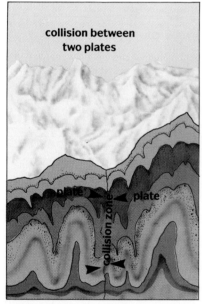

collision between
two plates

plate   plate

collision zone

Figure 18·8
The Himalayas are mountains that formed when two continental plates collided.

sub (under)

When two ocean plates collide, the edge of one plate bends downward and slides under the other. The process by which one plate is pushed below another is called **subduction**. The area where a plate is pushed below another plate is called a **subduction zone**. The lower plate bends and sinks into the asthenosphere, where it is destroyed by intense heat and pressure.

438

When an ocean plate sinks into the earth, it forms a trench. A **trench** is a deep valley on the sea floor formed by subduction. The Mariana Trench, where the Pacific Plate is sinking into the earth, is the deepest part of the ocean floor. It is 11 km below the surface of the ocean. When an ocean plate bends down into a trench, the plate melts. The hot, melted material may then rise to form volcanoes on the ocean floor.

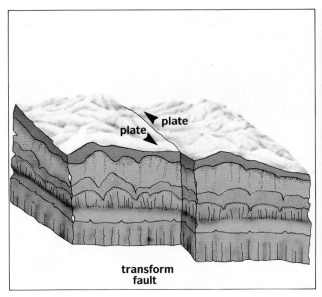

Figure 18·9

A transform fault is produced when two plates slide past each other *(left)*. The San Andreas Fault, found in California, is a transform fault *(right)*.

The third type of boundary occurs where plates slide past each other. The San Andreas Fault, shown in Figure 18·9 *(right)*, is this type of boundary. As the plates move past each other, sections of the plates become locked. Stress builds up until the plates suddenly slip past each other. The result is an earthquake.

REVIEW

1. What is the theory of plate tectonics?
2. What are the three types of plate boundaries?
3. What can happen to the earth's surface when plates collide?

CHALLENGE The North American, South American, Eurasian, and African plates move at a rate of about 2.0 cm a year. The Pacific, Nazca, and Cocos plates move at a rate of about 12.0 cm a year. Using Figure 18·7, on p. 437, explain what might cause this difference in speed.

439

18·3 Volcanoes

After completing this section, you will be able to

- **describe** the location of volcanoes.
- **describe** the materials given off by volcanoes.
- **describe** three types of volcanic cones.

The key terms in this section are
lava
magma
volcano

A **volcano** is a structure made of materials from within the earth that build up around an opening in the earth's surface. A volcano forms when **magma**, or molten rock in the earth, is forced up to the earth's surface. Magma that reaches the earth's surface is called **lava**.

There are about 600 known active volcanoes in the world. Volcanoes form in active parts of the earth's crust. Most volcanoes form as a result of activity between plates. Figure 18·10 shows the areas where volcanoes form.

One area where volcanoes form is a subduction zone. As one plate sinks under the other, the sinking plate melts as it slowly descends into the mantle. The resulting magma rises through the upper plate above and forms a chain of volcanoes, such as the Aleutian Islands in the Pacific Ocean.

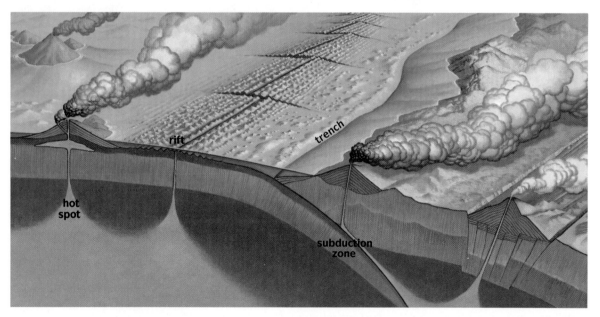

Figure 18·10

Volcanoes form above hot spots, in subduction zones, and along rifts.

Another area where volcanoes form is a rift. Volcanoes along a rift form from magma that rises out of the earth as the sea floor spreads. The volcanoes that formed Iceland were formed by magma from a rift in the Mid-Atlantic Ridge.

ACTIVITY   Convection and Hot Spots

OBJECTIVES
Demonstrate the concept of convection.
Formulate a conclusion about hot spots that supports the plate tectonic theory.

MATERIALS
2-hole rubber stopper to fit vial, 2 pieces of plastic capillary tubing to fit rubber stopper, small vial, 500-mL beaker, red food coloring, hot tap water, cold tap water

PROCEDURE

A. Place 350 mL of cold tap water in a 500-mL beaker.
B. Set up a vial, rubber stopper, and plastic capillary tubing as shown.
C. Add hot tap water to the vial, then add a few drops of red food coloring.
D. Place the vial in the beaker of cold tap water. Make sure the water covers the top of the capillary tubing.
E. Record your observations and explain what is happening.

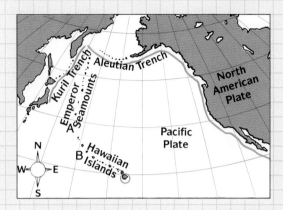

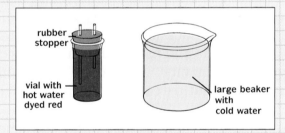

F. Sometimes islands and seamounts are formed over hot spots where plumes of lava rise. The hot spot lies beneath the plate and does not move. Examine the map and answer the following questions.

1. If the islands are forming over the hot spot, which one is older, *A* or *B*? Why?
2. Which island is younger, *A* or *B*? Why?
3. In what direction does the ocean floor seem to be moving at the present time? What evidence supports your answer?
4. What evidence do you have that there has been a change in direction in the movement of the ocean plate?
5. Where do you predict the next island will form?

RESULTS AND CONCLUSIONS
1. What kind of heat transfer did you demonstrate with the hot water and the cold water?
2. How do convection currents support the theory of plate tectonics?
3. How does the occurrence of hot spots support the theory of plate tectonics?

Some volcanoes, such as those in the Hawaiian Islands, are found in the middle of plates. These volcanoes are formed by superhot magma rising in columns from places in the mantle called *hot spots*. The magma can burn holes in a plate and rise to the surface to form volcanoes. As the plate moves over a hot spot, a chain of volcanoes forms.

VOLCANIC ERUPTION

When volcanoes erupt, they can give off lava, gases, and pieces of rock. There are two main types of lava. One type is called pahoehoe (pah HOH ee-hoh ee) lava. This kind of lava is hot, thin, and fast-flowing. When it hardens, it forms a wrinkled surface. The other kind of lava is called aa (AH ah) lava. This lava is cooler and thicker than pahoehoe lava. When aa lava cools, it forms a rough, blocklike surface.

Gases are given off by volcanoes. One such gas is water vapor. The water vapor comes from water that is dissolved in magma beneath the earth's surface. In addition to water vapor, such gases as carbon monoxide, sulfur dioxide, and hydrogen sulfide also escape.

Volcanoes also release rock materials. The smallest pieces of rock are called volcanic dust. Slightly larger rock fragments, about the size of sand, are called ash. In time, ash becomes fertile soil.

VOLCANIC FEATURES

Volcanic activity has formed many features of the earth. Much of the rock below the soil formed from lava. Many islands and mountain ranges were formed by volcanic activity. A common result of volcanic activity is a feature called a volcanic cone.

Figure 18·11

Pahoehoe lava has a ropelike appearance *(left)*. Aa lava has a rough appearance *(right)*.

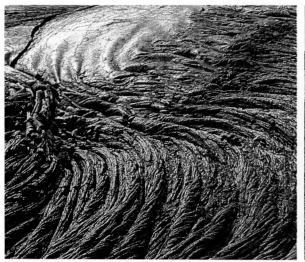

Volcanic cones can be classified by their shapes. A *shield cone* has a gentle slope and a broad base. This type of cone is formed from layers of thin lava flowing out around the volcano's opening. A *cinder cone* is a pile of ash and cinders that collects around a volcanic opening. This type of cone has steep sides and a narrow base. A *composite cone* is formed from alternating layers of lava and rocks. The layers are evidence of different types of volcanic activity. For example, there may have been periods of quiet eruptions in which lava was produced. Then at other times there may have been violent eruptions that produced rock fragments.

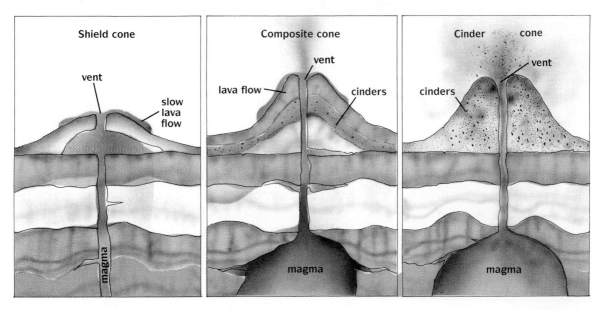

Figure 18·12
The three types of volcanic cones.

Located at the top of most volcanic cones is a bowl-shaped depression called a *crater*. A crater forms when lava hardens around the vent. The *vent* is the channel that connects the source of magma to the opening in a volcano. When magma moves up and out of the vent, the magma fills the crater before flowing out as lava. If the lava hardens, it forms a plug in the vent.

Some volcanoes have very large craters called *calderas* (kal DIHR uhz). A caldera may form when an explosion blows off the top of a volcano. A caldera may also form when magma drains out of the

Figure 18·13
Mount Fuji is a composite cone *(left)*. Crater Lake, found in Oregon, is a caldera *(right)*.

Figure 18·14
Shiprock, found in New Mexico, is a volcanic neck.

crater of a volcano. When the magma drains out, there is no longer any support for the volcano's top. Thus the top collapses, and a caldera is formed. Crater Lake, which is found in Oregon and shown in Figure 18·13, is an example of a caldera. What rock structure can be seen in the middle of Crater Lake?

Like all surface features of the earth, volcanoes are changed by erosion. Some parts of volcanoes are more easily eroded than others. Sometimes the hardened magma inside a volcano is made of rock that is not easily eroded. The rock may remain standing long after most of the cone of a volcano has eroded. The remaining structure is called a *volcanic neck*. An example of a volcanic neck is Shiprock, New Mexico, shown in Figure 18·14. What happened to the volcano in which Shiprock formed?

REVIEW

1. Where are volcanoes likely to form?
2. What types of materials can volcanoes give off?
3. What are a shield cone and a cinder cone? How is a composite cone related to the other two cone types?

CHALLENGE On November 14, 1985, a volcano erupted in the Andes, in South America. But lava did not flow down the volcano. Instead a layer of mud flowed down, burying four towns and killing more than 20,000 people. What caused mud instead of lava to flow down the volcano?

444

18·4 Earthquakes

More than a million earthquakes take place each year. Most are so weak that they barely rattle a teacup. Others, such as the 1906 earthquake in San Francisco, cause great destruction. Whether they are small tremors or large shifts in the earth's surface, almost all earthquakes happen when rock in the crust suddenly moves. Thus an **earthquake** is the shaking or trembling of the earth caused by the sudden movement of the earth's crust.

As you have learned, the earth's surface is broken into moving plates. As the plates move, they can slide past each other along their boundaries. A place where rocks have moved on one or both sides of a crack in the earth is called a **fault**.

After completing this section, you will be able to

- **describe** the cause of earthquakes.
- **explain** how earthquakes are detected.
- **relate** the effects of an earthquake to its magnitude.

The key terms in this section are
earthquake
fault
Richter scale

Figure 18·15
Earthquakes occur along plate boundaries.

Most earthquakes occur along plate boundaries. When plates slide past each other, the rocks between them are put under great strain. The strain occurs because rocks do not slide past each other easily. The surfaces of the rocks are rough and jagged. This roughness causes the rocks along the fault to lock together. As plates move, the rocks are squeezed, pulled, and bent. The bending causes strain to build up in the rocks. Eventually the strain becomes too great. Then, like a rubber band that snaps when stretched too far, the rocks slip along the weakest point on the fault. The energy released by this movement is felt as an earthquake.

This photograph shows the Transamerica Pyramid, an earthquake-resistant building in San Francisco. In what ways does the structure of the building make it less likely to suffer damage than the surrounding buildings?

Earthquakes can also occur away from plate boundaries. For example, no known plate boundaries exist in Missouri. Yet four major earthquakes took place in Missouri in 1811 and 1812. A large fault has been detected there. It may be an area of weak rock in the North American Plate. Earthquakes can also be caused by volcanic activity. Rising magma can seep into cracks in rock and trigger an earthquake.

In Denver more than a thousand earthquakes occurred between 1962 and 1966. During that time, large amounts of liquid wastes were pumped into wells. The earthquakes resulted when the liquids seeped into faults, making it easier for rock to slip.

EARTHQUAKE WAVES

Just as the snap on one end of a rope causes a ripple to move along the rope, the sudden movement of rock can send seismic waves through the earth. *Seismic* (SIZ mihk) *waves* are the waves produced in an earthquake. The waves move out from the moving rock in all directions. The point where the rocks actually move is called the *focus*. The place on the earth's surface directly above the focus is called the *epicenter* (EHP uh sehn tuhr). The focus and epicenter are shown in Figure 18·16.

When seismic waves reach the earth's surface, they cause the ground to vibrate. These vibrations can be recorded by an instrument called a *seismograph* (SIZ muh graf). Figure 18·17 shows the parts of a seismograph. Why doesn't the weight move?

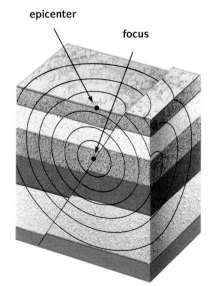

epicenter

focus

Figure 18·16
The epicenter is located on the surface above the focus.

Seismic waves are recorded as wavy lines on a seismogram, as shown in Figure 18·17 *(right)*. Seismic waves are used to locate the epicenter of an earthquake. The epicenter is where the earthquake usually is most severe.

Seismic waves are also used by scientists to study the earth's interior. Seismic waves that travel through the earth contain valuable information about the inside of the earth. For example, these waves were used to determine that the outer core of the earth is liquid.

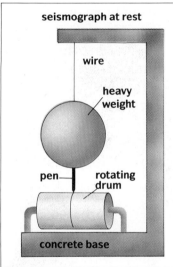
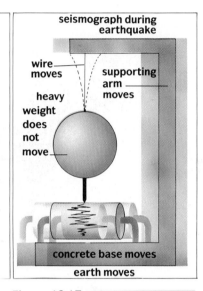

EFFECTS OF EARTHQUAKES

A method of measuring the energy released by an earthquake was developed by Charles Richter (RIHK tuhr). The **Richter scale** is a scale of magnitudes used to measure the relative sizes of earthquakes. Earthquakes with magnitudes of less than 2.5 are not felt by humans. The largest earthquakes recorded have had magnitudes near 8.9 on the Richter scale.

One of the most violent earthquakes to occur in North America in recent times took place in Mexico in 1985. That earthquake had a magnitude of about 8.1 on the Richter scale. Over 5000 people were killed, and many buildings collapsed. Dozens of aftershocks followed the earthquake. *Aftershocks* are smaller, less-intense earthquakes that follow a

Figure 18·17

An earthquake map at the National Earthquake Information Service *(left)*. Earthquake waves are recorded by a seismograph *(right)*.

major earthquake. They occur when the movement of rocks along a fault continues. Aftershocks can occur for more than a year after a major earthquake. In Mexico an aftershock with a magnitude of 7.5 came 18 hours after the earthquake.

Most earthquakes last only a few seconds, but the Mexican earthquake lasted almost a minute. The San Francisco earthquake of 1906 lasted for 40 seconds. Its magnitude was 8.3 on the Richter scale.

Earthquakes can cause great destruction. Their tremors can cause buildings to collapse and can cause water, gas, and sewer pipes to break. Fires often burn out of control when water pipes are broken. Many lives can be lost.

Often, more people are killed by an earthquake-related disaster than by the earthquake itself. One example of a disaster associated with earthquakes is a tsunami (tsoo NAH mee). A *tsunami* is a large ocean wave produced by an earthquake on the ocean floor. The wave can move at 500 km/h and be 30 m high when it reaches shore.

Figure 18·18
Damage caused by an earthquake.

Earthquakes are not uncommon on the earth. In fact, some places on the earth experience as many as 60 earthquakes in one day. Earthquake risks do exist. Therefore, people must plan and be prepared in the event that an earthquake occurs where they live. Here are some safety guidelines.

DO YOU KNOW?

It is said that some animals behave strangely before an earthquake. But scientists cannot rely on barking dogs or panicky fish as a warning system. Scientists are trying to make accurate predictions about where and when earthquakes will occur.

Earth scientists know that entire crustal plates move a certain amount each year. However, no one knows how much a particular area along the edge of a plate might move or slip. Some areas haven't slipped for many years. It is believed that pressure is building up in these areas and that these are the places where the greatest earthquakes will occur. These areas include some places along the San Andreas Fault in southern California.

Scientists particularly want to know how the crust behaves just before an earthquake occurs. Instruments such as seismographs and lasers can measure vibrations and strain in the crust. Computers can analyze the data gathered by these instruments. This can give earth scientists a better picture of changes that occur in the earth's crust and that lead up to an earthquake.

1. Indoors, stand against a wall or in a doorway.
2. Outdoors, stay in the open and away from electric wires.
3. In a moving vehicle, stop and stay inside.
4. At school, stay away from windows, and get under a desk.

After an earthquake,

5. Stay away from waterfront areas.
6. Expect aftershocks.
7. Do not drink tap water or flush toilets until the water and sewer lines have been checked.
8. Stay away from damaged buildings.

Planning for safety in an earthquake is also a consideration in building construction. More engineers are studying the ground they build on and are learning how to design buildings that will sway and not crumble when earthquakes occur.

REVIEW

1. What causes earthquakes?
2. How can earthquakes be detected?
3. What might be the magnitude of a small earthquake? Of a large earthquake?

CHALLENGE Another scale used to measure the strength of earthquakes is the Mercalli scale. It is based on the amount of damage done by an earthquake. Why would this scale not always be accurate in measuring the strength of an earthquake?

18·5 Mountains

Besides explaining the movement of the earth's plates, the theory of plate tectonics helps to explain the formation of mountains. A mountain is any piece of the earth's crust that rises more than 600 m above the surrounding surface. The tallest mountain in the United States is Mount McKinley, in Alaska. It is more than 6100 m tall. Mount Everest, in the Himalayas, is the tallest mountain on any continent and is over 8800 m tall. Did you know that some of the tallest mountains on the earth are under the surface of the ocean? These mountains rise thousands of meters above the ocean floor.

Based on their characteristics, mountains are classified into four main types. You have already learned about one type of mountain. These are volcanic mountains. **Volcanic mountains** form from lava and other volcanic materials. The Cascade Range of Washington and Oregon are volcanic mountains. The Cascade Range includes the volcanic cones Mount Ranier and Mount Hood.

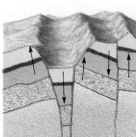

Figure 18·19
The four major types of mountains.

FOLDED MOUNTAINS

The largest and most common mountain ranges on the earth are folded mountains. **Folded mountains** form when sedimentary rock layers fold or bend. This folding of the surface may occur when an ocean plate and a continental plate collide. As the ocean plate slides under the continental plate, sedimentary rock trapped between the plates and at the continent's edge forms a series of parallel folds. The

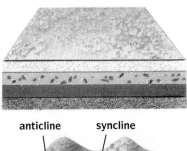

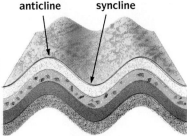

anticline   syncline

Figure 18·20
The Rocky Mountains are folded mountains *(left)*. Upward folds are called anticlines, and downward folds are called synclines *(right)*.

Appalachian Mountains and the Rocky Mountains are examples of folded mountains formed in this way. Recall that the collision of two continents formed the Himalayas.

Sedimentary rock layers are more likely to fold when they are buried below the surface of the earth. There the pressure on them makes them more pliable. Where the sedimentary layers fold upward, magma moves up and fills the space below the layers. Notice the parallel folds shown in Figure 18·20 *(right)*. The raised or arched rock layers at the ridges are called anticlines. An *anticline* is an upward fold in rock layers. The downward folds of rock layers that form the valleys are called *synclines*.

FAULT-BLOCK MOUNTAINS

Another kind of mountain forms at faults in the earth's surface. Again, pressure from moving plates causes the surface to buckle. Now, however, large blocks of crust separated by faults tip to the side. One edge of a block rises as the other edge sinks, forming a mountain. Such mountains, like the Sierra Nevada shown in Figure 18·21, are called fault-block mountains. **Fault-block mountains** are formed by the movement of large blocks of crust along faults. How are these mountains different from folded mountains?

Figure 18·21
The Sierra Nevada are fault-block mountains.

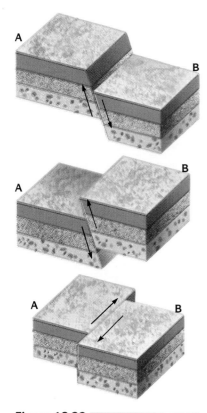

Figure 18·22

The three types of faults.

Figure 18·23

The Adirondacks, found in the eastern United States, are dome mountains.

Geologists classify a fault according to its angle and the direction in which the blocks of crust move. Notice in Figure 18·23 that if block *B* settles, the top layers of rock will move away from each other. This movement results in what is called a *normal fault*. However, if block *B* is lifted, its top layers will hang over the top layers of block *A*. This kind of movement results in a *reverse fault*. Finally, the blocks may move sideways along the fault. This movement results in a *lateral fault*. Rock is most likely to form a fault when the rock is on the surface and is brittle.

Dome mountains are the last type of mountain. **Dome mountains** form when magma within the earth pushes the surface upward. This movement creates a dome-shaped structure. Dome mountains may form when magma pushes upward through cracks that do not reach the surface. The rising magma lifts the surface layers. When the surface layers are weathered, a circular mountain range is left. The Adirondack Mountains, in the eastern United States, are a good example of dome mountains.

In time the forces of weathering and erosion will wear mountains down. But the processes of mountain building will continue. The Coast Ranges of North America and the Andes of South America, for example, are still being raised today.

REVIEW

1. Where are many of the earth's mountain ranges located?
2. What are the four main types of mountains?
3. How do mountains form?

CHALLENGE Many faults can be seen in the Rocky Mountains. Why, then, are these mountains called folded mountains?

CHAPTER SUMMARY

The main ideas in this chapter are listed below. Read these statements before you answer the Chapter Review questions.

- The theory of continental drift is supported by similar rocks, fossils, and mountain ranges and changes in climate on the continents. (18·1)
- The discovery of sea-floor spreading enabled scientists to explain how continents could move. (18·1)
- The theory of plate tectonics states that the earth's crust is broken into moving plates. (18·2)
- The theory of plate tectonics provides scientists with a way of explaining many features of the earth's crust. (18·2)
- Many of the features of the earth's crust are caused by plates coming into contact with one another. (18·2)
- Volcanoes form when magma rises from subduction zones, rifts, and hot spots. (18·3)

- There are three types of volcanic cones: shield cones, cinder cones, and composite cones. (18·3)
- Earthquakes are caused by the sudden movement of rock in the earth. They mainly occur along plate boundaries. (18·4)
- The Richter scale is a measure of the amount of energy given off by an earthquake. (18·4)
- Earthquakes can cause tsunamis. (18·4)
- Mountains generally form on or near plate boundaries. Mountains are produced by movements in the earth's crust. (18·5)
- The four main types of mountains are volcanic mountains, folded mountains, fault-block mountains, and dome mountains. (18·5)

The key terms in this chapter are listed below. Use each term in a sentence that shows the meaning of the term.

dome mountains	magma	theory of continental drift
earthquake	plate boundaries	theory of plate tectonics
fault	plates	theory of sea-floor spreading
fault-block mountains	Richter scale	trench
folded mountains	subduction	volcanic mountains
lava	subduction zone	volcano

Chapter Review

VOCABULARY

Write the letter of the term that best matches the definition. Not all the terms will be used.

1. Process by which one plate is pushed below another
2. Theory that states that the earth's crust is broken into moving plates
3. Theory that says the ocean floor spreads out from the Mid-Ocean Ridge
4. A deep valley formed by a subduction zone
5. A crack along which rock moves
6. Molten rock in the earth
7. Structure made up of materials from within the earth
8. The shaking or trembling of the earth
9. Mountains formed by the bending of sedimentary rock layers
10. Mountains formed when magma pushes the earth's surface upward

a. dome mountains
b. earthquake
c. fault
d. fault-block mountains
e. folded mountains
f. lava
g. magma
h. subduction
i. theory of plate tectonics
j. theory of sea-floor spreading
k. trench
l. volcano

CONCEPTS

Choose the term or phrase that best answers the question or completes the statement.

1. The theory of continental drift was not accepted by scientists because
   a. they had not seen a continent move.
   b. they did not understand how continents could move.
   c. similar fossils did not appear on different continents.
   d. rock layers on the continents' edges did not match.
2. What does the theory of plate tectonics help scientists to explain?
   a. earthquakes
   b. volcanoes
   c. mountains
   d. all of the above
3. Which of the following are materials given off by volcanoes?
   a. soil
   b. cinders and cones
   c. blocks and shale
   d. none of the above

4. Earthquakes can be detected from long distances by their
    a. noise.
    b. seismic waves.
    c. smoke.
    d. magnitude.
5. Which of the following types of mountains is likely to have anticlines and synclines?
    a. fault-block
    b. dome
    c. folded
    d. volcanic

Write the correct term for each feature in the diagram.

6.   **9.**

7.   **10.**

8.

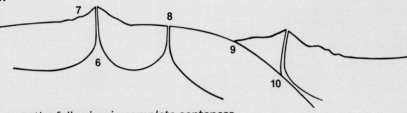

Answer the following in complete sentences.

11. Compare the theory of sea-floor spreading and the theory of continental drift.
12. Describe the three types of plate boundaries.
13. Explain how each kind of volcanic cone forms.
14. How does the release of strain in rock cause earthquakes?
15. Compare the formation of folded mountains with that of fault-block mountains.

---

1. There is evidence of large sand dunes in the sandstone formations near London, England. What may have caused the sand dunes?
2. The Alps are mountains in Europe. Propose a way in which they may have been formed. Justify your answer.
3. Why are the focuses of earthquakes much deeper in subduction zones along the edges of continents than in rifts in the Mid-Ocean Ridge?
4. How might large reservoirs of water cause earthquakes?

---

1. Find out more information about the *Glomar Challenger*. What projects are its scientists working on now? What instruments do they use?
2. Use resource materials to learn more about Iceland. What type of plate boundary is associated with its formation? What features on Iceland give clues about its history?

CHAPTER 19

WATER IN THE ATMOSPHERE

If you live near a mountain peak, you may have observed the type of clouds shown in the photograph. Because they are shaped like lenses, these clouds are called lenticular clouds. They have been known to be mistaken for flying saucers.

Clouds can produce rain, snow, and hail. But most clouds do not produce any precipitation. To understand why, you must first understand the processes that operate in the atmosphere.

- *Where do clouds come from?*
- *Under what conditions do clouds produce precipitation?*
- *What processes form rain, snow, and hail?*

19·1 The Water Cycle

ex- (out)
vapor (steam)

WATER

Water is one of few materials that exists on the earth in all three states of matter: solid, liquid, and gas. Water in liquid form is found in oceans, lakes, and streams, and as droplets in clouds. Water in solid form is called ice. It is found at the polar ice-caps and in clouds as snowflakes. Water in gas form is called water vapor. Water vapor is present in air. The **water cycle** is the continuous movement of water between the earth and the air. Figure 19·1 illustrates the paths that water can follow and how water changes during the water cycle.

One change that occurs in the water cycle is evaporation (ih vap uh RAY shuhn). **Evaporation** is the process by which liquid water changes to water vapor. You know that puddles dry up and that wet clothes hung on a clothesline become dry. In both cases, water evaporates.

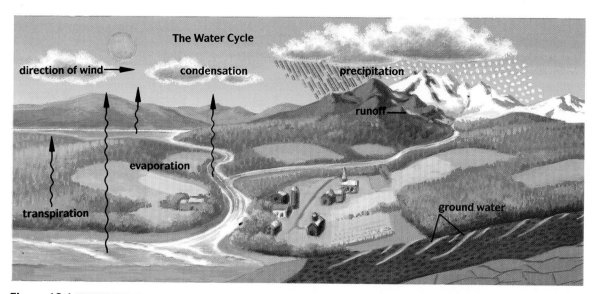

Figure 19·1
The parts of the water cycle.

Water is also added to the atmosphere by transpiration (tran spuh RAY shuhn). *Transpiration* is the process by which plants release water vapor through their leaves. Water that is collected by plant roots is lost into the air through transpiration.

Once in the atmosphere, water vapor may become liquid water through a process called condensation (kahn den SAY shuhn). **Condensation** occurs when water vapor changes into liquid water. The moisture that forms on a bathroom mirror after a hot shower and the water that collects on a cold drinking glass both form by condensation. Clouds form when water vapor condenses in the atmosphere.

com- (together)
densus (thick)

Figure 19·2
When warm, moist air comes into contact with a cold surface, water vapor condenses.

Sometimes, water vapor changes directly from a gas to a solid. This change occurs when vapor is forced out of the air at temperatures below freezing. It is in this way that snowflakes and the frost on a window form. The process in which a vapor changes directly to a solid or a solid changes directly to a vapor is called *sublimation* (suhb luh-MAY shuhn).

A cycle is a series of regularly occurring events. As you can see in Figure 19·1, page 458, the water cycle has no beginning and no end. The driving force behind the water cycle is energy from the sun. What process in the water cycle is caused directly by the sun's energy? Most water vapor that enters the air has evaporated from oceans, which make up 70 percent of the earth's surface. The rest of the water vapor has evaporated from streams, rivers, lakes, plants, animals, and industry. Each minute, millions of metric tons of water evaporates into the atmosphere.

PRECIPITATION

When air in the atmosphere cools, water vapor may condense into drops of liquid water or may sublimate to form ice crystals. The drops of liquid water or the ice crystals grow in size until they fall back to the earth. Water that returns to the earth as rain, snow, sleet, or hail is called **precipitation** (prih sihp uh TAY shuhn).

Figure 19·3

Water returns to the earth's surface through condensation *(left)* or as precipitation *(middle* and *right)*.

Precipitation falls on open water—lakes, streams, oceans—and on land. The precipitation which falls on land may travel to open water as surface runoff. Or the water may soak into the ground and move underground to open water. Water moving underground is called *ground water*. From the open water, water evaporates and the water cycle repeats.

The water cycle is essential to living things. Without the continuous return of water to the land, land plants and animals could not exist. There would be no water to drink and to grow food.

REVIEW

1. What changes occur during the water cycle?
2. How does water move from one place to another during the water cycle?
3. What is the importance of the water cycle?

CHALLENGE How would producing rain by seeding clouds affect the water cycle?

19·2 Humidity

RELATIVE HUMIDITY

Where does water go when it evaporates? When water evaporates, water molecules move into spaces between air molecules. **Humidity** (hyoo-MIHD uh tee) is water vapor in air. Humidity can vary from nearly 0 percent over a desert to almost 4 percent over a tropical rain forest.

The air's ability to hold water vapor, or the air's capacity, depends on the temperature of the air. As temperature increases, the air's capacity increases. Figure 19·4 shows the relationship between temperature and the air's capacity. What is the air's capacity at 20°C? At what temperature will the air's capacity be equal to 0? What is the air's capacity at 5°C? An increase in temperature causes molecules in the air to spread, which creates more space for water molecules.

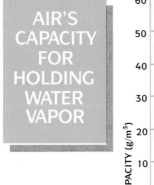

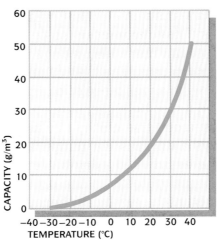

Figure 19·4
The capacity of air increases as the temperature increases.

Meteorologists (mee tee uh RAHL uh jihsts), people who study the weather, often compare the amount of water vapor in the air with the air's capacity. The amount of water vapor in the air compared with the maximum water vapor that the air can hold at a given temperature is called the **relative humidity**.

461

Figure 19·5

If the amount of water vapor in the air remains constant as the temperature increases, the relative humidity will decrease.

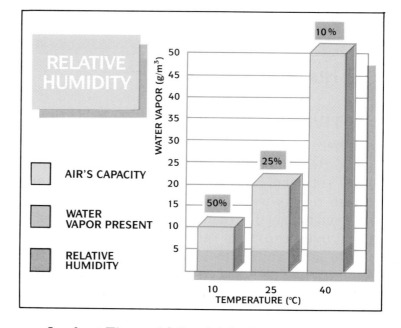

Figure 19·6

A psychrometer contains a wet bulb and a dry bulb.

Look at Figure 19·5, which shows how relative humidity changes as the temperature changes. How does the relative humidity at 10°C compare with the relative humidity at 40°C? You can see that as the temperature increases and the water vapor present remains the same, the relative humidity decreases.

One instrument that measures relative humidity is a **psychrometer** (si KRAHM uh tuhr). As you can see in Figure 19·6, a psychrometer contains two thermometers. The bulb of one thermometer is covered with a wet piece of cloth. This thermometer is called a wet-bulb thermometer. When water evaporates from the cloth, the wet-bulb thermometer shows a decrease in temperature. The other thermometer is called a dry-bulb thermometer. Since no evaporation takes place on the bulb of this thermometer, the dry-bulb thermometer's temperature does not change.

CALCULATING RELATIVE HUMIDITY

When the air is dry, water evaporates quickly from the wet-bulb thermometer, and this thermometer shows a large decrease in temperature. Thus the difference between the temperature readings of the two thermometers is large. When the air is holding a large amount of water vapor, little water evaporates from the wet-bulb thermometer. The difference between the temperature readings is small. Therefore the difference between the temperature readings of these thermometers is an indication of the amount of water vapor in the air.

Table 19·1 can be used to find the relative humidity from the temperature readings on a psychrometer. The numbers across the top of the table indicate differences between the wet-bulb and dry-bulb readings in degrees Celsius. The numbers down the left side of the table list dry-bulb thermometer readings in degrees Celsius. The following procedure is used to determine relative humidity.

1. Read the temperatures on a psychrometer.
2. Find the difference between the temperatures.
3. On the left side of the table, find the row marked by the dry-bulb temperature.
4. Find the column for the difference between the temperatures. Read the relative humidity where the row and column meet.

Table 19·1 *Relative Humidity (%)*

DRY-BULB TEMPERATURE	DIFFERENCE BETWEEN WET-BULB AND DRY-BULB TEMPERATURES (°C)																	
(°C)	1	2	3	4	5	6	7	8	9	10	11	12	13	14	15	16	17	18
11	89	78	67	56	46	36	27	18	9									
12	89	78	68	58	48	39	29	21	12									
13	89	79	69	59	50	41	32	23	15	7								
14	90	79	70	60	51	42	34	26	18	10								
15	90	80	71	61	53	44	36	27	20	13	6							
16	90	81	71	63	54	46	38	30	23	15	8							
17	90	81	72	64	55	47	40	32	25	18	11							
18	91	82	73	65	57	49	41	34	27	20	14	7						
19	91	82	74	65	58	50	43	36	29	22	16	10						
20	91	83	74	66	59	51	44	37	31	24	18	12	6					
21	91	83	75	67	60	53	46	39	32	26	20	14	9					
22	92	83	76	68	61	54	47	40	34	28	22	17	11	6				
23	92	84	76	69	62	55	48	42	36	30	24	19	13	8				
24	92	84	77	69	62	56	49	43	37	31	26	20	15	10	5			
25	92	84	77	70	63	57	50	44	39	33	28	22	17	12	8			
26	92	85	78	71	64	58	51	46	40	34	29	24	19	14	10	5		
27	92	85	78	71	65	58	52	47	41	36	31	26	21	16	12	7		
28	93	85	78	72	65	59	53	48	42	37	32	27	22	18	13	9	5	
29	93	86	79	72	66	60	54	49	43	38	33	28	24	19	15	11	7	
30	93	86	79	73	67	61	55	50	44	39	35	30	25	21	17	13	9	5

ACTIVITY   How Is Relative Humidity Measured?

OBJECTIVE
Measure the relative humidity in several locations.

MATERIALS
piece of cardboard 15 cm × 30 cm, 2 Celsius thermometers, clear tape, 4-cm piece of shoelace, cup of water, textbook, large index card

PROCEDURE
A. Place a piece of cardboard 15 cm × 30 cm in front of you. Place two thermometers side by side on the cardboard. Make sure that the bulb of each thermometer extends over the edge of the cardboard. Tape the thermometers to the cardboard.

B. Slide a piece of shoelace 4 cm long over the bulb of one thermometer. Dip the shoelace into the cup of water. This thermometer is the wet-bulb thermometer. The other thermometer is the dry-bulb thermometer.

C. Place the cardboard with the thermometers on a textbook so that the bulbs of the thermometers hang over the edge of the book.

D. While carefully watching the thermometers, fan the two bulbs with an index card. When the temperature reading on the wet-bulb thermometer stays the same for one minute, read that temperature. Then read the dry-bulb thermometer temperature.

   1. What is the wet-bulb reading?

   2. What is the dry-bulb reading?

E. Calculate the difference between the readings.

   3. What is the difference?

F. Using Table 19·1, determine the relative humidity of your classroom.

   4. What is the relative humidity of your classroom?

G. With your teacher's permission, rewet the shoelace, and repeat steps **C** through **E** outside your school.

   5. What is the relative humidity outside your school?

   6. In what rooms of your school would you expect to find high relative humidity? In what rooms would you expect to find low relative humidity?

H. With your teacher's permission, check your guesses by measuring the relative humidity in those places.

RESULTS AND CONCLUSIONS
1. Is the relative humidity today higher indoors or outdoors? Explain your answer.

2. Did you find different relative humidities for different parts of the school? Why?

What is the relative humidity when the dry–bulb temperature is 22°C and the difference between the dry–bulb and wet–bulb readings is 2°C?

REVIEW
1. What happens to the amount of water air can hold as the temperature increases? As it decreases?
2. What is relative humidity?
3. What is the relative humidity if the temperature is 17°C and the difference between the two readings is 5°C?

CHALLENGE What would the relative humidity be if both the wet bulb and the dry bulb showed the same temperature?

19·3 Condensation

For condensation to occur, air must become saturated, or filled, with water vapor. Air can become saturated as water evaporates from a body of water, such as a lake or an ocean. More often, however, air becomes saturated as its temperature decreases. The boxes in Figure 19·7 represent air's capacity at different temperatures. The water in the boxes represents how much water vapor is present in the air. The first box shows the air's capacity at 20°C. Notice that the amount of water vapor in the box is 25 percent. If the temperature decreases to 10°C, the air's capacity decreases. However, the percent of water vapor has increased to 50 percent. If the temperature decreases to 0°C, the amount of water vapor increases to 100 percent.

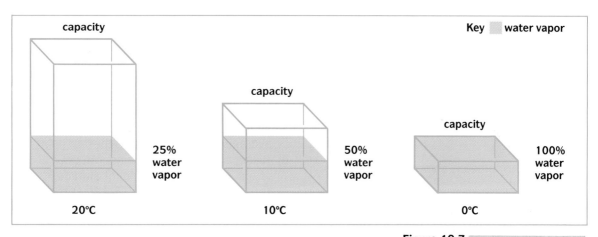

Figure 19·7

As the temperature decreases, the capacity of air decreases. What effect does this have on the relative humidity?

What is the relative humidity? When the air's capacity equals the amount of water vapor in the air, the air becomes saturated. The temperature to which air must be cooled to become saturated is called the **dew point.** In which box in Figure 19·7 has the air temperature reached the dew point?

When relative humidity is high, the dew point is close to the air's temperature. The temperature does not have to be lowered much for the air to become saturated. The air is already nearly saturated. When the relative humidity is low, the air is

Dew is water that forms from the condensation of water vapor.

dry. The dew point is much lower than air temperature. A large decrease in temperature is needed to reduce the air's capacity enough for it to become saturated.

When the air becomes saturated, water vapor does not always condense. For water vapor to condense from air the water vapor must have a surface to condense on. **Dew** is water vapor that condenses on cold surfaces, such as grass, plants, and automobiles, on cool mornings. Notice in Figure 19·8 that dew has formed on the pine needles.

Ordinary air may seem to be free of smoke and dust. However, if you observe a ray of sunlight in a darkened room, you would see that the air contains floating dust particles. These particles can serve as surfaces on which water vapor can condense. In air, water vapor condenses on dust, smoke, salt, and other small particles that are floating there. Small particles in air that water condenses on are called

ACTIVITY   How Is the Dew Point Measured?

OBJECTIVES
Determine the dew point.
Estimate the altitude at which clouds form.

MATERIALS
Celsius thermometer, shiny can, water, ice, stirring rod

PROCEDURE
A. Using a thermometer, measure the temperature of the air. Record this temperature.
B. Half fill a shiny can with water. If condensation collects on the can, replace the water with warmer water. Dry the outside of the can. Repeat this procedure until no more condensation forms.
C. Place a piece of ice in the water. While carefully watching the outside of the can for moisture, use a stirring rod to slowly stir the ice and water. As soon as moisture appears on the can, remove the ice and measure the temperature of the

water. Record this temperature.
D. Repeat steps **B** and **C** two more times, and average your three readings. The average of these readings is the dew point.
E. Rising air decreases in temperature about 1 °C for each 100 m of altitude through the troposphere. Subtract the dew point reading from the air temperature reading. Multiply the difference by 100. This figure tells you at what altitude (in meters) the temperature reaches the dew point. If today's air is pushed up to that height, clouds will form.

RESULTS AND CONCLUSIONS
1. What was the air temperature?
2. What was the dew point?
3. At what altitude would clouds form?
4. The dew point will decrease a small amount as altitude increases, because of the changing pressure. In what way does this affect your prediction?

Packed snow on a slope contains many layers. If any one of the layers is too weak to hold the snow above it, an avalanche can occur. A sudden cold snap in early winter can create a weak layer of snow. The ground at this time may still be warm. Heat rising through the snow can change the structure of the crystals in a layer, so that they do not stick to each other or to the snow above. The layer of snow becomes weak.

Snowflakes that are unable to stick to weak layers beneath them pull harder on snowflakes that are uphill. Eventually the flakes near the surface pull apart and create a crack in the snow. The snow below the crack has nothing to cling to, and it dangles dangerously. An avalanche can be set off by a skier, pushing on the snow.

Attempts to predict avalanches have come a long way from the old method of poking holes in the snow. Snow guides now take instruments up a slope. With these instruments, the guides can measure snow characteristics such as density and the tension between flakes. Other information, including wind strength, wind direction, snow temperature, angle of the slope, and crystal type, is also gathered. The aim is to develop computer programs that will use all this information to tell forecasters what conditions may lead to avalanches.

condensation nuclei. Condensation nuclei are always present in the air. Fog and clouds form when water condenses onto condensation nuclei.

If the dew point is below freezing, water vapor does not condense to form drops of water. Instead the water sublimates, or changes directly from water vapor to ice. This process forms the delicate crystal structure that you recognize in frost or snowflakes. **Frost** is ice that forms on objects when water vapor sublimates.

REVIEW

1. How can air become saturated with water vapor?
2. How is the dew point affected by relative humidity?
3. How do dew and frost form?

CHALLENGE The clouds that form behind jet airplanes are called *contrails,* short for *condensation trails*. What is the source of the water vapor and condensation nuclei that form these clouds? Why does the water vapor condense?

19·4 Clouds

After completing this section, you will be able to

- **explain** how clouds form.
- **describe** three basic types of clouds.
- **describe** the kind of weather associated with each type of cloud.

The key terms in this section are
cirrus clouds
cloud
cumulus clouds
stratus clouds

HOW CLOUDS FORM

At any one time, about 50 percent of the earth is covered by clouds. A **cloud** is a collection of water droplets or ice particles floating in the atmosphere. Most clouds form in the troposphere, the bottom layer of the atmosphere. The shape and position of clouds are clues in forecasting weather. Clouds indicate the direction and speed of wind in an area, as well as the amount of water vapor in the air.

Three conditions must exist for water to condense from air. First the air must contain water vapor. Second the air must contain condensation nuclei. Finally the air temperature must drop to the dew point. Air generally has both water vapor and condensation nuclei. In what ways, then, does air cool to the dew point?

One way in which air can be cooled is by coming into contact with a cool surface. For example, air can be cooled if it moves over a cooler body of water. This is why air that blows in from the ocean during the summer is cool.

Another way air cools is as heat radiates from it into space. For example, air cools during the night, and it cools more quickly on a clear night

Figure 19·9
Fog is a cloud that forms close to the earth's surface.

than on a cloudy night. This is because on a cloudy night the clouds trap heat that is radiating into space. Fog often forms in the early morning after a clear night. At this time the air temperature near the ground drops to the dew point.

Air also cools as it rises. For example, air rises when it moves across a warm part of the earth's surface and is heated. As the air rises, the pressure around it decreases. This causes the rising air to expand. The temperature of any gas decreases as the gas expands.

KINDS OF CLOUDS

Careful observation has shown that there are three basic cloud shapes. **Cumulus** (KYOO myuh-luhs) **clouds**, shown in Figure 19·10, are fluffy clouds, often with flat bases. These clouds form as warm air rises through the atmosphere. Cumulus clouds are found at all altitudes, and they generally indicate fair weather. If the upward push of air is strong, these clouds may extend many kilometers into the atmosphere, forming a thunderhead. Another name for a thunderhead is *cumulonimbus* (kyoo myuh loh NIHM buhs) *cloud*. When *-nimbus* or *nimbo-* is part of a cloud name, it indicates that the cloud is precipitating. A cumulonimbus cloud may bring violent weather, including thunder, lightning, hail, and tornadoes.

cumulus (heap)

Figure 19·10
Cumulus clouds. What causes the clouds to have a flat bottom?

stratus (spreading out)

Stratus (STRAY tuhs) **clouds** are clouds that spread out in a layer where a large body of air is slowly lifted into the atmosphere. They usually indicate rainy weather. Look at the stratus clouds in Figure 19·11 (*left*). These clouds are not as tall as cumulus clouds but cover a wider area. Stratus clouds may block the sun for many hours, even days, because it takes so long for them to pass. Nimbostratus clouds produce a light but steady rain or snow that can last for more than a day.

Figure 19·11
Stratus clouds *(left)* and cirrus clouds *(right)*.

cirrus (curl)

Cirrus (SIHR uhs) **clouds** are thin, feathery clouds that form at high altitudes. The temperature at such altitudes is always well below freezing, so cirrus clouds are made of ice crystals. Notice in Figure 19·11 (*right*) the shape of cirrus clouds. Cirrus clouds are thin and wispy. This is because they form where the air is thin and the winds are strong. They are sometimes called mare's tails because of their appearance. Cirrus clouds are fair-weather clouds. Notice in Figure 19·12, page 471, that clouds are also named according to the altitudes where they form.

cirrus

cirrostratus

cirrocumulus

— 7km

altocumulus

altostratus

cumulonimbus

cumulus

— 2km

stratocumulus

stratus

nimbostratus

fog

REVIEW

1. How do clouds form?
2. How are the three basic kinds of clouds different?
3. What kind of weather generally is brought by a cumulus cloud? By a stratus cloud? By a cirrus cloud?

CHALLENGE Cumulus clouds usually form in the afternoon rather than in the morning. Explain why this is true.

Figure 19·12
Clouds are classified according to their shape and altitude.

19·5 Precipitation

As you have learned, precipitation is water that returns to the earth as rain, snow, sleet, or hail. All clouds contain water, but not all clouds produce precipitation. Clouds are made of droplets that are either tiny drops of liquid water or tiny particles of ice. Figure 19·13 illustrates different sizes of cloud droplets compared with the size of a raindrop. Notice how much larger the raindrop is than the other droplets.

Cloud droplets fall slowly because of their small size, and the slightest upward movement of air can keep them afloat. Because of their small size, these droplets also evaporate quickly as they fall through the warmer and drier air near the earth. For these reasons, the water in a cloud does not always reach the ground. To reach the ground the droplets must form large raindrops.

Figure 19·13

Comparative sizes of water droplets and drops in a cloud.

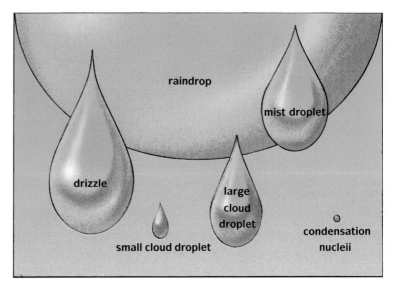

RAIN

Rain, the most common form of precipitation, is liquid water that falls to the earth. One way in which raindrops form is by cloud droplets colliding and joining. Scientists believe that cloud droplets of different sizes are more likely to join than are drop-

Manufactured snow is formed by snowmaking machines that blow a mist of water into the air at temperatures below freezing. The snow forms when tiny water droplets in the mist freeze and fall to the ground. Is manufactured snow the same as natural snow? Explain your answer.

lets of the same size. The large cloud droplets fall faster than do smaller cloud droplets and tend to collect smaller droplets along the way. Eventually enough cloud droplets collect to form a raindrop. It takes more than a million cloud droplets to make a raindrop. Some scientists also believe that the movement of cloud droplets creates electric charges on the droplets. These charges could speed the growth process by drawing droplets together.

Another way in which raindrops form is by the melting of snowflakes. Many clouds are made up of ice crystals because these clouds form where temperatures are below freezing. The ice crystals collect and grow rapidly as water vapor sublimates on them. Eventually they form snowflakes that fall through the clouds. As the snowflakes fall, they may melt in clouds where the temperature is above freezing. There the snowflakes form raindrops.

One factor that influences how large raindrops become is the vertical height of the cloud. A raindrop that falls through a tall cloud can combine with many others and become much larger. A cumulonimbus cloud, for example, is very tall and thus can produce the heavy rain of a thunderstorm. In contrast, small water droplets called *drizzle* form in thin stratus clouds. The droplets fall only a short distance through this type of cloud.

Figure 19·14
The shape of a snowflake.

Figure 19·15
The formation of sleet *(left)* and hail *(right)*.

OTHER FORMS OF PRECIPITATION

Snow is the solid form of precipitation that occurs when snowflakes do not melt as they fall. They do not melt when the air temperature between the cloud and the ground remains below freezing. Like raindrops, snowflakes grow by colliding with and joining others as they fall. All snowflakes have six sides or points, but no two snowflakes seem to be exactly alike.

Sleet, or freezing rain, forms when raindrops freeze after they leave a cloud, as they fall to the earth. Figure 19·15 *(left)* illustrates a situation that would produce sleet. Why, do you think, is sleet often mixed with rain?

Hail is made of rounded pieces of ice formed by strong updrafts in cumulonimbus clouds during thunderstorms. Hail begins as raindrops that are forced by updrafts high into a cloud, where the temperature is below freezing. The raindrops freeze

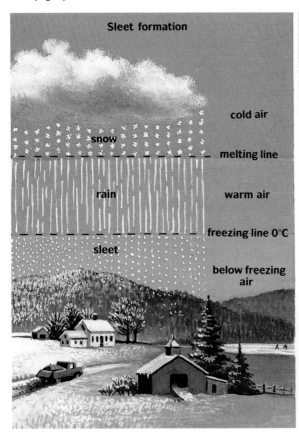

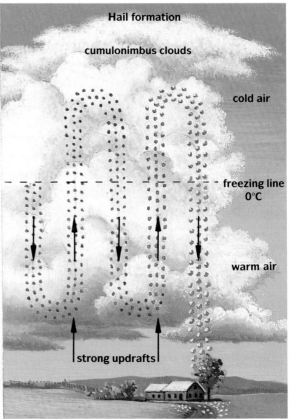

and fall as ice pellets toward the earth. They pick up droplets as they fall. The pellets may also be caught in updrafts and sent high into the cloud. There the droplets freeze in a layer around the pellets. The process can occur repeatedly before the pieces grow so large that they fall through the updrafts. Figure 19·15 (*right*), page 474 illustrates this process. Hail can do tremendous damage to crops, break windows and damage other property.

Occasionally, objects on the surface of the earth may have just cooled to below freezing when rain falls. When raindrops wet the just-frozen surfaces, a layer of ice forms. The layer of ice that forms from rain on objects whose temperatures are below freezing is called *glaze*.

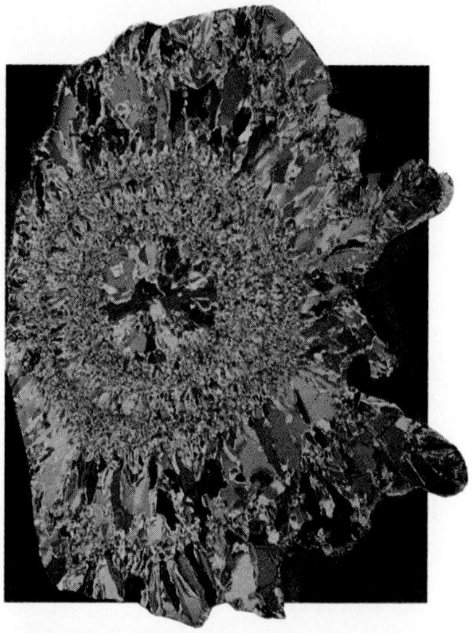

Figure 19·16
A cross section of a hailstone. What causes the layers in the hailstone?

REVIEW

1. What are two ways in which rain can form?
2. Why do tall clouds produce large raindrops?
3. What is the difference between how snow and hail form?

CHALLENGE Explain why hail is unlikely to fall from stratus clouds.

CHAPTER SUMMARY

The main ideas in this chapter are listed below. Read these statements before you answer the Chapter Review questions.

- The water cycle is the continuous movement of water between the earth and the air. (19·1)
- Relative humidity is the amount of water vapor in the air compared with the maximum amount that could be held at a given temperature. (19·2)
- For water vapor to condense, the air must become saturated, and there must be a surface for the water vapor to condense on. (19·3)
- Clouds form when rising air cools to the dew point. Clouds are named according to their shapes and altitudes. (19·4)
- Precipitation forms when cloud droplets or snowflakes become large enough to fall. Precipitation includes rain, snow, sleet, drizzle, and hail. (19·5)

The key terms in this chapter are listed below. Use each term in a sentence that shows the meaning of the term.

cirrus clouds	evaporation	rain
cloud	frost	relative humidity
condensation	hail	snow
cumulus clouds	humidity	stratus clouds
dew	precipitation	water cycle
dew point	psychrometer	

Chapter Review

VOCABULARY

Use the key terms from the previous page to complete the following sentences correctly.

1. The exchange of water between the earth and the atmosphere is called the _____.
2. The process in which liquid water changes into water vapor is _____.
3. The amount of water vapor in the air compared with the maximum water vapor that air can hold at a given temperature is called _____.
4. Water vapor in the air is called _____.
5. Dew that collects on plants on cool mornings forms by the process of _____.
6. The temperature at which water condenses from the air is the _____.
7. Flat, spread-out clouds that form when a large body of air is slowly lifted are _____.
8. Heaped, fluffy, fair-weather clouds are _____.
9. An instrument used to measure relative humidity is a/an _____.
10. Pellets of ice sometimes created during thunderstorms are called _____.

CONCEPTS

Write the correct term for each number in the diagram.

1. _____.
2. _____.
3. _____.
4. _____.
5. _____.

Identify each statement as True or False. If a statement is false, replace the underlined term or phrase with a term or phrase that makes the statement true.

6. When the temperature increases, the relative humidity <u>increases</u>.
7. Particles that can serve as condensation nuclei include <u>dust, smoke,</u> and <u>salt</u>.
8. Most clouds form in the <u>stratosphere</u>.
9. When the temperature falls to the dew point and the dew point is below freezing, <u>hail</u> can form.
10. <u>Drizzle</u> forms in thin clouds where the droplets do not join with many others as they fall.

Answer the following in complete sentences.

11. What is the difference between evaporation and condensation?
12. How is humidity affected by temperature?
13. What is the relationship between the dew point and relative humidity?
14. Why does rising air cool?
15. Compare and contrast sleet and hail.

---

1. Why is precipitation greater in areas near the equator than in areas near the poles?
2. Why does a high relative humidity on a warm day make you feel uncomfortable?
3. Why does running a fan make you feel cooler?
4. If you blow up, seal, and release a balloon, when will it rise more readily—on a cold day or on a warm day?

APPLICATION/ CRITICAL THINKING

---

1. Using a pump, inflate a bicycle tube or basketball. Feel the temperature of the pump. Then let the air out of the tube or basketball, and feel the air as it passes out of the stem. How does the temperature of the air compare with the temperature of the pump? How do you explain this?
2. Measure the amount of the next rainfall by following this procedure. Obtain a large, empty juice can and a graduate. Fill the can with water to a depth of 1.0 cm. Pour this water into the graduate. Using a glass-marking pencil, mark the level of the water as 1.0 cm on the graduate. Mark off levels for 2.0 cm, 3.0 cm, and 4.0 cm. Mark off fractions of these levels, too. Then place the empty can outside. After the next rainfall, pour the water collected in the can into the graduate to measure the amount of rainfall in centimeters.

EXTENSION

CHAPTER 20

FORECASTING WEATHER

We live at the bottom of a sea of air that is in constant motion. Violent storms can result when air masses with different temperatures and amounts of moisture collide. The photograph shows one such storm, a tornado. Notice the white funnel cloud. As it moves along the ground, the tornado picks up dust and debris. With winds reaching a speed of almost 500 km/h, a tornado can destroy anything in its path.

- *What conditions lead to the formation of tornadoes?*
- *What are some signs that indicate a change in weather?*
- *How do meteorologists predict the weather?*

20·1 Making Local Forecasts

After completing this section, you will be able to

- **describe** the factors used to make local forecasts.
- **use** the Beaufort scale to determine wind speed.
- **list** conditions that affect local forecasts.

The key term in this section is
forecast

fore (before)

Day-to-day weather changes are caused by the passing of air masses and fronts. An *air mass* is a large body of air that has similar humidity and temperature throughout. A *front* marks the front edge of an air mass. Air masses in general move across North America from west to east. If you learn to recognize the signs that come with air masses and fronts, you can learn to predict the weather. A prediction about future weather is called a **forecast**.

AIR PRESSURE AND WIND

One condition of the atmosphere that is measured when forecasting weather is air pressure. Air pressure is measured with a barometer. Air masses can be regions of high pressure or regions of low pressure. High-pressure air masses generally contain cool, dry air. Low-pressure air masses generally contain warm, moist air. Thus, if the air pressure is rising, cooler and drier weather can be expected within a few days. If the air pressure is falling, however, warmer and more humid weather can be expected within a few days.

Figure 20·1

The movement of air around a high-pressure air mass. In what direction does the air move?

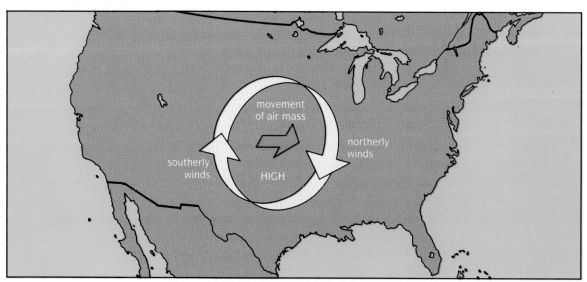

480

Another sign to consider when forecasting weather is the direction of the wind, as shown by a wind vane. Air in a high-pressure system, or a high, circulates outward from the center of the mass, in a clockwise direction. The air in a low-pressure system, or a low, circulates inward, toward the center of the low, in a counterclockwise direction. The direction of the wind around you indicates what part of a pressure system is passing over you.

WEATHER CHANGES

Figure 20·2 shows a high-pressure system over the eastern United States. The pressure system is traveling directly east across the country. As the air mass approaches Boston, the air pressure rises. Winds approach from the northwest. When the center of the system reaches Boston, the air pressure remains constant. The winds now approach from the west. When the system leaves Boston, the pressure decreases. The winds finally approach from the south. By noting the changing pressure and wind direction, you can determine what type of air mass is approaching and the type of weather it will bring. What changes in pressure and wind direction will take place in Boston if the approaching weather system is a low?

Table 20·1 lists the weather predicted by different combinations of wind direction and air pressure in eastern North America. What type of

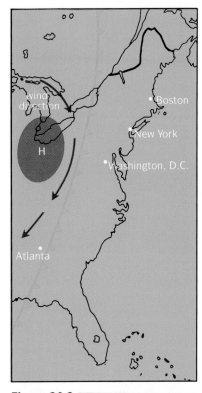

Figure 20·2

As a high-pressure system moves east, winds will approach Boston from the northwest. As the system moves away from Boston, winds will approach from the southwest.

Table 20·1 *Forecasting Weather*

CHANGE IN DIRECTION OF WIND	BAROMETER READING (CM OF MERCURY)	WEATHER INDICATED
Variable	76.7 or above, steady	• Continued fair, with little temperature change
SW to NW	76.2 to 76.7, rising rapidly	• Fair and cooler, followed within 2 days by warmer weather and rain
S to SE	76.2 to 76.7, falling slowly	• Rain within 24 hours, warmer
SE to NE	76.2 to 76.7, falling rapidly	• Increasing wind, rain within 12 hours
SE to NE	76.2 or below, falling slowly	• Rain within 18 hours, continuing 1 to 2 days
E to NE	76.2 or above, falling rapidly	• In summer, rain within 12 to 24 hours; in winter, rain or snow with increasing wind
S to SW	76.2 or below, rising slowly	• Clearing within a few hours, fair and cooler for several days
E to N	75.6 or below, falling rapidly	• Severe northeast wind; in winter heavy snow followed by a cold wave

weather is expected if winds change from south-west to northwest and the barometer reading is 76.4 cm and rising rapidly?

Another important sign of future weather is the cloud cover. Wind from the southeast and falling air pressure indicate that a front is approaching. Figure 20·3 shows two different fronts approaching. If cirrus clouds are seen to the west followed by cirrostratus and altostratus clouds, a warm front is approaching. Although the rain from the front is still far away, when it arrives it may last for a long time. The clouds associated with a warm front extend many kilometers ahead of the front. If to the west, cirrus clouds are seen followed by a tall, dark wall of cumulonimbus clouds, a cold front is approaching. This storm will arrive soon and could be violent. However, a storm resulting from a cold front usually does not last long. Fair weather will quickly follow as the front passes.

Figure 20·3
Cirrus clouds followed by cumulo-nimbus clouds *(bottom)* indicate an approaching cold front. Cirrus clouds and cirrostratus clouds *(right)* indicate an approaching warm front.

One way to judge the strength of a weather system is to measure its wind speed. You can estimate wind speed based on the wind's effects. One system of estimating wind speed is called the *Beau-*

Table 20·2 *The Beaufort Scale of Wind Strength*

DESCRIPTION OF WIND	WIND SPEED (km/h)	EFFECT OF WIND
Calm	Less than 1	Air still; smoke rises vertically
Light air	1 to 5	Wind direction shown by smoke drift; weather vanes inactive
Light breeze	6 to 11	Wind felt on face; leaves rustle
Gentle breeze	12 to 19	Leaves and small twigs move constantly; wind extends light flags
Moderate breeze	20 to 28	Wind raises dust and loose papers; moves twigs and thin branches
Fresh breeze	29 to 38	Small trees in leaf begin to sway
Strong breeze	39 to 49	Large branches move; telephone wires whistle; umbrellas difficult to control
Moderate gale	50 to 61	Whole trees sway; hard to walk
Fresh gale	62 to 74	Twigs break from trees; walking against wind very difficult
Strong gale	75 to 88	Slight damage to buildings
Whole gale	89 to 102	Trees uprooted; considerable damage to buildings
Storm	103 to 117	Widespread damage; rarely occurs inland
Hurricane	More than 117	Extreme destruction

fort scale. This scale is shown in Table 20·2. As you can see, the scale relates the speed of the wind to the wind's effects. For example, if wind is felt on the face and if leaves rustle, the wind speed is estimated to be 6 – 11 km/h. The wind is described as a light breeze. If whole trees move in the wind and it is hard to walk, how fast is the wind? What would the description be for this wind?

When using wind direction or cloud type to predict weather, local geography must be considered. Nearby oceans, mountains, and lakes can result in local winds. The direction of these winds may differ from that of winds resulting from large air masses. Large bodies of water can cause precipitation by adding moisture to the air. Such factors make forecasting more difficult.

REVIEW

1. What factors can you use to make your own local forecast?
2. How is the Beaufort scale used to determine the wind speed?
3. Name two conditions that might make your local forecast different from a regional forecast.

CHALLENGE What is the scientific basis for the saying "Dark cloud in the west, stay indoors and get some rest"?

20·2 Weather Maps

Before the National Weather Service (NWS) makes a forecast, it collects and organizes weather data from around the world. The NWS gathers data from almost 10,000 stations worldwide, nearly 2000 of them in the United States. From the information gathered, weather maps are produced. **Weather maps** are maps that provide an overall picture of weather activity across the earth. These maps help meteorologists as they study weather patterns and forecast the weather.

Eight times a day, weather stations across the United States report conditions to the NWS. These conditions are measured from the ground and include temperature, air pressure, and the change in air pressure during each 3-hour period. Wind speed, wind direction, dew point, visibility, cloud cover, cloud types, and any precipitation are also reported. The data are put together to produce a special map called a *surface map*.

Figure 20·4

A surface map.

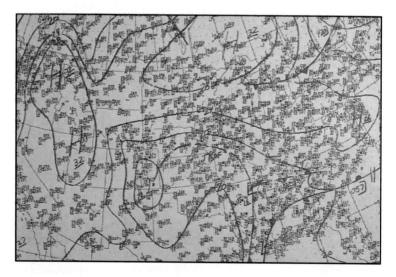

STATION MODELS

An NWS surface map shows the weather reported at each weather station. Each station is represented by a group of symbols called a station model. The *station model* describes the data collected at that particular weather station. Figure 20·5 shows an example of a station model and illustrates some common symbols. These symbols are for cloud cover, wind speed, temperature, dew point, and other weather conditions.

Look at the station model shown in Figure 20·5. What is the temperature at the station? How much of the sky is cloud-covered at the station? What is the barometric pressure?

Figure 20·5

Symbols shown on a weather map.

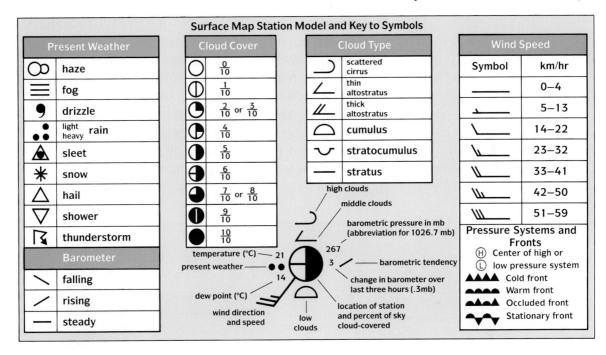

ISOBARS AND ISOTHERMS

Several steps are taken to produce a surface map. First the station models are printed on the map. Then **isobars,** lines that connect places having equal air pressure, are drawn. The air pressure, measured in units called millibars (mb), is shown at the end of each isobar. When the isobars are finished, some areas on the map may be completely circled by them. The circled areas that represent low pressure are labeled as lows or *L*. The circled areas that represent high pressure are labeled as highs or *H*. Occasionally, **isotherms,** lines that connect places having equal temperature, are also marked.

iso- (equal)
baros (weight)

therme (heat)

485

Today, surface maps including station models, isobars, and isotherms are drawn by computers. Then meteorologists analyze the map, marking the lines for the fronts, and shading the areas of precipitation. With a surface map, simple weather forecasts can be made.

WEATHER PATTERNS

Since weather systems tend to move in straight lines, weather forecasting can be improved through the use of a series of maps. Notice in Figure 20·6 (*A, B, C*) that both the warm front and the cold front are moving west to east across the country. When each of the maps is traced onto a single map, as shown in Figure 20·6 (*D*), the pattern of movement shows both the direction and the speed of the weather system. A forecast would be based on the movements of the system over a period of three to five days. In what direction is the cold front moving?

Figure 20·6

The movements of weather systems can be followed on a series of weather maps.

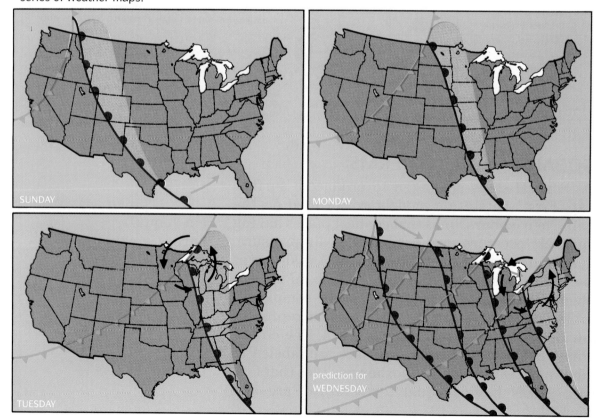

ACTIVITY　How Are Forecasts Made?

OBJECTIVE
Predict future weather by using weather maps for several days.

MATERIALS
3 newspaper weather maps, 3 different colored pencils, metric ruler

PROCEDURE
A. Save newspaper weather maps of the United States for 3 consecutive days. Today should be the third day. On a blank piece of paper, trace the outline of the United States.

B. With a colored pencil, trace the main features—highs, lows, and fronts—of the first day's weather map onto your map outline. With a second color, trace the features of the second day's map onto your map. With a third color, trace the features of the third day's map onto your map.

C. Using a metric ruler, determine how far each low has traveled each day. Determine the direction in which each low is traveling, and mark on your map where you expect each low will be tomorrow.

D. Repeat step **C** for any highs on your map.

E. Mark the ends of each front and one point near the middle of each front on your map. Repeat step **C** for each of the fronts by following the movement of the center of each front.
  1. In general, in what direction did the weather systems move?
  2. What, if any, formations occurred? Where did they occur?
  3. What formations produced rain?

F. Study the movements of the highs, lows, and fronts for the 3-day period.
  4. Predict the weather for your area over the next 24 hours.

RESULTS AND CONCLUSIONS
1. How did the weather maps for the 3 days explain the weather that you experienced? For example, if it rained, why did it? If it was clear, why was it?
2. How did your prediction compare with the actual weather?
3. Explain any differences between your prediction and the actual weather.

Even when a number of maps are used, a forecast is only accurate for about 12 hours. Beyond this time, other factors can affect the weather pattern. For example, new air masses entering from north or south may change the movement of another air mass. Or a large air mass may stall, stopping everything behind it. Mountains can also change the path of a weather system. And winds in the upper troposphere can cause a system to move north or south.

It is important to know about weather patterns everywhere, even places where people don't live, such as over the ocean. A worldwide network for weather observation has been established to fill in these places. At intervals across the ocean are buoys that transmit readings of the weather conditions to weather stations on land. Ships, which depend on weather forecasts for their safety, also report conditions as they travel. Through the television and infrared cameras they carry, weather satellites keep a constant watch on the surface of the earth. Figure 20·7 is a satellite photograph of a section of the earth's surface. Notice the cloud patterns in the photograph. What areas of the United States were covered by clouds when this photograph was taken?

Figure 20·7
A satellite photograph of a weather system.

STORMS

One of the most difficult weather conditions to forecast is a small-scale storm, such as a thunderstorm or tornado, which can develop very quickly. Radar is used to study such storms. Radar measures the size and the number of raindrops in the air. Radar waves pass through dry air unaffected, but they reflect from drops of water. The greater the number of drops in the air or the larger the drops in the air, the stronger the signal reflected to the station. Today, radar stations watch the entire United States for precipitation. Figure 20·8 shows a radar map of the United States. The shaded areas show where precipitation is occurring. How do the radar map and satellite photograph compare?

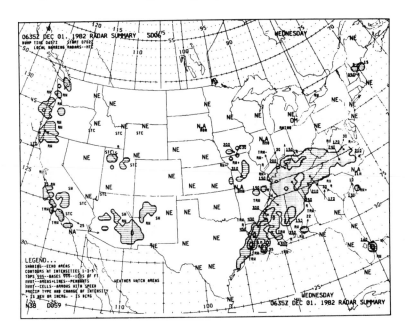

Figure 20·8
A radar weather map.

A newer kind of radar, Doppler radar, measures not only the rain but also the speed and direction of the winds within a storm. Thus the wind patterns that produce storms can be identified before the precipitation starts. Forecasts made using Doppler radar are more accurate for predicting when storms will start. Such forecasts can predict the severity of storms and where they will strike.

Long-range forecasts are based on winds in the upper troposphere and on seasonal averages of temperature and precipitation. The NWS issues 30-day and 90-day forecasts. But the long-range forecasts are general. A long-range forecast might suggest that the following month will be warmer and drier.

REVIEW

1. What information is found on a weather map?
2. How is a weather map made?
3. What are the weather conditions shown in the station model in Figure 20·5?

CHALLENGE Local weather is more likely to change in winter than in summer. Why is this so?

20·3 Climate

There can be great differences in weather from day to day and from season to season. Yet records show that average seasonal patterns repeat themselves year after year. These repeating patterns make up the climate of a region. **Climate** is the average of the weather conditions in a region over a long period of time.

The two main conditions that determine climate are the temperature and precipitation. The climate of a region is described by the averages, totals, and extremes of these conditions. For example, in a desert there is less than 25 cm of rain a year. A desert has large daily changes in temperature. It warms quickly during the day and cools quickly during the night. How would you describe the climate of a tropical rain forest?

LATITUDE

One important factor that influences climate is latitude. Figure 20·9 shows light rays from the sun hitting the surface of the earth. Notice that near the equator the light rays strike directly. During winter in the Northern Hemisphere, the light rays strike at an angle. Light rays striking the earth at an angle

Figure 20·9

The amount of energy that the earth receives varies with the angle at which sunlight strikes the earth's surface.

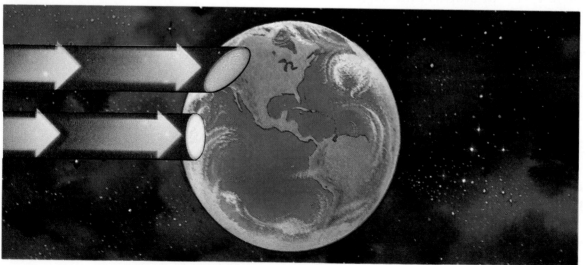

490

spread out, covering a larger area than do light rays striking more directly. The earth's surface receives less energy when the rays are spread out. At the equator, sunlight strikes more directly and is therefore more concentrated. At the poles, sunlight strikes less directly. Generally climates are warmest near the equator and coolest near the poles.

The tilt of the earth is partly responsible for seasonal changes in temperature. When a hemisphere is leaning toward the sun, the season in that hemisphere is summer. When a hemisphere is leaning away from the sun, the season in that hemisphere is winter.

ALTITUDE

Another factor that influences climate is altitude. Notice in Figure 20·10 that St. Louis, Missouri, is at about the same latitude as Denver, but the altitude of St. Louis is only 163 m compared with 1610 m in Denver. The yearly average temperature in St. Louis is 13.3°C compared with 10.1°C in Denver. This difference in temperature is partially caused by the difference in altitude. Many mountains are snow-covered all year because the temperatures at the tops of mountains rarely rise above freezing.

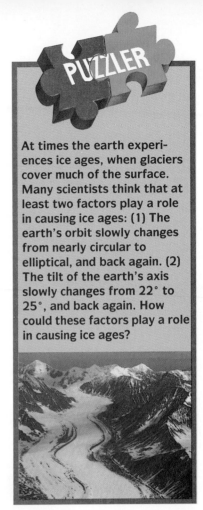

PUZZLER

At times the earth experiences ice ages, when glaciers cover much of the surface. Many scientists think that at least two factors play a role in causing ice ages: (1) The earth's orbit slowly changes from nearly circular to elliptical, and back again. (2) The tilt of the earth's axis slowly changes from 22° to 25°, and back again. How could these factors play a role in causing ice ages?

Figure 20·10
Altitude has an effect on climate.

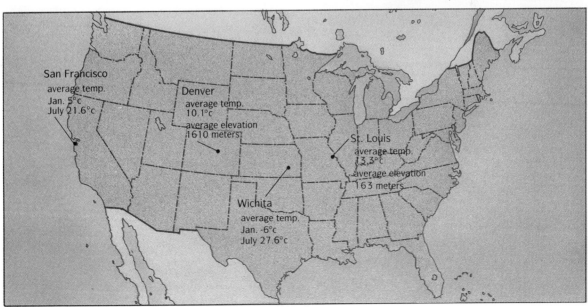

San Francisco
average temp.
Jan. 5°c
July 21.6°c

Denver
average temp.
10.1°c
average elevation
1610 meters

St. Louis
average temp.
13.3°c
average elevation
163 meters

Wichita
average temp.
Jan. -6°c
July 27.6°c

EFFECT OF WATER AND LAND

Large bodies of water have two important effects on climate. First, air over a body of water picks up moisture. Thus the climate of regions near large bodies of water tends to be more humid and have more precipitation than climates away from large bodies of water. Second, water does not change temperature as quickly as land does. In San Francisco, California, the normal low for January is 5.0°C, and the normal July high is 21.6°C. In Wichita, Kansas, which is at about the same latitude, the normal January low is −6.0°C, and the normal July high is 27.6°C. What accounts for San Francisco's smaller variation in temperature?

Climate can also be influenced by the shape of the land. As an air mass moves up a mountain, for example, the temperature of the air decreases, often to the dew point. When this happens, as shown in Figure 20·11, water vapor is released from the air.

Figure 20·11

Air cools when it rises over mountains. When the air cools, water in it condenses.

REVIEW

1. What is the difference between weather and climate?
2. What two main conditions determine the climate of a region?
3. What are the factors that influence climate?

CHALLENGE What do you think causes the "pea-soup" fogs that London, England, is so famous for?

20·4 Climate Zones

TYPES OF CLIMATE ZONES

Meteorologists have classified the earth's climates into three major climate zones. These zones —tropical, temperate, and polar—are defined by their yearly temperature ranges. The yearly temperature range is the difference between the warmest average monthly temperature and the coldest average monthly temperature. Notice in Figure 20·12 that each zone is found both north and south of the equator. Although lines are drawn on maps to mark the boundaries of these zones, on the earth there are no definite boundaries.

After completing this section, you will be able to

- **compare** the three major climate zones.
- **give examples** of temperate climate regions in the United States.

The key terms in this section are
polar climate
temperate climate
tropical climate

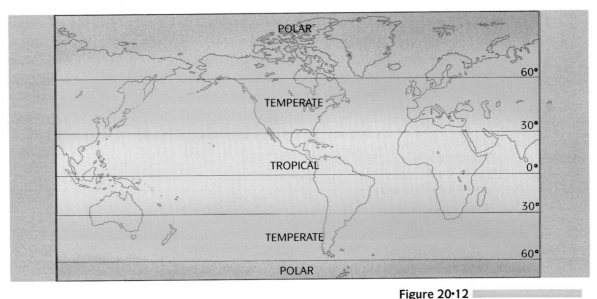

Figure 20·12
The major climate zones of the earth.

A **tropical climate** is found where the average temperature during the year stays above 18°C. The tropical climate zone is found between latitudes 30° north and 30° south. There the earth receives the most direct sunlight and the largest amount of heat.

A **polar climate** is found where the average temperature during the year stays below 10°C. The polar climate zones are found between the North Pole and 60° north and the South Pole and 60° south. In polar zones, sunlight hits the surface at an angle much of the time.

Between the tropical climate zone and the polar climates zones are zones where warm air meets cold air. The climate in these zones is called a temperate climate. A **temperate climate** is found where the average summer temperature is above 18°C and the average winter temperature is below 10°C. Temperate climate zones are found both north and south of the equator. Almost all of the United States has a temperate climate.

CLIMATE REGIONS

Based on local temperature and precipitation conditions, an area can be classified as a *climate region*. Figure 20·13 shows the climate regions of North America. North America extends from the tropical zone of Central America to the polar zone of northern Canada. The temperate zone is divided into many climate regions because of the many variables that influence its weather. Recall that such variables include altitude, the shape of the land, the presence of bodies of water, and the prevailing movement of air masses.

The United States has many of the temperate climate regions. The northwestern coast of the country receives moist air from over the Pacific

Figure 20·13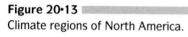
Climate regions of North America.

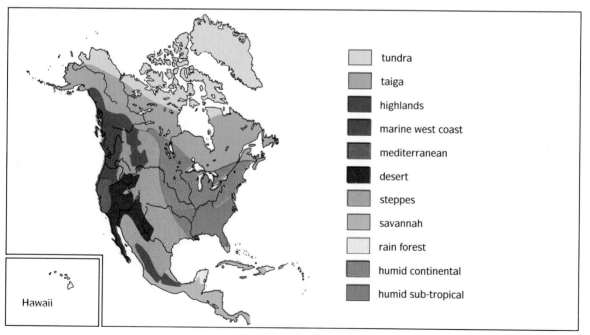

Figure 20·14
Temperate steppes *(left)* and Mediterranean climate *(right)*.

Ocean. This region receives 50–75 cm of precipitation a year, which creates what is called a *marine climate*. Air along the California coast is dry in the summer. This region, which receives about 25 cm of rain a year, has a *Mediterranean climate*. Running along the California coast is a mountain range called the Coastal Ranges. As moist air reaches the mountains, it rises and releases most of its water. The dry winds that flow down the eastern slopes create the temperate deserts of the West. These deserts have a cold winter and a hot summer. The dry air moving across these deserts interacts with moist air masses from the south to release precipitation on the Central Plains. This addition of water forms a climate region called the temperate steppes (stehps). *The temperate steppes* has a moist climate with a cold winter and a hot summer. Grasslands flourish here.

The eastern portion of the United States is divided into the humid continental climate and humid subtropical climate. The humid continental region is influenced more by cold polar air masses than is the other region.

REVIEW

1. Compare the temperate, polar, and tropical climate zones.
2. What are three of the temperate climate regions found in the United States? How is each different?

CHALLENGE Why does air become dryer when it sinks?

20·5 Changing the Climate and Weather

CHANGING THE WEATHER

Rain does not always occur where it is needed. Long periods of time without rain can destroy crops and cause starvation in many parts of the world. Many attempts have been made to make rain. In one method, called **cloud seeding**, dry crystals such as dry ice crystals, are added to a cloud. The dry crystals act as condensation nuclei. Cloud seeding has been used to bring rain to areas that need it. Cloud seeding has also been used to force large storm systems to release rain before they are ready, possibly reducing their power.

Figure 20·15

The L–shaped hole in the clouds was produced by cloud seeding with dry–ice crystals.

Cloud seeding, however, has not been very effective in producing rain, and some scientists are concerned about its possible drawbacks. First, clouds must be present, since seeding cannot produce them. Second, seeding a cloud may make a storm more powerful. Scientists do not yet understand the effect that creating rain in one place has on the weather of another place.

CHANGING THE CLIMATE

There is no easy way to change a climate on a large scale. But people have been successful in changing the climate in very small areas. The climate in a small area is called a **microclimate**. Farmers may create microclimates to help their plants grow. A greenhouse, for example, extends the growing season by creating a warm, moist microclimate for seedlings before the warm weather arrives. Irrigation is used to add extra water to the soil. Rows of trees between the fields and the prevailing local winds form windbreaks that protect the plants and slow the evaporation of water from the soil.

micro- (small)

The building of cities has created microclimates that differ from climates of surrounding areas. Often a meteorologist's weather forecast calls for different conditions in a city and in a nearby suburb. These differences occur for many reasons. The concrete and asphalt used to build a city collect and store heat better than do the fields

ACTIVITY How Do Microclimates Differ?

OBJECTIVES
Identify some microclimates near your school.
Collect data on each microclimate for comparison.

MATERIALS
psychrometer, thermometer

PROCEDURE
A. Make a table in which to record temperature and humidity data for 5 days.
B. With your teacher's permission, choose two or three microclimates around your school to compare. Choose areas that are different from each other. For example, you might choose spots at the center of a ball field, under a shady tree, and alongside a building. Write the names of your locations in your table.

C. Measure the temperature and relative humidity at each location once a day for 5 days. Your measurements should be taken in the same place in each location each day. Record your results.
  1. What variable should you control to make sure your results are accurate?

RESULTS AND CONCLUSIONS
1. What was the average temperature for each location?
2. What was the average relative humidity for each location?
3. How did the areas that you measured compare in temperature and humidity?
4. How did the areas that you measured compare with different areas measured by your classmates?
5. How would you explain any differences?

SCIENCE & TECHNOLOGY

Africa is in the clutches of an extreme climate change. In 1968, after 10 years of wet weather, a drought began. The drought continues today, centering on the Sahara's southern border and stretching across the continent to Ethiopia and Somalia.

Scientists are trying to find the cause of the devastating drought. Some researchers at the National Meteorological Center in Maryland may be close to an answer. They have found a link between droughts in southeastern Africa and El Niños in the Pacific Ocean, half a world away! El Niños are major warmings of the surface waters of the ocean. The scientists in Maryland have found that 22 of the past 28 El Niños were accompanied by below normal rainfall in southern Africa. Links such as these are one step toward understanding what causes a drought.

and forests around the city. Also the buildings act like large windbreaks. Thus a city is usually warmer than the areas around it.

In a city, precipitation does not soak into soil or sit on the surface and evaporate into the air. Instead the water collects in sewers and is removed, leaving the air in the city drier than the air in areas around the city. Smoke, car exhaust, and dust are more likely to be found in air over cities. These particles act as condensation nuclei. The rain that is produced by clouds that form from these nuclei can be acidic and may be causing serious damage to the environment of the entire earth.

Climate change of a large scale might result from damage to the ozone layer of the atmosphere. This layer protects living things from the sun's ultraviolet radiation. Some chemicals that people have released into the air have been shown to chemically react with ozone, changing it into new substances. If the ozone layer is being reduced, living things on the earth may develop problems caused by increased exposure to ultraviolet radiation. A reduction in ozone might also cause the earth's climates to become warmer. Much work is now being done to determine if such changes are taking place.

The addition of carbon dioxide to the atmosphere by cars and industry may be changing the

Figure 20·16

Smog is a microclimate formed by smoke and car exhaust.

498

earth's climate. In a process called the greenhouse effect, sunlight enters the earth's atmosphere and warms the earth's surface. When warmed, the earth's surface gives off heat waves. But these heat waves do not leave the atmosphere. They are blocked by carbon dioxide, causing a general warming of the atmosphere.

REVIEW

1. What are some microclimates around you?
2. How can cloud seeding be used to change weather?
3. What problems might arise if people try to change the weather and climates?

CHALLENGE Some years ago the route of a river was changed, shortening it by about 50 percent. The surrounding tropical land became drier, and plant and animal species began dying off. How might the change in the river have caused the altered climate in the area?

CHAPTER SUMMARY

The main ideas in this chapter are listed below. Read these statements before you answer the Chapter Review questions.

- Weather forecasts are based in part on changes in air pressure, on wind speed and direction, and on cloud cover. (20•1)
- Geographic conditions, such as nearness to oceans, lakes, and mountains, can affect local weather. (20•1)
- Weather data gathered by weather stations, satellites, and radar are used to produce weather maps. (20•2)
- Weather maps are used to make forecasts. (20•2)
- Temperature and precipitation are the two main conditions that determine a region's climate. (20•3)
- Both latitude and altitude influence a region's climate. Nearness to large bodies of water and the shape of the land can influence a region's climate. (20•3)
- The three major climate zones are the polar climate, the temperate climate, and the tropical climate. (20•4)
- Within each climate zone there are a variety of climate regions, based on conditions of temperature and precipitation. (20•4)
- Attempts to change weather, such as by cloud seeding, have been largely unsuccessful and may cause problems. (20•5)
- Microclimates include farmed areas, greenhouses, and cities. (20•5)

The key terms in this chapter are listed below. Use each term in a sentence that shows the meaning of the term.

climate	isotherms	temperate climate
cloud seeding	microclimate	tropical climate
forecast	polar climate	weather maps
isobars		

Chapter Review

VOCABULARY

Use the key terms from the previous page to complete the following sentences correctly.

1. Lines on a weather map that connect places having equal air pressure are called _____.
2. Maps that provide overall pictures of weather activity across the earth are called _____.
3. A climate that is found where the average summer temperature is above 18°C and the average winter temperature is below 10°C is a _____.
4. A climate in a small area, such as in a greenhouse or in a city, is called a/an _____.
5. A prediction about future weather is called a/an _____.
6. Lines on a weather map that connect places having equal temperature are called _____.
7. The average weather conditions in a region over a long period of time is the _____.
8. A climate that is found where the average temperature stays above 18°C all year is a/an _____.
9. A technique involving the use of dry crystals to act as condensation nuclei to produce rain is _____.
10. A climate that is found where the average temperature stays below 10°C all year is a/an _____.

CONCEPTS

Look at the surface map below. Refer to Figure 20•5, page 485 and answer the following questions.

1. What is the temperature at weather station A?
2. What is the wind direction at weather station B? What is its speed?
3. What kind of front is passing over C?
4. What changes will occur when front D passes?
5. In what direction does the air seem to be circulating around the low?

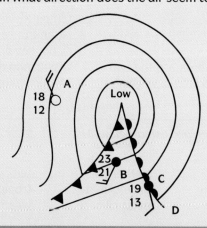

Choose the term or phrase that best answers the question or completes the statement.

6. Which of the following conditions can complicate the forecasting of local weather?
   a. mountains
   b. large lakes
   c. both **a** and **b**
   d. neither **a** nor **b**

7. The Beaufort scale estimates the speed of the wind from
   a. an anemometer.
   b. a wind vane.
   c. the sound it makes.
   d. the effects of the wind.

8. Worldwide data on weather is collected by
   a. aircraft.
   b. satellites.
   c. weather balloons.
   d. weather maps.

9. What are the two main conditions that determine a region's climate?
   a. temperature and precipitation
   b. wind speed and direction
   c. temperature and air pressure
   d. wind direction and precipitation

10. As carbon dioxide is added to the atmosphere, the temperature will
    a. increase
    b. decrease
    c. remain the same

Answer the following in complete sentences.

11. What conditions affect the weather for your area?
12. What information is included on a weather map?
13. How does climate differ from weather?
14. What is the climate of the temperate steppes?
15. How might a reduction in the amount of ozone in the atmosphere affect the earth's climate?

---

1. Identify the factors that determine the climate in your region.
2. Identify some ways in which your family controls the microclimate in your home.
3. How might the presence of a large inland sea in central Canada affect the climate of North America?

APPLICATION/ CRITICAL THINKING

---

1. Keep a daily record of temperature, air pressure, wind direction, cloud cover, and precipitation in your area. Look for relationships among the data. Then use the daily data to predict the weather for the next few days in your area.
2. The earth's climate during the Mesozoic Era, 65 million years ago, seems to have been warmer and more humid than the climate on the earth today. What factors may have produced the climate conditions of that time?

EXTENSION

CHAPTER 21

THE EARTH'S OCEANS

On many maps and globes, oceans are shown as smooth, blue surfaces. Yet beneath the ocean surface are a mountain taller than Mount Everest and a valley many times deeper than the Grand Canyon. The ocean floor is as rugged and varied as any place on the earth's continents. The ocean separates the land masses of the earth, affects the weather and climate, and supplies the atmosphere with water. Where the ocean meets the land, waves pound the shore and remove sand and rock. The photograph shows the effects of waves over time. The rocks shown were once part of a huge cliff.

- *What is the shape of the land under the ocean?*
- *What causes waves in the ocean?*
- *How can wave erosion be prevented?*

21·1 Composition of Seawater

ORIGIN OF THE OCEANS

Early in its history, the earth was a much hotter place. Liquid water could not collect on the earth's surface beause the surface was too hot. Volcanic activity constantly released gases. The process in which gases are released by volcanic activity is called **degassing** (dee GAS ihng). Only when the earth cooled could gases condense to form clouds and then rain water. This rain water formed the first oceans.

COMPOSITION OF THE OCEANS

salis (salt)

Thousands of samples of seawater from around the earth have been studied. Scientists have found that seawater is a complex solution. It contains most of the elements found on the earth. If a kilogram of seawater is left to evaporate, an average of 35 g of salt remains. The **salinity** (suh LIHN uh tee), or saltiness, of seawater is defined as the number of grams of dissolved salt in a kilogram of seawater. Thus the average salinity of seawater is 35 g/kg. In addition to salt, seawater contains smaller amounts of other compounds and elements. Figure 21·1 lists the most common elements in seawater. What two elements make up most of the dissolved minerals? What substance do these two materials form?

Figure 21·1

What percent of seawater is dissolved minerals?

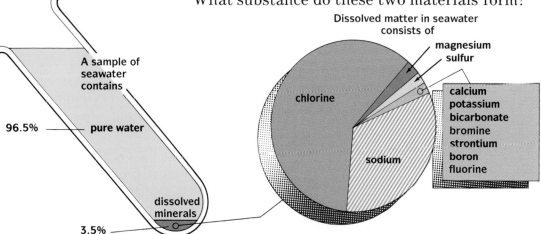

A sample of seawater contains

96.5% — pure water

3.5% — dissolved minerals

Dissolved matter in seawater consists of

chlorine

magnesium
sulfur

calcium
potassium
bicarbonate
bromine
strontium
boron
fluorine

sodium

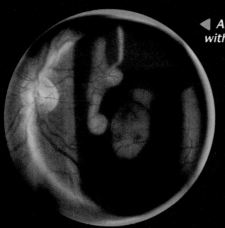

An image is projected on nerve tissue within the eye.

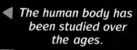

A magnified cross section of a nerve.

The human body has been studied over the ages.

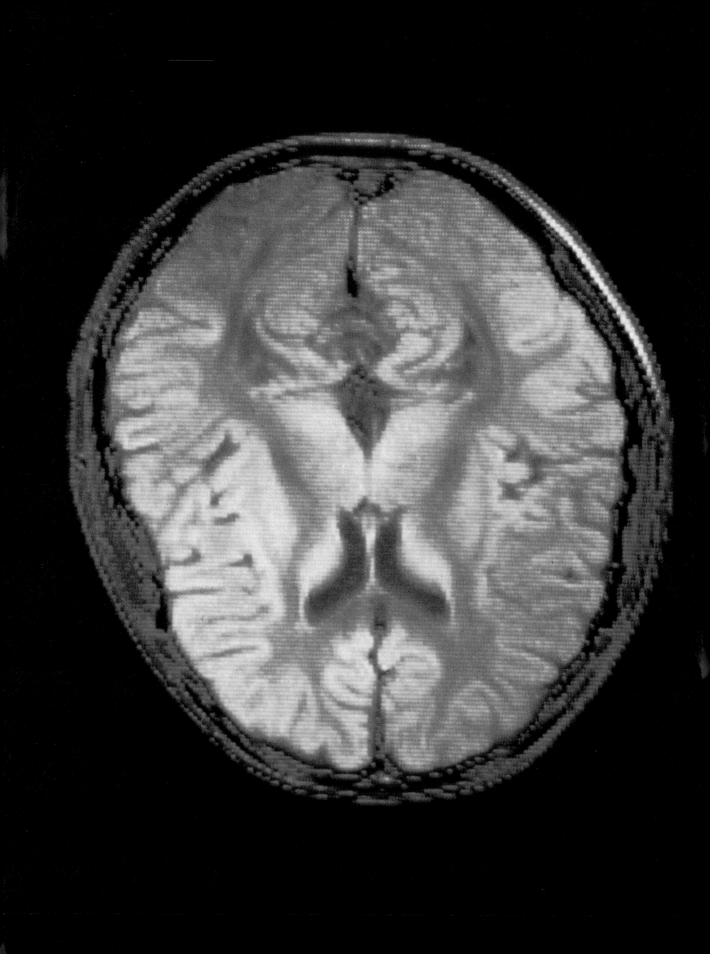

OCEAN BASIN FLOOR

At the end of each continental margin begins the ocean basin. The **ocean basin** is a deep depression that holds the surface water of the earth. The main features of the ocean basin, shown in Figure 21·5, are abyssal (uh BIHS uhl) plains, seamounts, trenches, and the Mid-Ocean Ridge.

Abyssal plains are flat areas of the ocean floor. The abyssal plains are the most level areas on the earth's surface. They are formed when sediments cover any rough parts of the ocean floor.

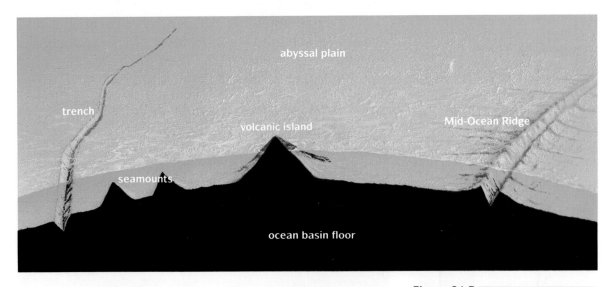

Figure 21·5
The ocean floor contains trenches, seamounts, volcanic islands, abyssal plains, and the Mid-Ocean Ridge.

Seamounts are underwater volcanic mountains on the abyssal plains. Most seamounts are found in the Pacific Ocean. The largest seamount is the island of Hawaii. It rises more than 10 km above the ocean floor, making it the tallest mountain on the earth. The Mid-Ocean Ridge is a continuous chain of mountains on the floor of the major oceans. The ridge is about 65,000 km long. It is the largest surface feature on the earth.

REVIEW

1. What are the earth's four major oceans?
2. What are the main features of the continental margin?
3. What are the main features of the ocean basin?

CHALLENGE Explain the presence of a thick layer of sediments found at the foot of submarine canyons.

21·3 Ocean Deposits

OCEAN FLOOR SEDIMENT

Unlike the land surface of the earth, the ocean floor has a nearly constant environment. Thick layers of sediments can collect on the ocean floor because it remains undisturbed for long periods of time. There are three sources of sediments on the ocean floor: the land, living things in the ocean, and ocean water.

Land sediment is formed by weathering and erosion of the land surface. Most of this sediment is carried by rivers from the land to the ocean. Wind can also carry land sediment to the ocean.

Figure 21·6
The ocean floor has a nearly constant environment.

A second source of sediments on the ocean floor is called *ooze*. Ooze is made up of shells, skeletons, and other hard materials that remain when tiny sea animals and plants die.

A third type of sediment on the ocean floor comes from the minerals dissolved in ocean water. For example, minerals can form *manganese nodules*, round objects on the ocean floor. The nodules can contain valuable metals, such as manganese, iron, copper, and nickel.

CORAL REEFS

In tropical or warm oceans, colorful deposits called coral reefs form where the water is shallow. **Coral reefs** are rocklike structures formed in warm, shallow water by colonies of tiny sea animals called corals.

There are three types of coral reefs: fringing reefs, barrier reefs, and atolls. A fringing reef is a type of coral reef that forms around an island or along a coast.

A barrier reef is a coral reef that is separated from coastal land by water. Such a reef may be hundreds of kilometers long. The Great Barrier Reef is the largest coral reef on the earth. This reef lies off the northeastern coast of Australia.

An **atoll** (AT ohl) is a ring-shaped reef that surrounds a body of water. It does not appear to be connected to land, but it is actually attached to an underwater volcano. An atoll begins as a fringing reef around a volcanic island. As the island sinks and is worn away by waves, the coral reef grows upward and forms a barrier reef. If the island sinks below the ocean surface, an atoll remains.

Figure 21·7
A coral reef is formed by tiny sea animals called corals.

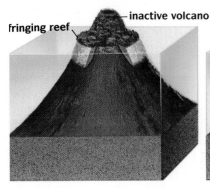
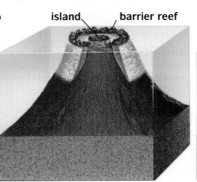

Figure 21·8
Three steps in the formation of an atoll: a fringing reef *(top)*, a barrier reef *(middle)*, and an atoll *(bottom)*.

REVIEW

1. What are three sources of sediments in the ocean?
2. Compare the three kinds of coral reefs.
3. What are the steps in the formation of an atoll?

CHALLENGE Where on the ocean floor would the finest land sediments be found? Where would the coarsest land sediments be found? Explain your answers.

21·4 Waves and Currents

After completing this section,
you will be able to

- **explain** the changes in a wave as it enters shallow water.
- **describe** two surface currents that affect North America.
- **explain** the effects of deep ocean currents.

The key terms in this section are
breaker   **upwelling**
Gulf Stream

OCEAN WAVES

Almost all water waves are caused by wind. When it blows over the surface of water, wind causes the water to flow. Because the water has more mass, it moves more slowly than the air. As a result, the water "piles up," forming a wave. The wind can now push on the side of the wave, making it grow larger.

The height that a wave reaches depends on three factors: the speed of the wind, the length of time the wind has been blowing, and the amount of open water that the wind blows across. The largest waves in the ocean form when the wind is strong and steady, and blows across the ocean surface for hundreds of kilometers. The greatest wave height ever measured in the open ocean is 40 m.

The motion of a water particle as a wave passes can be illustrated by a cork floating in water. As you can see in Figure 21·9, the cork is lifted up as the wave approaches. The cork is carried back and up to the crest, or top, of the wave. As the wave moves away, the cork moves down and forward to its original position. What shape path does the cork move in as it rises and falls?

Figure 21·9 ▨▨▨▨▨▨▨

A cork floating in water shows the motion of water at the surface as a wave passes through.

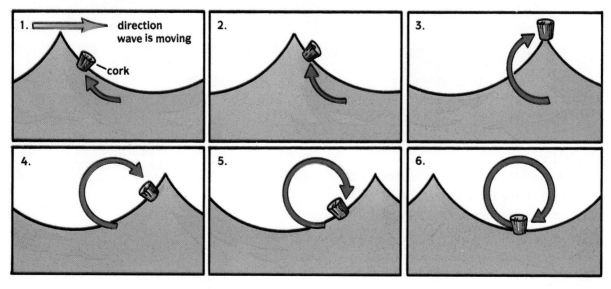

As a wave moves into shallow water near shore, the movement of the water changes. The wave length shortens, and the wave height increases. The water at the bottom of the wave slows down. When the wave height becomes too great, the crest breaks, and the water in it falls forward as shown in Figure 21·10.

Figure 21·10
A breaker forms when the wave height becomes too great.

A breaking wave is called a **breaker**. The water from a breaking wave is called the surf. The white foam produced in a breaker comes from the air that the water traps as it crashes down. A wave can also break on the open sea if the wind is strong enough. A strong wind can blow the crest off a wave, forming a breaker called a *whitecap*.

The most destructive waves in the ocean are tsunamis. Unlike most other waves, tsunamis are not formed by wind. They are caused by undersea volcanic explosions and earthquakes. The largest tsunami ever recorded was 64 m high. It was seen off the coast of Siberia in 1737. As tsunamis break and crash against the shore, they cause great destruction to buildings and houses along the shoreline.

SURFACE CURRENTS

Wind blowing across the ocean causes a surface current. A surface current forms when the surface water begins moving in the same direction as the wind. However, currents do not continue moving in the same direction as the wind. Land can cause the currents to change direction by blocking their path. Also, the earth's rotation causes currents to bend to the right in the Northern Hemisphere and to the left in the Southern Hemisphere. This bending of a current's path is called the *Coriolis* (kawr ee oʜ lihs) *effect*. The Coriolis effect causes currents to move in a circular pattern.

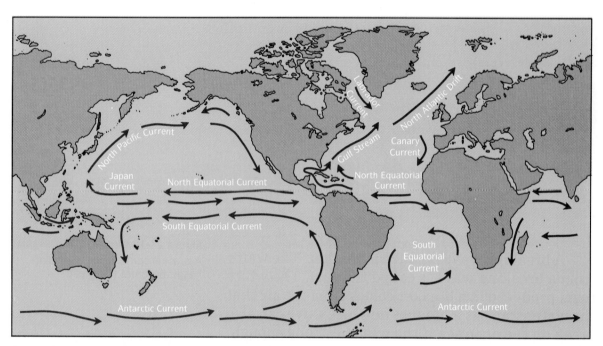

Figure 21·11

The major ocean surface currents. Which current affects the eastern coast of the United States? Which current affects the western coast of the United States?

In the Atlantic Ocean there are two major currents. They are the *North Equatorial Current* and the *South Equatorial Current*, as shown in Figure 21·11. The energy for these currents comes from the trade winds blowing toward the equator. The Coriolis effect and the continent of South America force the North Equatorial Current northward. The current splits as some of the water flows across the northern part of Cuba and the rest flows along the shores of the Gulf of Mexico. The parts come together again in the Straits of Florida to form the **Gulf Stream**. The Gulf Stream flows northward along the Atlantic Coast of the United States.

The Pacific Ocean has currents similar to those in the Atlantic Ocean. Look again at Figure 21·11. Notice that the North Equatorial Current in the Pacific turns north, forming the Japan Current. The current then travels northeast, across the Pacific Ocean, as the *North Pacific Current*. Why do northern California beaches have colder water than New England beaches of the same latitude?

DEEP OCEAN CURRENTS

Surface currents may reach down 100 m in the ocean. Other currents, called deep ocean currents, can occur several kilometers below the ocean surface. These currents are caused by differences in the density of the water.

The density of water depends on its temperature and its salinity. When water at the surface cools, it becomes denser and sinks. Water also becomes denser when its salinity increases. The freezing of water, like its evaporation, leaves behind salt. Thus when water freezes, the density of the remaining water increases. This causes the water to sink. As it sinks to the ocean bottom, the denser water pushes the water on the bottom outward in all directions.

Along some coasts, such as the west coast of the United States, wind can cause deep ocean water to rise, in a process called **upwelling**. In upwelling, wind causes warm surface water along the coast to move out to sea. Cold deep water below rises to replace the surface water.

Figure 21·12

Deep ocean currents form from differences in the density of water *(left)* and in the temperature of water *(right)*.

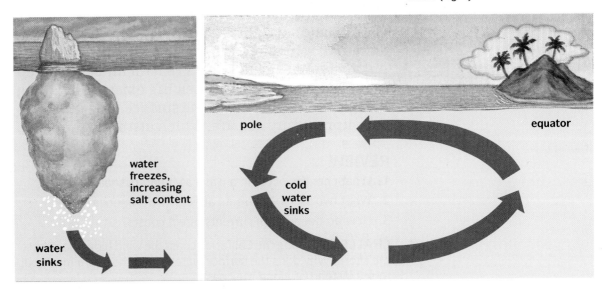

water freezes, increasing salt content

water sinks

pole

cold water sinks

equator

How Do Cold and Hot Water Mix?

OBJECTIVE

Demonstrate how cold water and hot water mix.

MATERIALS

2 beakers, food coloring or ink, plastic drinking straw

PROCEDURE

A. Fill a beaker with very cold water.

B. Fill another beaker with very hot water.

C. Add enough food coloring to the hot water so that the color is easily seen. Use a drinking straw to stir the mixture.

D. Use the straw to remove some of the colored water. Do this by inserting the straw into the colored water. Tightly cover the top of the straw with your finger. **Caution:** Do not use your mouth. With the top covered, lift the straw straight up out of the water.

E. Keeping the top covered, put the open end of the straw in the cold clear water, near the bottom of the beaker. Remove your finger from the top of the straw to release the colored water.

1. What happens to the colored water?

F. Repeat steps **D** and **E**, but this time put some cold colored water into hot clear water.

2. What happens to the cold water?

RESULTS AND CONCLUSIONS

What effect did the temperature have on the way the two liquids mixed?

EXTENSION

Try the experiment again, this time using hot and cold *salt* water. Are the results similar?

Near the surface of the ocean, where the water is warm and sunlight reaches, plant life and tiny sea animals can deplete the water's supply of food or nutrients. But the nutrients remain unused in deep ocean water, where little sea life exists. Upwelling brings those nutrients to the surface. The nutrients can support tiny sea life, which attracts many fish.

REVIEW

1. What changes occur in a wave as it enters shallow water?

2. What two surface currents affect North America?

3. How do deep ocean currents affect coasts?

CHALLENGE Along the California coast the wind blows parallel to the shore. Why does the surface water along the shore move out to sea instead of along the coast?

21·5 Shoreline Features

BEACHES

The boundary between the land and the ocean is called the **shoreline**. Where the shoreline has not been eroded much, it is rocky and contains cliffs. The shoreline on the northwest coast of North America contains many cliffs. Where the shoreline has been eroded, large amounts of rock material, such as sand, gravel, and pebbles, collect on the shore. A collection of rock material along a shore is called a **beach**. Beaches cover much of the eastern shore of North America.

Not all beach material comes from the breaking down of cliffs and rocks that make up some shorelines. Gravel and sand can be carried to shorelines and deposited there by rivers. Beaches are usually thought of as having light-colored sand. However, many beaches do not have sand. Instead they may be covered by dark sand or pebbles or rocks, as shown in Figure 21·13.

The size and amount of the material on a beach is determined by the age of the beach. An old beach

After completing this section, you will be able to

- **explain** how beaches form.
- **describe** several features caused by the deposit of sand.
- **identify** several features of rocky shorelines.

The key terms in this section are
beach
longshore current
shoreline

Figure 21·13

A pebble beach in California *(left);* a black sand beach in Hawaii *(top right);* a white sand beach in New Jersey *(bottom right).*

has more material and finer material. The west coast of North America, for example, is young and has narrow beaches with little sand. But the east coast, being much older than the west coast, has wide beaches with large deposits of sand.

The color of the sand on a beach can vary greatly, depending on its origin. Beaches on the island of Hawaii, for example, are covered with black sand. This sand forms from the weathering of lava flows. The light-colored sand on beaches of the east coast of North America comes from the weathering of granite. The white sand on beaches of southern Florida comes from the weathered remains of skeletons and shells of tiny sea animals.

The size of a beach may vary from summer to winter. During the summer a beach may be wide and contain sand. During the winter the waves are larger and can wash away sand, leaving only gravel and reducing the width of the beach. The sand may be deposited offshore in a ridge called a *sand bar*. When summer returns, gentle waves can slowly return the sand to the beach. Wind on the beach may cause the sand to be deposited in mounds or ridges called sand dunes.

Figure 21·14

A beach is made of sediment eroded from the land.

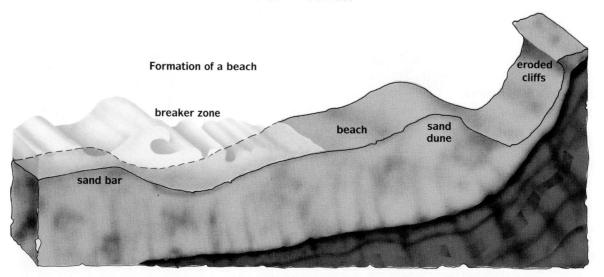

Formation of a beach

breaker zone

beach

sand dune

eroded cliffs

sand bar

Off the Gulf Coast and along much of the eastern shore of the United States, deposits called barrier islands are found. A *barrier island* is a long island of sand in the ocean. A barrier island runs

PUZZLER

Sea walls are built behind beaches to protect houses from storm waves, as well as to preserve shorelines. But, as you can see in the photograph, a sea wall can cause a beach to erode. Explain why this happens.

parallel to the shoreline. Barrier islands may range in width from 100 m to 2 km and extend in length for hundreds of kilometers.

Many scientists believe that barrier islands may have once been sand dunes. Beginning about 15,000 years ago, at the end of the last ice age, the sea level began rising. The rise in sea level was caused by the melting of great ice sheets. As the sea level rose, the sand dunes became surrounded by ocean.

Other deposits of sand are left by longshore currents. A **longshore current** is an ocean current that moves along the shoreline. Longshore currents can carry large amounts of sand. In places where the current slows down, the sand is deposited. For example, where the shoreline turns in at a bay, such a current can leave a deposit of sand called a spit. A spit extends from the land into the mouth of a bay.

Longshore currents also deposit sand around piers and similar structures that people make and that extend into the ocean. Some of these structures are built with the purpose of trapping sand for beaches. For example, piles of rocks called jetties are built to prevent erosion of beaches. Jetties extend from the beaches into the ocean and trap sand that is carried by longshore currents. However, jetties cause longshore currents to become depleted of sand. Thus, beaches farther down the current lose their supply of sand, and over time they erode faster.

Figure 21·15
A jetty is placed on a beach to prevent erosion by waves.

519

ROCKY SHORELINES

Some of the most unusual features of rocky shorelines are sea cliffs, sea caves, sea arches, and sea stacks. They form from headlands, or rocky points that extend into the sea. As waves pound the rock, water and air are forced into cracks. This action eventually causes large slabs of rock to split off, forming a vertical cliff called a *sea cliff*.

The slabs of rock are further broken down into small pieces. The pieces of rock are picked up by the waves and help to abrade the wall of the sea cliff further. If the cliff contains soft rock, the waves and pieces of rock hollow out part of the cliff, forming a *sea cave*.

The waves may cut straight through a wall of the sea cave. This forms a *sea arch*, a kind of stone bridge that connects the land with one support in the sea. If the roof of the arch falls, the column of rock left standing in the water is called a *sea stack*. You can find sea cliffs, sea caves, sea arches, and sea stacks along the coasts of Oregon, Washington, California, and Maine.

Figure 21·16
Sea caves *(left)*, sea arches *(middle)*, and sea stacks *(right)*.

REVIEW

1. How do beaches form?
2. What are several features caused by the deposit of sand?
3. What are several features of rocky shorelines?

CHALLENGE Why do waves erode shorelines that have cliffs more quickly than they erode shorelines that have beaches?

21·6 Tides

CAUSE OF TIDES

The periodic rise and fall in the level of the ocean is called the **tides**. For people living along the shore, tides can be as important as the weather. Tides can cause the water level to rise as much as 15 m, twice a day, covering large areas of the shore with water. Each day, changes in the water level occur at every shoreline.

Tides are caused by the gravitational pull of the sun and the moon. The moon is much closer to the earth than is the sun, so the moon has a much greater effect on the tides. On the side of the earth facing the moon, ocean water is pulled toward the moon and away from the earth. This causes the level of the ocean to rise and forms a tidal bulge, or high tide.

A tidal bulge also occurs on the other side of the earth, facing away from the moon. Here the solid earth is closer to the moon than is the ocean. As a result, the solid earth is pulled to the moon more than is the water. The water appears to be pulled from the earth in another tidal bulge. Thus at any one time there are two tidal bulges on the earth.

After completing this section, you will be able to

- **explain** the cause of tides.
- **compare** neap tides with spring tides.
- **describe** the factors that can affect tides in local areas.

The key terms in this section are
neap tides
spring tides
tides

Figure 21·17
The greatest tidal range occurs during the spring tide *(left)*. A smaller tidal range occurs during the neap tide *(right)*.

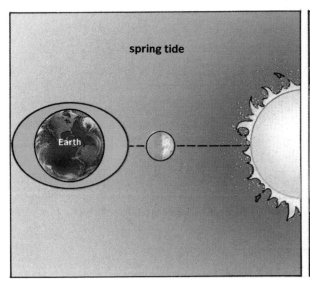
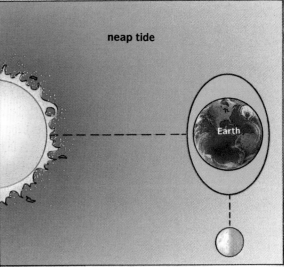

spring tide

neap tide

The tides in the Bay of Fundy, in Canada, are the largest in the world, with a tidal range of more than 15 m.

An experimental power plant that harnesses the tide there can produce about 50 million kW-h of electric power a year. This is enough electricity for about 500 homes. The power plant uses a turbine that catches the en-ergy of flowing water. This turbine generates electricity only when the tide flows out. When the tide comes in, gates to the turbine are opened, and the water flows into a holding pond. When the tide turns and begins to flow back out, the trapped tidal water rushes through the turbine. Electric power can be pro-duced for about 6 hours.

The two areas of ocean between the bulges supply water to fill the bulges. Thus the water level in these areas falls, forming two low tides. The difference in the water level between low tide and high tide is called the *tidal range.*

SPRING AND NEAP TIDES

The sun also causes two tidal bulges. But because the sun's pull of gravity on the ocean is much weaker than the moon's, the tidal bulges caused by the sun are very small. However, twice a month the sun and moon are in the same line with the earth. Then the sun's pull is added to the moon's pull. This forms higher-than-usual tides called **spring tides**. At the same time the low tides are lower than normal. Thus, the tidal range is greatest during the spring tides.

The sun and the moon can form a right angle with the earth. Then the moon's effect on the ocean is partly reduced by the sun's pull. There is little change in the level of water between high tide and low tide. These weaker tides are called **neap tides**. Notice the positions of the earth, moon, and sun in Figure 21·17 (*right*), page 521.

The tidal bulges remain in place as the earth rotates. This causes many places on the earth to have two high tides and two low tides each day. But because the moon is also moving in the same direction as the earth rotates, the tides occur about 50 minutes later each day.

Figure 21·18

High tide *(top)* and low tide *(bottom).*

TIDAL RANGE

The tidal range in the open ocean is less than a meter. The tidal range near coastal areas can vary, depending on three factors: the shape of the ocean basin, the depth of the ocean basin, and the shape of the coastline. In the Mediterranean Sea the tidal range is about a third of a meter. In the Bay of Fundy, on the southeastern coast of Canada, the tidal range is about 15 m. In fact the tide there rises about 3 m in 10 minutes!

REVIEW

1. What is the cause of tides?
2. How do neap tides and spring tides differ?
3. What factors affect tides in local areas?

CHALLENGE The moon travels in an elliptical path rather than in a circular path around the earth. How do you think this affects tides?

CHAPTER SUMMARY

The main ideas in this chapter are listed below. Read these statements before you answer the Chapter Review questions.

- Seawater is a complex solution that contains salts, minerals, and gases dissolved in water. (21·1)
- The salt content of seawater is relatively stable throughout the ocean. However, the amounts of gases dissolved in seawater vary. (21·1)
- The earth has four major oceans: the Pacific Ocean, the Atlantic Ocean, the Indian Ocean, and the Arctic Ocean. (21·2)
- The ocean floor has mountains, seamounts, trenches, and abyssal plains. (21·2)
- Some of the sediments deposited on the ocean floor come from weathering and erosion of land surfaces. (21·3)

- In tropical or warm oceans, deposits called coral reefs form around islands or near coastlines. (21·3)
- Almost all ocean waves are formed by wind blowing across the ocean surface. (21·4)
- Surface currents are formed by wind, but deep-ocean currents are caused by differences in the density of water. (21·4)
- Features such as beaches and cliffs are the result of wave action. (21·5)
- Large amounts of sand can be moved along beaches by longshore currents. (21·5)
- The gravitational pull of the moon and sun causes the level of the ocean to rise and fall periodically. (21·6)

The key terms in this chapter are listed below. Use each term in a sentence that shows the meaning of the term.

atoll	continental shelf	longshore current	shoreline
beach	coral reefs	neap tides	spring tides
breaker	degassing	ocean basin	tides
continental margin	Gulf Stream	salinity	upwelling

Chapter Review

VOCABULARY

Write the letter of the term that best matches the definition. Not all the terms will be used.

1. The underwater area that borders a continent
2. The highest high tides
3. A deep current that rises to the ocean surface
4. A breaking wave
5. Rocklike structures formed from shell-like material
6. An ocean current that moves along the shore
7. The amount of dissolved salt in a kilogram of seawater
8. The process in which gases are released by volcanoes
9. A warm current that flows by North America's eastern coast
10. A collection of rock material along a shore

a. beach
b. breaker
c. continental margin
d. coral reefs
e. degassing
f. Gulf Stream
g. longshore current
h. ocean basin
i. salinity
j. shoreline
k. spring tides
l. upwelling

CONCEPTS

Identify each statement as True or False. If a statement is false, replace the underlined term or phrase with a term or phrase that makes the statement true.

1. The first oceans were formed from <u>rain</u> water.
2. The largest ocean on the earth is the <u>Pacific Ocean</u>.
3. Most sediments that reach the ocean floor are carried by <u>wind</u>.
4. Waves break on a beach because the water becomes <u>deep</u>.
5. The <u>moon</u> has a greater influence on the tides than does the sun.

Choose the term or phrase that best answers the question or completes the statement.

6. Which of the following elements are found in the greatest amounts in seawater?
   a. chlorine and sodium
   b. calcium and strontium
   c. magnesium and bromine
   d. sulfur and fluorine
7. Thick layers of sediments can collect on the ocean floor because
   a. it is very cold.
   b. the water is heavy.
   c. conditions rarely change.
   d. there are many living things.
8. Fishers look for areas of upwelling because
   a. the water there is warmer.
   b. there are fewer storms.
   c. the water there is colder.
   d. the water there contains more sea life.

9. Old beaches tend to be
   a. narrow and rocky.
   b. wide and sandy.
   c. narrow and sandy.
   d. wide and rocky.
10. Which of the following formations can develop at a rocky point along a shoreline?
   a. a trench
   b. an atoll
   c. a sea stack
   d. a seamount

Answer the following in complete sentences.

11. What role do volcanoes have in making the ocean salty?
12. Compare the topographies of the continental margin and the ocean basin.
13. Describe three kinds of coral reefs.
14. How does a large wave form on the ocean?
15. Compare the way tides are caused on the side of the earth facing the moon with the way they are caused on the opposite side.

APPLICATION/ CRITICAL THINKING

1. During an ice age, much of the earth's water is "locked up" in glaciers. How would sea level be affected by an ice age? How would the salinity of the ocean be affected?
2. How might the thickness of the sediments on the continental shelves be used to determine the age of the earth?
3. The climate of southern Florida is affected by the Gulf Stream more than by the climate of northern Florida. How does this explain the fact that the climate in southern Florida is warmer than that in northern Florida?
4. Winds north of the Sargasso Sea, in the North Atlantic Ocean, blow toward the east, but winds south of the sea blow toward the west. Why, then, is seaweed in the Sargasso Sea pushed toward the center of the sea?

EXTENSION

1. Find out for how long people have been able to live in artificial enclosures under the sea. What do such experiments indicate about the future?
2. Find out why cliff divers at Acapulco, Mexico, must jump at the right moment if they are to dive safely.
3. There are certain places on the earth that are ideal for surfing. Find out where those places are and why special breakers occur there.
4. Do library research to find out how the salinities of the Red Sea, the Black Sea, the Mediterranean Sea, and the Great Salt Lake compare.

Science in Careers

You would not have to be an astronaut or astronomer to be involved in a space program. As an aerospace assembler, you could put together the machinery and parts that go into spacecraft, telescopes, and equipment used in the aerospace industry.

Aerospace assemblers work for private industry and for the government. They must be able to work with their hands and to recognize details. A high school diploma and on-the-job training are usually required. Courses in shop and science are helpful.

AEROSPACE ASSEMBLER

VOLCANOLOGIST

You have learned about the different kinds of volcanoes. Many active volcanoes are spectacular. Some provide dazzling displays of streaming lava. Still others are life threatening, destroying towns with rivers of boiling mud and clouds of poisonous gas.

Volcanologists are scientists who study volcanoes. These people may take samples of lava from a volcano to learn about the earth's interior. Many volcanologists are trying to discover ways of predicting violent eruptions of volcanoes.

Volcanologists often travel to different parts of the world to visit active volcanoes. The scientists collect samples of volcanic gases, ash, and lava. And they use instruments to record seismic activity and changes in the contours of the land.

Many volcanologists teach at universities. Some work for the government. After receiving a college degree, most volcanologists go on to receive advanced degrees. Classes in earth science, physics, chemistry, and math will be helpful to persons who wish to enter the field of volcanology.

People in Science

During the 1960s, Dr. George Robert Carruthers, a research physicist, was developing instruments that would improve the ability to detect radiation from space. He knew that stars give off radiation that is invisible to the eye.

Some of this invisible radiation is located in the ultraviolet region of the spectrum. Dr. Carruthers knew that the earth's atmosphere blocks out most of this radiation similar to the way clouds block out visible light from the sun.

Dr. Carruthers developed a device that would be used outside the atmosphere, in space. This device is called the Far Ultraviolet Camera Spectrograph. It was taken to the moon on Apollo 12 in 1972.

Carruthers's instrument takes pictures of objects radiating ultraviolet radiation. It also separates this radiation into a spectrum. The instrument has allowed astronomers to investigate the chemical and physical properties of stars and interstellar gas in great detail.

Dr. George Robert Carruthers PHYSICIST

Issues and Technology

Acid Rain

It is rotting the bodies of cars and weakening the structures of metal bridges. It is wearing away monuments, like the Egyptian temples at Karnak, the American Indian cliff dwellings at Mesa Verde, and the Statue of Liberty. It gets into lakes and kills wildlife. It falls on trees and kills them. It is reported to have turned a Swedish woman's blonde hair to a shade of green. What could have such world-wide effects? It is acid rain, one of the most controversial environmental problems today. Everyone knows that acid rain is harmful. But people don't all agree on where it comes from and who should pay for its damage.

Most scientists agree that acid rain forms from gases released by the burning of fossil fuels—oil, coal, and gas. The primary sources of such gases are electric power plants, industrial boilers, and metal smelters. When fossil fuels are burned, sulfur dioxide and nitrogen oxide gases are given off. These invisible gases pour out of smokestacks into the air. Once in the air and in the presence of sunlight, these gases react with other chemicals. The reactions turn the gases into sulfuric acid and nitric acid. They fall to earth as acid rain or acid snow.

Extremely tall smokestacks—some over 300 m high—have made the problem worse. They were originally built high to remove pollution from areas where factories are located. The idea was that the pollution could be sent soaring high enough into the sky to harmlessly drift away. But the stacks are so tall that they put the pollution into high-altitude wind streams. In this way, pollutants are carried hundreds or thousands of kilometers downwind from the source.

In North America the industrial areas of the Midwest and Northeast are main sources of sulfur dioxide and nitrogen oxides. Therefore, large amounts of acid rain fall downwind of those areas, in the northeastern United States and eastern Canada. Tests have shown that rain in the northeastern United States is sometimes 10 to 30 times more acidic than normal rain. A 1978 storm brought rain as acidic as lemon juice to one part of Pennsylvania.

Figure 1 is a pH scale. A pH scale shows how acidic or basic (alkaline) a substance is. This scale shows the pH of several substances, including acid rain. The stronger the acid, the lower the pH number. Numbers greater than 7 indicate that the substance is alkaline. A pH of 7 is neutral.

APPLYING CRITICAL THINKING SKILLS

1. What is the acidity of unpolluted rain?
2. What is the range of acidity for acid rain?
3. Is seawater acidic? How do you know?
4. Is unpolluted rain acidic? If so, why is acid rain a problem?

Most of the damage caused by acid rain occurs in spring. Acids are held in snow all winter. Then they are suddenly released as the snow melts. The acids enter lakes quickly. The shock of raised acid levels

Figure 1

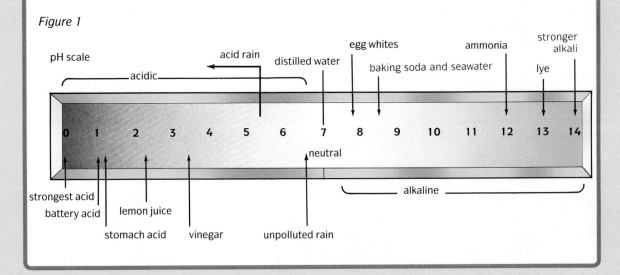

527

often causes the fish to die. The acidity of the water irritates the gills of fish. So the gills form a protective layer of mucus. But the high levels of acid cause too much mucus to form. It clogs the gills, and the fish suffocate.

Acid rain also helps to draw metals, like aluminum, lead, and mercury, out of the soil. These metals concentrate in lakes. The metals kill bacteria, aquatic plants, and animals that are part of the food chain. Lakes attacked by acid rain are often beautifully crystal clear. That is because all life in these lakes has disappeared.

Figure 2 shows the relationship between the acidity of water and its effect on some living things found in lakes. Notice that organisms differ in their ability to tolerate acid rain.

APPLYING CRITICAL THINKING SKILLS

1. Which creature can stand the most acidity?
2. What kinds of creatures can stand less acidity?
3. Which of these creatures could live in a lake in which the water had the acidity of acid rain?
4. What activities of humans are likely to be affected by an increase in the acidity of lakes?

In northern Europe the damage caused by acid rain has been similar to that occurring in North America. Foul-tasting contaminated water sup-plies, dead lakes, and dying forests are alarming many people. Over 20,000 Swedish lakes are estimated to be without fish. In Germany, one half of the nation's trees have been injured by acid rain.

The problem is also serious in Canada. Since much of Canada's acid rain results from American industrial pollution, there is strain between the two countries, who have been close friends.

There are processes for removing some of the pollution that causes acid rain. Devices called scrubbers work on sulfur dioxide. They shoot jets of wet lime at waste gases before they go up a smokestack. The alkaline lime reduces the strength of the acids that form from sulfur dioxide. In many cases the scrubbers reduce sulfur dioxide emissions by over 90 percent. That cuts down on acid rain.

Over a dozen European countries and Canada have pledged to encourage the use of scrubbers and other antipollution devices. These countries want to reduce the amount of sulfur dioxide in the air by 30 percent by the early 1990s. The United States and Great Britain have refused to make such a pledge. And they are two of the largest producers of the harmful gases.

One reason for holding back is money. It is expensive to install antipollution devices. Much of the cost gets passed along to the public. Thus the use of

Figure 2

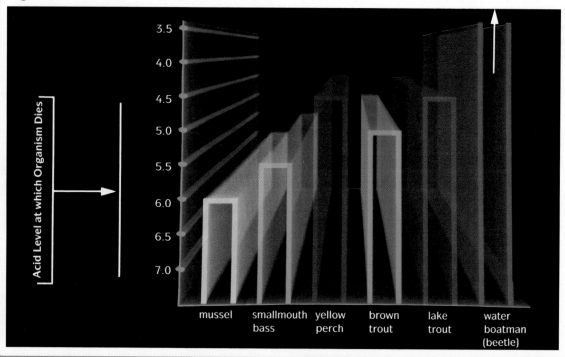

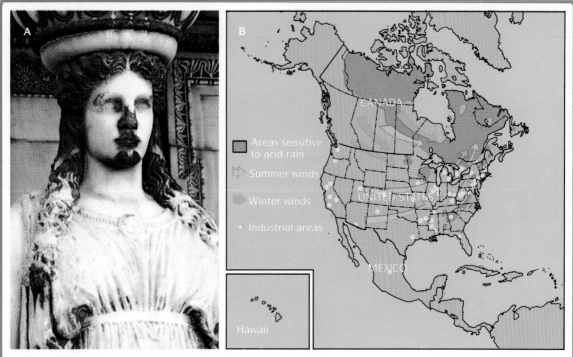

Figure 3

antipollution devices in power plants would probably mean a rise in electric bills. The use of such devices in manufacturing plants could mean higher prices for the goods produced in those plants. Many people who would have to pay the increased costs do not live in areas affected by acid rain. Is it fair for them to pay for a problem occurring thousands of kilometers away?

Meanwhile, some people say that the source of acid rain has not yet been proven. They say that spending money on antipollution devices may not help to solve the problem. At this time, industries in the United States are not required to install antipollution devices, like scrubbers.

Those people who are against controls on sulfur content in air point to statistics for support. They say that in some instances sulfur content in air has gone down while acidity of rain has gone up. Many other factors—such as natural acidity of decayed forest vegetation, pesticides leaking into soil and water, and overfishing—may have as much to do with the disappearance of fish as does acid rain.

The United States Environmental Protection Agency (EPA) estimates that the cost of repairing and replacing structures damaged by acid rain has been more than $5 billion. But that doesn't take

into account environmental problems. And it doesn't take into account how this pollution could be affecting human health.

Should something be done now? If so, who should pay for the damage? If we wait, what will be the long-term effect?

Figure 3 shows industrial areas in North America. The figure also shows areas that are sensitive to damage by acid rain. The arrows show the main wind patterns and routes for the spread of acid rain.

APPLYING CRITICAL THINKING SKILLS
1. In North America, what country has the most industrial areas where sulfur dioxide and nitrogen oxides are produced?
2. What country has the most areas that are sensitive to acid rain?
3. How do you think the acid rain situation affects relations between Canada and the United States?
4. Judging from wind patterns, do you think acid rain would be more of problem in eastern Canada and the northeastern United States in summer or in winter? Why?
5. If scrubbers and other pollution control devices are needed, who should pay for them? Why?

INVESTIGATING
THE HUMAN BODY

Think of the many tasks humans can accomplish. Humans can run a 4-minute mile, perform intricate surgery, and compose symphonies. All of these tasks are directed by a complex nervous system. In this unit you will learn how the nervous system controls the body. This organ system, along with other systems of the body, is reproduced by each new individual. In this unit you will also learn about human reproduction and development.

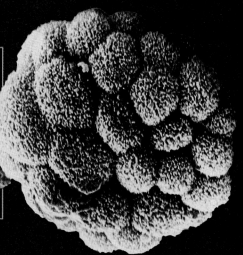

An early stage of human ▲ development, as the fertilized egg undergoes cell division.

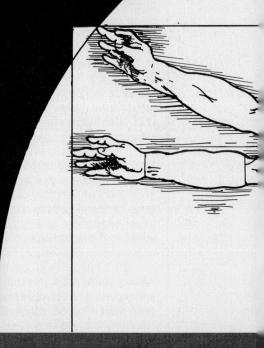

▲ *This family shows three stages of human development.*

CHAPTER 22

CONTROL SYSTEMS

Can you tell what is shown in the photograph? This image of the brain was made by an NMR machine. NMR stands for nuclear magnetic resonance. To produce an image with an NMR machine, an object is surrounded by a magnetic field. This field in turn magnetizes the nuclei of atoms within the object. The magnetism of different substances within the object shows up as different colors.

An NMR machine may be used to detect problems that in the past would have been found by surgery or by X ray. The benefit of using NMR is that an individual is not subjected to potentially harmful X rays. In addition, NMR can be used to clearly show soft tissues of the body that may not show up in X rays.

This NMR brain scan shows a cross section of the brain. The outer rings show the fat surrounding the skull, the skull, and the fluid that surrounds the brain. The yellow and white area is the brain itself. Notice the many folds of the brain. These folded areas allow the part of the brain that is involved in reasoning and voluntary movement to have a large surface area.

- *What are the main parts of the brain?*
- *How does the brain function with other parts of the nervous system?*
- *What are the parts of the nervous system?*

22·1 Sending Electrical Messages

THE NERVOUS SYSTEM

When you are frightened, your heart may beat faster. When you are cold, your body may shiver. What causes these changes in the body? Most of the body's reactions to the outside world are controlled by the nervous system. The **nervous system** is a control system made up of the brain, spinal cord, and nerves. The spinal cord carries messages from the brain to other parts of the body. The coordination of such actions as walking or breathing is also controlled by the nervous system.

The nervous system receives *stimuli* from outside the body. Stimuli are events or conditions that cause an organism to react. The stimuli trigger the nervous system. The nervous system then sends messages to various parts of the body, causing them to respond to the stimuli.

NEURONS

The nervous system is made up of neurons. **Neurons** are nerve cells; they carry messages throughout the body. The central part of a neuron is the *cell body*. Look at the neuron shown in Figure

Figure 22·1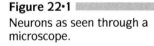
Neurons as seen through a microscope.

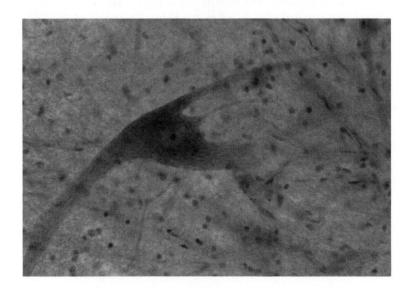

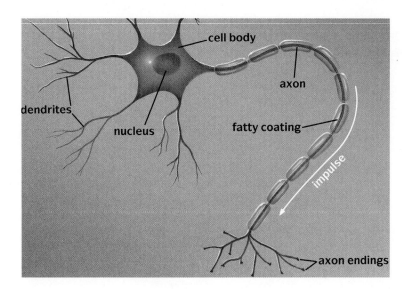

Figure 22·2 ▨▨▨▨▨▨▨▨▨
The structure of a neuron.

22·2 and notice the many fibers that extend from the cell body. Many of these fibers are dendrites.

Dendrites are the extensions of a neuron that carry messages to the cell body. The single, long fiber that extends from the other side of the cell body is an axon. An *axon* is the extension of a neuron that carries messages away from the cell body. Most neurons have many dendrites but only one axon.

The message that travels along a neuron is called an **impulse**. An impulse is received by one or more dendrites and then flows to the cell body and on to the axon. From the axon the impulse may travel on to the next neuron. In this way, impulses move rapidly throughout the body.

Dendrites and axons are sometimes covered by a fatty coating that prevents impulses from jumping randomly from one neuron to another. The coating also increases the speed at which impulses are carried along an axon or dendrite.

Although impulses move from neuron to neuron, neurons do not touch each other. Between any two neurons, there is a gap called a **synapse**. Locate the synapses and an enlargement of one shown in Figure 22·3 on the next page.

syn- (together)

How do impulses cross a synapse? Suppose an impulse is moving along a neuron. When the impulse reaches the end of the axon, a chemical is

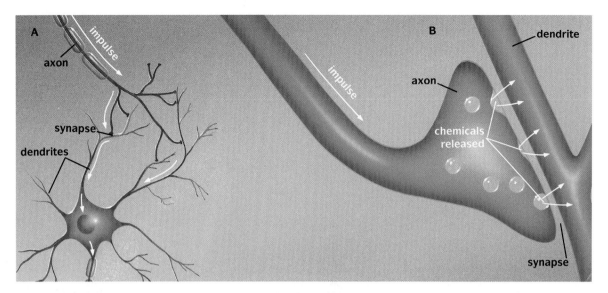

Figure 22·3

Neurons showing axon and dendrite endings *(A)*. Notice that a message crosses a synapse from the axon to the dendrite *(B)*.

released from the axon into the synapse. This chemical moves across the synapse to the dendrites of the next neuron. The chemical causes an impulse to start in the second neuron. Thus the impulse moves from neuron to neuron.

NEURON TYPES

There are three types of neurons: sensory, motor, and association. *Sensory neurons* carry impulses toward the spinal cord or brain. For example, when you stroke a cat, impulses are carried from your fingers to your brain by sensory neurons.

Motor neurons carry impulses from the brain or spinal cord to other organs. For example, impulses from motor neurons cause muscles to contract. *Association neurons* are found within the spinal cord or brain. These neurons serve as links between sensory neurons and motor neurons.

REVIEW

1. What are the functions of the nervous system?
2. What are the main parts of a neuron?
3. How does an impulse pass from one neuron to another?

CHALLENGE The following kinds of wires are found in a computer system: wires that run from a keyboard to the computer box; wires that are contained within the computer box; and wires that run from the computer box to a printer. Explain how each of these three types of wires is similar to one of the three types of neurons.

22·2 The Nervous System

CENTRAL NERVOUS SYSTEM

The **brain** is the main control center of the nervous system. The brain is protected by the skull. Billions of neurons make up the brain. This complex organ is connected to the spinal cord. The **spinal cord** is a structure that carries messages between the brain and the other parts of the body. The spinal cord contains nerve tissue and is enclosed by the backbone. The brain and spinal cord together make up the *central nervous system*, which is shown in Figure 22·4A.

The brain has three main parts, as shown in Figure 22·4B. Notice that the cerebrum is the largest part. The **cerebrum** is the part of the brain that functions in learning, memory, and reasoning. It also functions in interpreting messages from and directing the control of many parts of the body. The cerebrum consists of a right half and a left half. Each half of the cerebrum controls the opposite half of the body.

After completing this section, you will be able to

- **identify** and **describe** the parts of the central nervous system.
- **describe** the function of the peripheral nervous system.
- **explain** how reflexes occur.

The key terms in this section are
brain   medulla
cerebellum   reflex
cerebrum   spinal cord

Figure 22·4

The brain and spinal cord make up the central nervous system *(A)*. The three parts of the brain *(B)*.

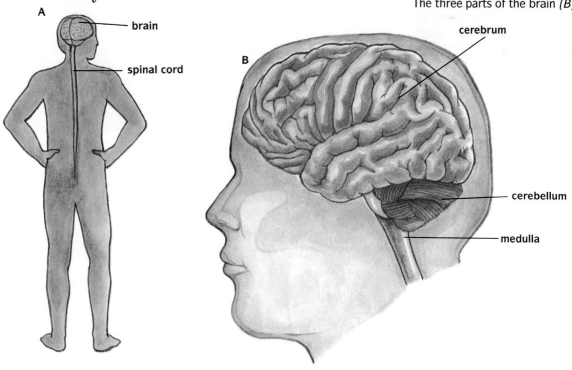

A

brain

spinal cord

B

cerebrum

cerebellum

medulla

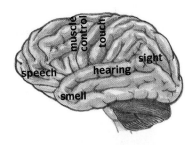

Figure 22·5
Functions of the cerebrum.

Figure 22·5 shows a "map" of the cerebrum. You can see that different parts of the cerebrum have different functions. Where is information that comes from the eyes received? Locate the part of the cerebrum that controls the muscles. Just behind this part is a region that receives information about the sense of touch. Other parts of the cerebrum function in hearing, smelling, and speaking.

The **cerebellum** is the part of the brain that controls muscle coordination and body balance. Where is the cerebellum located? Balancing on a beam or performing a high jump, as shown in Figure 22·6, involves many muscles working together. Even the simple act of moving a leg forward to take a step involves the coordinated work of more than 50 muscles. Impulses to the muscles begin in the cerebrum and pass through the cerebellum, resulting in smooth movement of the body.

Figure 22·6
What part of the brain allows these athletes to maintain their balance?

Look back at Figure 22·4B. Where is the medulla located? The **medulla** is the part of the brain that controls involuntary actions needed for life. Involuntary actions are those not under conscious control. Breathing and the beating of the heart, as well as actions such as coughing and sneezing, are controlled by the medulla.

The brain and spinal cord are covered with protective membranes and surrounded by fluid. The fluid cushions the brain and spinal cord, protecting them from injury.

PERIPHERAL NERVOUS SYSTEM

Notice in Figure 22·7 that many nerves pass from the central nervous system to all parts of the body. A nerve is a group of neuron fibers. The nerves that connect the central nervous system with other organs form the *peripheral nervous system*. This system, shown in Figure 22·7, carries messages between the central nervous system and other parts of the body.

The peripheral nervous system and spinal cord control some actions that do not involve the brain. For example, when you step on a sharp object, you automatically lift your foot, as a reflex. Your brain has not directed the action. A **reflex** is a quick, automatic response to a stimulus.

The path that an impulse takes in a reflex is called a *reflex arc*. The reflex arc shown in Figure 22·8 involves three neurons — sensory, association, and motor. The brain is not part of the reflex. Look at Figure 22·8 as you read about the reflex.

1. Contact of the foot with a sharp object causes a pain stimulus that is received by a receptor in the skin of the foot. A *receptor* is a structure that

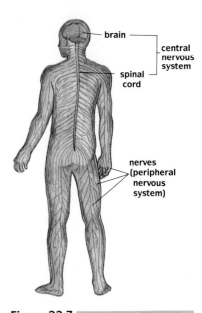

Figure 22·7

The peripheral nervous system.

Figure 22·8

The association neuron of a reflex arc is found in the spinal cord.

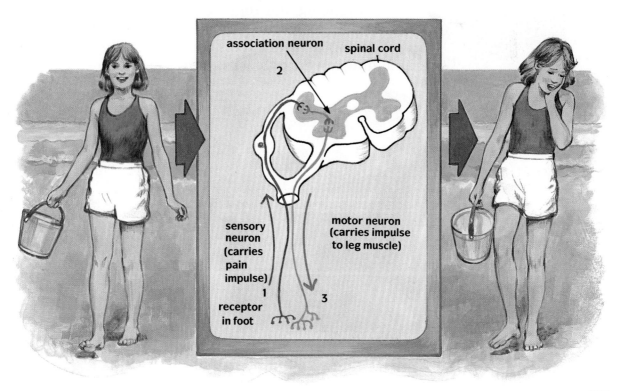

receives a stimulus. An impulse travels from the receptor through a sensory neuron to the spinal cord.

2. In the spinal cord the impulse passes through an association neuron. The association neuron causes an impulse in a motor neuron.

3. The impulse travels along the motor neuron to the muscles of the leg. The impulse causes the muscles to contract and lift the foot off the sharp object.

LEARNING

Think about some of the skills you have gained since you were born. You may remember learning how to swim, to ride a bicycle, or to do some other activity. When you began learning such activities, you had to think about many parts of the tasks at one time. As you practiced, the activities became more automatic. Finally you could perform the tasks without thinking about them. *Learning* is the complex process by which the ability to do a new task is gained. Learning is a function of the nervous system.

Practicing and repeating steps may be important parts of learning. Some scientists think that practicing a task affects synapses. The children building towers of blocks, shown in Figure 22·9, are

Figure 22·9

The girl shooting baskets *(left)* and the children playing with blocks *(right)* are learning by practicing.

OBJECTIVES
Determine how repetition affects learning.
Construct a graph to show how repetition affects learning.

MATERIALS
fifteen 3-cm x 3-cm cardboard squares, clock or watch with second hand

PROCEDURE
A. On squares of cardboard, write the first 15 letters of the alphabet, 1 letter on each square.
B. Scramble the squares, and lay them out on your desk, letter side up.
C. Have a classmate keep time with a clock or watch. When your classmate says "go," use your index finger to touch each of the squares in *alphabetical order*. Record the number of seconds it took to touch all the letters in order.

D. Repeat step **C** four more times.
E. Draw a graph like the one shown above, and graph your results.

RESULTS AND CONCLUSIONS
1. How long did it take to touch the letters the first time? Did the amount of time increase or decrease with each trial? Explain why this change occurred.
2. Predict what the graph would look like if you repeated the task ten more times.

repeating a set of actions. These actions use the same neurons and synapses. Practice seems to make messages move across synapses more easily.

Learning also involves forming a memory of how to do an activity. It is thought that memories are stored in the cerebrum, but scientists are not sure in what form memories are stored.

REVIEW
1. Name the parts of the central nervous system. What are the main functions of each part?
2. What is the peripheral nervous system? What is its function?
3. List the three types of neurons through which an impulse travels in a reflex arc. What is the function of each type of neuron?

CHALLENGE Describe the reflex involved in touching a hot stove. Explain why saying "ouch" and shaking your hand afterward are not part of the reflex. After you have had experiences with hot stoves, it becomes automatic for you not to touch them. Why is this automatic behavior not a reflex?

22·3 The Senses

Heat, sound, and light are examples of the many stimuli that act on the nervous system. Each of these stimuli is detected by a different kind of receptor. Some receptors are the endings of dendrites; other receptors are structures attached to dendrites. Some receptors are found in *sense organs*. For example, the eye is a sense organ that contains light receptors.

Sense organs send impulses along nerves to the brain, where the impulses are interpreted. Although receptors in the eye detect light, you are aware of the light only when impulses from the eye are received by the brain.

SIGHT

Study the drawing of the eye in Figure 22·10. Light enters the eye through the **cornea**, the clear area at the front of the eye. Behind the cornea is the colored part of the eye, called the iris. The **iris** is a ring of muscle that contracts or relaxes in response to light. This action, which is a reflex, causes the pupil to change size. The **pupil** is the opening in the middle of the iris. The size of the pupil controls the amount of light entering the eye. When would the pupil be small?

Figure 22·10
The structure of the eye.

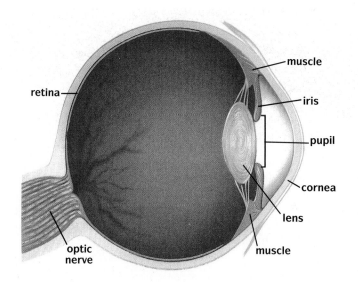

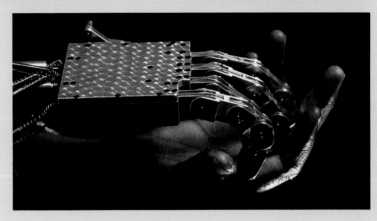

A mechanical hand may soon help people who are both blind and deaf to communicate. The hand is run by a computer and can spell out letters of the manual alphabet. The manual alphabet is a series of hand signals used by deaf people. A blind-deaf person reads by touching the hand as it spells. It may be possible in the future to also use this hand for telephone communication.

Light passes through the pupil to the lens. The **lens** is a clear, flexible structure that focuses light. Muscles attached to the lens cause it to get thicker or thinner. The lens focuses light onto the retina. By changing shape, the lens can focus light from near or distant objects. The **retina** is a layer of receptor cells located at the back of the eye. The lens of the eye focusing images on the retina can be compared to the lens in a movie projector focusing light on a movie screen.

The retina contains two kinds of receptor cells: rods and cones. **Rods** are receptors that detect the presence or absence of light and that allow you to see in dim light. **Cones** are receptors that allow you to see color. Cones function well in bright light only. Which receptors do you make most use of at night?

The rods and cones are connected to sensory neurons that form the *optic nerve*. Impulses from the rods and cones are sent along the optic nerve to the sight center of the cerebrum. In the cerebrum the image is interpreted.

HEARING AND BALANCE

Sounds are caused by vibrations of objects. If you pluck a guitar string, it will vibrate, sending sound waves through the air. The sound waves cause structures within the ear to vibrate. These vibrations are changed into impulses that travel to the brain, where they are interpreted as sound.

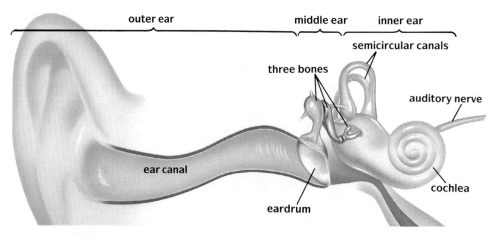

Figure 22·11
The structure of the ear.

The *outer ear* as shown in Figure 22·11 gathers and funnels sound waves. The outer ear is made up of two parts: the visible part of the ear and the canal. The canal carries sound waves to the eardrum. The **eardrum** is a round membrane that vibrates when sound waves strike it. The eardrum separates the outer ear from the middle ear.

The *middle ear* contains three tiny bones. Vibrations of the eardrum pass through these three

ACTIVITY How Do Sounds Reach the Ear?

OBJECTIVE
Compare the ways in which sounds are received by the ear.

MATERIALS
tuning fork, rubber hammer, metric ruler

PROCEDURE
A. Have your partner strike a tuning fork with a rubber hammer and hold the vibrating tuning fork directly in front of you, about 20 cm away.
   1. Describe the sound you hear.
B. Have your partner strike the tuning fork and hold it by the side of your head, about 20 cm from your left ear. Repeat this test with your right ear.
   2. How do the sounds you hear compare with the sound you heard in step **A**?
C. Have your partner strike the tuning fork

and hold the base of it against your forehead.
   3. How does this sound compare with the sounds you heard in steps **A** and **B**?
D. Repeat step **C**, but cover both ears.
   4. How does what you hear compare with the sounds you heard in step **C**?

RESULTS AND CONCLUSIONS
1. Which sound was softest? Why?
2. Which sound was loudest? Why?
3. Sound waves usually reach your ear by moving through the air. In which steps did this occur?
4. In which steps were sound waves not able to reach your ear by moving through the air? Why was this not possible?
5. How did sound waves reach your ear when they could not travel through the air?

bones. One bone in the middle ear rests on the cochlea, a structure in the *inner ear*. The **cochlea** is a coiled, fluid-filled tube that contains sound receptors. Vibrations pass through this fluid to reach the receptors. The receptors send impulses through the *auditory nerve* to the hearing centers of the cerebrum.

Notice also in Figure 22·11 that the inner ear contains three semicircular canals. **Semicircular canals** are structures that help the body keep its balance. Like the cochlea, these canals contain receptor cells and fluid. When the angle of the head changes, such as in bending down, the fluid in the semicircular canals moves. The movement of the fluid causes the receptor cells to send impulses to the brain. The brain uses this information to control the body's movement and balance.

SMELL AND TASTE

Odors are caused by molecules of substances diffusing through the air. These molecules stimulate receptors in your nose. Locate the receptors in Figure 22·12. The receptors send impulses along nerves to the section of the cerebrum behind the nose. Here the impulses are interpreted.

Within the tongue, the sense organ of taste, are many receptors called *taste buds*. Like the receptors

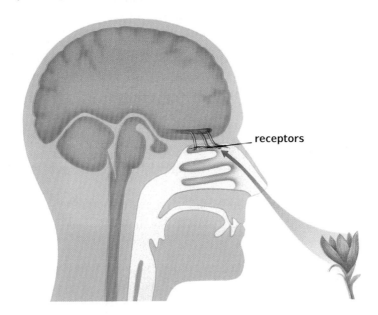

Figure 22·12
Receptors for smell are located in the nose.

receptors

for smell, taste buds respond to molecules of different substances. As you eat, food molecules dissolved in saliva cause the taste buds to send impulses to the brain, where they are interpreted.

TOUCH

Notice in Figure 22·13 that there are five different types of stimuli that the skin can detect. These stimuli are received by different types of receptors in the skin. Some of these receptors are the ends of sensory neurons. Other receptors in the skin are special structures attached to dendrites.

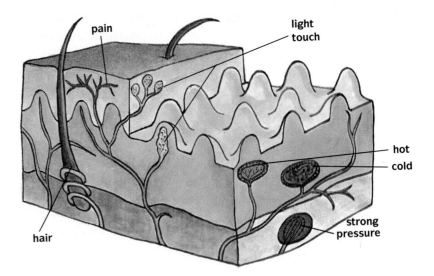

Figure 22·13
The skin contains five kinds of receptors.

Notice that the skin has separate receptors for light touch and strong pressure. Pressure receptors are found deep in the skin. What are the other types of receptors in the skin?

REVIEW

1. Give four examples of sense organs.
2. List the eye structures through which light passes to reach the retina.
3. Explain how sound vibrations move through the ear.
4. What stimulates receptors in the nose? In taste buds?
5. What kinds of receptors are found in the skin?

CHALLENGE Fish have receptors that detect moving objects by their vibrations in the water. These receptors are similar to a type of receptor found in humans. Which type? Explain.

22·4 Chemical Regulation

In addition to the nervous system, control functions are also carried out by the endocrine system. The **endocrine system** is a control system made up of glands. Glands are organs that make chemicals that control certain body functions. *Endocrine glands* release their chemicals directly into the blood. Thus, endocrine glands are different from other glands, which release their chemicals through ducts, or tubes.

The chemicals produced by endocrine glands are called **hormones**. Because hormones are released into the blood, they travel more slowly than do nerve impulses. A nerve impulse may travel the length of the body in less than a second; a hormone may take many minutes. Thus, directions from the endocrine system take longer to be carried out than do those from the nervous system. However, the effects of chemical control last longer. As you read about it, locate each gland in Figure 22·14.

Figure 22·14
The endocrine system.

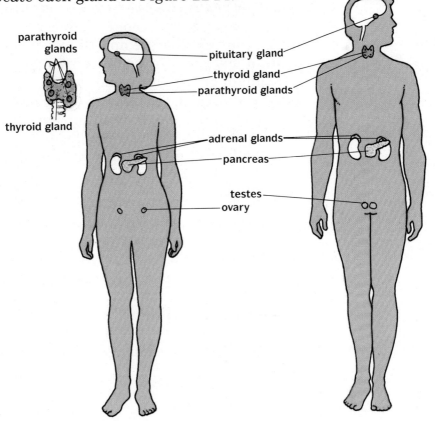

Figure 22·15

Many basketball players are very tall. Which gland produces the hormone that stimulates growth?

● *Pituitary Gland* The pituitary gland, a small gland at the base of the brain, releases many hormones. Some of these hormones control other glands.

One of the hormones released by the pituitary gland, *growth hormone*, stimulates growth in many of the body's tissues. For example, growth hormone causes bones to grow and causes protein to form within muscles. In some individuals the wrong amount of growth hormone is released by the pituitary gland. With too little growth hormone, a child will not grow enough; with too much, a child may grow far beyond normal size. Such problems can be treated if they are detected early in life.

● *Adrenal Glands* An adrenal gland is found just above each of the two kidneys. Each adrenal gland has two layers. The outer layer makes several hormones that help to control the body's use of sugar and minerals. The inner layer of an adrenal gland makes the hormone *adrenalin*. Adrenalin is released when a person is under stress or involved in intense exercise. Adrenalin causes the heart to beat faster and increases the flow of blood to the brain and muscles. These changes help the body respond to stress.

• *Thyroid and Parathyroid Glands* The thyroid gland, located in the neck, makes a hormone that controls the rate at which the body uses energy. If the thyroid gland releases too little hormone, the use of energy will slow down. What will happen if the thyroid gland releases too much hormone?

The thyroid gland also makes a hormone that helps to control the amount of calcium and phosphorus in the blood. Calcium and phosphorus are part of bones and teeth and are also used in many body processes. This second thyroid hormone works together with a hormone released by the parathyroid glands. Where are the four parathyroid glands located?

• *Pancreas* The pancreas, located just under the stomach, is really two glands in one. Part of the pancreas releases enzymes into a duct for use in digestion. The pancreas also contains endocrine tissue, shown in Figure 22·16. This tissue releases hormones into the blood.

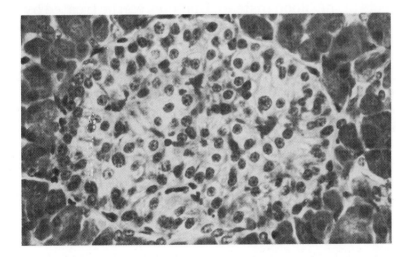

Figure 22·16
Endocrine tissue of the pancreas.

One of these hormones is *insulin.* Insulin controls the amount of glucose in the blood. Glucose is a sugar that is the body's main source of energy. After food is eaten, glucose enters the blood from the digestive system. A high level of glucose in the blood causes insulin to be released by the pancreas. When insulin is released, it causes glucose to move from the blood into cells of the body. As the amount

PUZZLER

Diabetes is a disorder of the endocrine tissue of the pancreas. In this disorder, glucose does not enter the cells but instead collects in the blood. Insulin injections can control the disorder. Sometimes, people who use insulin have very low levels of glucose in the blood. What would explain such a condition in a person with diabetes?

of glucose in the blood decreases, the pancreas stops making insulin.

In some people the pancreas makes little or no insulin. This results in a disorder called *diabetes*. Without insulin, glucose cannot enter cells but collects in the blood instead. Diabetes can be treated by reducing the amount of sugar that is eaten and by taking insulin.

● *Ovaries and Testes* Ovaries are the female reproductive organs; testes are the male reproductive organs. Both of these types of organs produce sex cells as well as function as endocrine glands. The ovaries and testes produce sex hormones, which prepare the body for reproduction. As the body matures, these hormones cause the development of sex characteristics. These changes include the growth of facial hair in males and the development of breasts in females.

REVIEW

1. What is a hormone?
2. Name the glands that make up the endocrine system. What are the main functions of each gland?
3. Describe the disorder that results from lack of insulin.

CHALLENGE When a person is under stress, adrenalin causes more blood to flow to the brain and muscles. How do you think these changes help the body deal with stress?

550

22·5 Drugs and the Body

A **drug** is a chemical that causes physical, emotional, or behavioral changes in the body. Many drugs cause changes in the way the nervous system works. The proper use of drugs is for the treatment of illness or disease. *Drug abuse* is the misuse of drugs. For example, painkilling drugs may be needed after an injury. But taking painkillers just to "feel good" is drug abuse. Taking someone else's prescription medicine is also drug abuse.

A person who abuses a drug may become *dependent* on the drug. Then, the body becomes used to the presence of the drug, making the person feel a need to keep taking the drug. With some drugs, dependence may lead to addiction. **Addiction** is a condition in which the body requires a drug. Once a person is addicted to a drug, it is very difficult to stop its use. When a person stops taking an addictive drug, he or she may have chills, headaches, nausea, and other problems. Drug abusers sometimes die or are disabled by an overdose of drugs. Most drugs fall into one of the four groups listed in Table 22·1 on the next page. These groups are stimulants, depressants, narcotics, and hallucinogens.

After completing this section, you will be able to

- **compare** proper drug use and drug abuse.
- **identify** the major kinds of drugs and **give examples** of each.

The key terms in this section are
addiction
drug

addictus (give over to)

Figure 22·17
Many drugs have harmful effects on the body.

Table 22·1 *Some Abused Drugs and Their Effects*

TYPE OF DRUG	EXAMPLES	EFFECTS
Stimulants	Amphetamines Caffeine Cocaine Nicotine	Increased activity in the nervous system; nervousness and overactivity; increased heartbeat rate and breathing; increased alertness and decreased tiredness.
Depressants	Alcohol Barbiturates	Decreased activity in the nervous system; drowsiness or sleepiness; decreased heartbeat rate and breathing, reduced stress or worry.
Narcotics	Codein Heroin Morphine	Reduced sensitivity to pain; drowsiness or sleepiness; decreased activity in the nervous system; decreased heartbeat rate and breathing.
Hallucinogens	LSD Marijuana PCP	Changed pattern of thoughts and emotions: user sees, hears, smells, or feels things that are not real.

STIMULANTS

Drugs that increase the activity of the nervous system are called *stimulants*. Stimulants usually cause the heart rate, blood pressure, and breathing rate to increase.

Caffeine and *nicotine* are widely used stimulants. Caffeine is a drug found in coffee, tea, cocoa, and some soft drinks. Large amounts of caffeine are harmful to the body. Nicotine is a drug in tobacco. Nicotine increases the heart rate and blood pressure. Smokers become dependent on nicotine.

Amphetamines (am FEHT uh meenz) and *cocaine* are also stimulants. Amphetamines, which are sometimes used as diet pills or to increase alertness, can cause dependency. Cocaine is a dangerous stimulant that leads to dependency. A form of cocaine called *crack* causes rapid addiction. Crack also affects the brain and often causes death.

DEPRESSANTS

Drugs that reduce the activity of the nervous system are called *depressants*. These drugs change the movement of chemicals across the synapses between neurons. Depressants usually slow the heart and breathing rates and reduce stress and worry.

The most-abused depressant is *alcohol*. It is found in drinks such as beer, wine, and liquors. Small amounts of alcohol may act as a stimulant for a short time. Large amounts of alcohol cause a person to become sleepy or even to lose consciousness. Loss of coordination and slurred speech are also effects of this drug.

Many people are able to use alcohol in small amounts without ill effects. But some people develop a dependence on alcohol, called *alcoholism*. Over a period of time alcoholism causes a disease called cirrhosis (suh ROH sihs). This disease damages the liver, preventing it from functioning properly. Liver cells are replaced by deposits of fat and fibers. In what ways does the failed liver shown in Part *A* of Figure 22·18 differ from the normal liver shown in part *C*? Cirrhosis is a major cause of death among alcoholics.

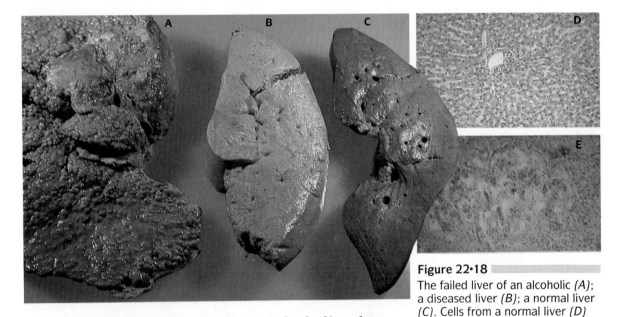

Figure 22·18
The failed liver of an alcoholic *(A)*; a diseased liver *(B)*; a normal liver *(C)*. Cells from a normal liver *(D)* and from a diseased liver *(E)*.

Sometimes, people who are not alcoholics abuse alcohol by drinking and then driving. Drunk driving is a major cause of deaths and injuries in traffic accidents.

Barbiturates (bahr BIHCH uh rayts) are depressants that are prescribed for people who have trouble sleeping. These drugs are also used to reduce nervousness and worrying. Barbiturates slow the rate of breathing; with large doses, breathing may stop. Overuse of these drugs can lead to unconsciousness and death.

NARCOTICS AND HALLUCINOGENS

Narcotics are drugs that reduce pain and give a feeling of well-being. Opium, morphine, codeine, and heroin are narcotics. The use of these drugs leads to dependence and addiction. Although addiction to narcotics can sometimes be overcome, the process is long and difficult.

Drugs that cause hallucinations are called *hallucinogens* (huh LOO suh nuh jehnz). A person having a hallucination vividly imagines seeing, hearing, feeling, or smelling something. For example, hallucinogens may cause a person to hear music when none is playing.

Marijuana is a hallucinogen. In low doses, marijuana acts as a depressant; in higher doses it causes hallucinations. The substances LSD, also called acid, and PCP, known as angel dust, are strong hallucinogens. Both of these drugs cause brain damage when they are taken in large doses.

SMOKING

Nicotine is not the only harmful substance that is inhaled when tobacco is smoked. Carbon monoxide, a poisonous gas, is also inhaled. This gas damages red blood cells and reduces their ability to carry oxygen. Smoking is a major cause of heart disease and other problems of circulation.

Tobacco smoke also contains tar. Tar is thought to be the cause of several lung diseases. Compare

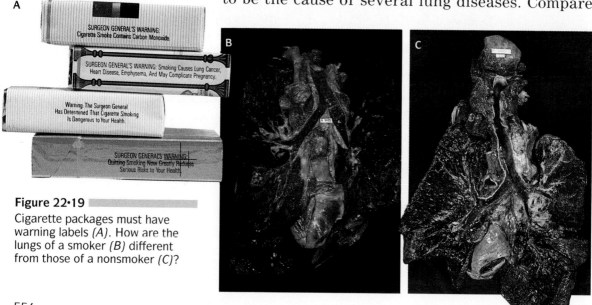

Figure 22·19

Cigarette packages must have warning labels *(A)*. How are the lungs of a smoker *(B)* different from those of a nonsmoker *(C)*?

the lungs of a smoker, shown in part *B* of Figure 22·19, with those of a nonsmoker, shown in part *C*. The most serious lung disease caused by smoking is lung cancer.

REVIEW

1. What is the difference between proper drug use and drug abuse?
2. List the four main groups of drugs, and give an example for each.
3. What are some problems caused by abuse of alcohol?

CHALLENGE A chewing gum containing nicotine is sometimes prescribed to help people quit smoking. Explain how such a gum might work for this purpose.

CHAPTER SUMMARY

The main ideas in this chapter are listed below. Read these statements before you answer the Chapter Review questions.

- The nervous system is one of the body's control systems. The nervous system receives and responds to stimuli. Neurons carry impulses within the body. (22·1)
- The central nervous system includes the brain and spinal cord. The main parts of the brain are the cerebrum, the cerebellum, and the medulla. The cerebrum is responsible for thought and for conscious control of many parts of the body. The cerebellum controls muscle coordination and body balance. The medulla controls involuntary functions needed for life. (22·2)
- The peripheral nervous system carries messages to and from the central nervous system. The peripheral nervous system and the spinal cord control many reflex actions. Learning is a function of the nervous system

and is a process by which the ability to do a new task is gained. (22·2)
- Sense organs contain receptors that receive stimuli from the environment. Impulses are sent from sense organs to the brain, where the impulses are interpreted. Receptors are found in the eyes, ears, nose, tongue, and skin. (22·3)
- The endocrine system is another of the body's control systems. Endocrine glands release hormones into the blood. Hormones control many of the body's functions. (22·4)
- The misuse of drugs is drug abuse and usually results in harm to the body. Abused drugs include stimulants, depressants, narcotics, and hallucinogens. Smoking leads to a number of health problems, including heart disease and cancer. (22·5)

The key terms in this chapter are listed below. Use each term in a sentence that shows the meaning of the term.

addiction	cornea	iris	reflex
brain	drug	lens	retina
cerebellum	eardrum	medulla	rods
cerebrum	endocrine system	nervous system	semicircular canals
cochlea	hormones	neurons	spinal cord
cones	impulse	pupil	synapse

Chapter Review

VOCABULARY

Use the key terms from the previous page to complete the following sentences correctly.

1. The part of the brain that functions in learning, memory, and reasoning is the _____.
2. The part of the brain that controls muscle coordination and body balance is the _____.
3. A quick, automatic response to a stimulus is called a/an _____.
4. Eye receptors that detect color are called _____.
5. The cells that make up the nervous system are called _____.
6. The clear area at the front of the eye is called the _____.
7. A message that travels along a neuron is called a/an _____.
8. Receptors for the sense of balance are located in the _____.
9. A chemical that causes physical, emotional, or behavioral changes in the body is called a/an _____.
10. The chemicals made by endocrine glands are called _____.

CONCEPTS

Choose the term or phrase that best answers the question or completes the statement.

1. The cerebrum is responsible for all of the following *except*
   a. interpreting information from sense organs.
   b. reasoning.
   c. coordination of movement.
   d. control of muscles.
2. Impulses pass across synapses by means of
   a. electrical impulses.
   b. chemicals.
   c. contact between neurons.
   d. reflex arcs.
3. Which of the structures of the ear is *not* concerned with hearing?
   a. eardrum   c. middle ear
   b. cochlea   d. semicircular canals
4. Which of the following pairs of senses are most similar?
   a. vision and hearing   c. taste and smell
   b. vision and balance   d. hearing and touch
5. Endocrine glands
   a. release chemicals into ducts, or tubes.
   b. are part of the nervous system.
   c. act more quickly than does the nervous system.
   d. release hormones into the blood.

Complete the following sentences.

6. A neuron that carries impulses from the brain to a muscle is an example of a/an _____ neuron.
7. The part of the brain that controls heart rate and breathing rate is the _____ .
8. The lens focuses _____ on the retina.
9. A disease in which little or no insulin is produced is called _____ .
10. Drugs that reduce pain and give a feeling of well-being are called _____ .

Answer the following in complete sentences.

11. What is an impulse? In what direction does an impulse move along a neuron?
12. What is the peripheral nervous system? What are its functions?
13. List in order the structures through which an impulse travels in a reflex arc.
14. Explain how sound vibrations are passed from the outer ear to the inner ear.
15. In what ways is the endocrine system similar to the nervous system? In what ways do the two systems differ?
16. What are the effects on the body produced by smoking? Which substances cause these effects?

APPLICATION/ CRITICAL THINKING

1. How is the eye similar to a camera?
2. When the light is dim, are colors easier to see or more difficult to see? Explain your answer in terms of receptors in the eye.
3. An injury to the brain might be fatal if the medulla rather than the cerebrum were damaged. Explain why.

EXTENSION

1. Caffeine is found in coffee, tea, and some other foods. Go to a supermarket, and read the list of ingredients on different foods. Make a list of the foods that contain caffeine. Some headache and cold medications also contain caffeine; find out which ones do. Explain why these medicines might contain caffeine.
2. Write a report on the difference between sensation and perception. Include a discussion of optical illusions. How do optical illusions relate to the difference between sensation and perception? Include drawings of some optical illusions.
3. Find out about an organization called Students Against Drunk Driving (SADD), which is based in Marlborough, Massachusetts. Report your findings to the class.

23

REPRODUCTION

*I*f you ever thought that all babies look alike, look again at the photograph. Not only do these babies show different expressions, the babies also differ in their physical characteristics. Some of the babies are smaller than others. Some have a full head of hair; others have no hair.

These babies are the same, however, in their basic structure. The head of each baby is quite large in proportion to the rest of the body. Parts of many of the babies' bones are made up of soft, flexible tissue that will later be replaced by more rigid material.

Before birth these babies would have appeared even more similar. There are several stages in the development of a human, which are the same for all individuals.

- *What are the stages of development before birth?*
- *How does a baby receive nourishment before birth?*
- *What determines the traits of individuals?*

23·1 Reproductive Systems

After completing this section, you will be able to

- **describe** the structures and functions of male and female reproductive systems.
- **identify** changes that occur at puberty.
- **describe** the major events in the menstrual cycle.

The key terms in this section are

fertilization	penis
ovary	testes
oviduct	uterus
ovulation	vagina

Reproduction is the process by which organisms make more of their kind. Humans reproduce by sexual reproduction, the joining of egg and sperm. The process of joining egg and sperm, or sex cells, is called **fertilization**. Eggs and sperm are produced in and joined in the organs that make up the *reproductive system.*

Fertilization is the first step in the development of a new individual. Look at the baby in Figure 23·1. He has changed in many ways since his birth. But none of these changes are as great as those that occurred in the fertilized egg as it developed into the baby before birth. You will learn more about these changes, and the processes and structures of reproduction, in this chapter.

Figure 23·1

The members of this family are in many different stages of development.

THE MALE REPRODUCTIVE SYSTEM

Figure 23·2 on the facing page shows the male reproductive system. The testes are located in a sac-like structure outside of the body. **Testes** are the reproductive organs that produce sperm, the sex cells of the male. From the testes, sperm pass into a long tube called the *sperm duct.*

Notice the three different types of glands shown in Figure 23·2. These glands release fluids

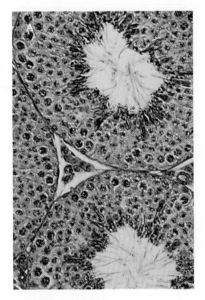

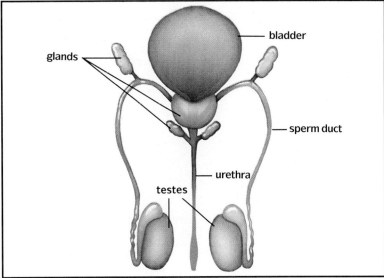

glands

bladder

sperm duct

urethra

testes

Figure 23·2

The male reproductive system. The photograph shows a cross section of one of the testes. The two large spaces are tubes in which sperm are made.

into the sperm duct, providing a liquid in which the sperm can swim. The mixture of fluid and sperm flows from the sperm duct into the *urethra* (yu REE-thruh), a tube inside the penis. The **penis** is the male organ through which sperm pass to the outside of the body.

Besides making sperm, the testes also make sex hormones that cause changes in a male's body at puberty. *Puberty* is the time when the body becomes sexually mature and can reproduce. At puberty the testes begin to make sperm. Also, at this time most boys get taller, hair starts to grow on the face and body, and the voice deepens.

THE FEMALE REPRODUCTIVE SYSTEM

As you read about the female reproductive system, find each structure in Figure 23·3 on the next page. An **ovary** is a reproductive organ that makes eggs. The ovaries are located in the abdomen; each ovary is about 3 cm long. The **oviducts** are tubes through which eggs pass from the ovaries to the uterus. The **uterus** is the organ in which a baby develops. The uterus is a hollow, pear-shaped organ with thick, muscular walls.

The uterus is connected to the vagina. The **vagina** is the passage from the uterus to the outside of the body. This passage is the place where sperm

ovum (egg)
ductus (to lead)

561

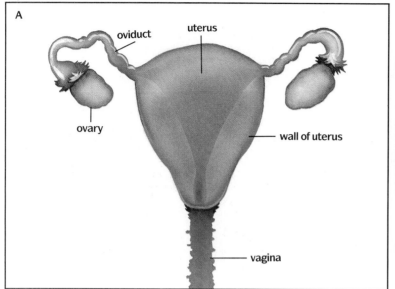

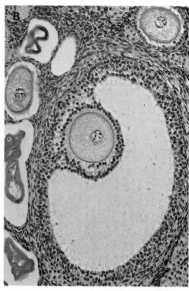

Figure 23·3

The female reproductive system. The photograph shows a cross section of an ovary. The circular structure near the center is a mature egg cell.

enter the body of the female. The vagina is also the passage through which a baby is born. For this reason, the vagina is also called the birth canal.

Besides making eggs, the ovaries also make female sex hormones that cause changes in a female's body at puberty. The ovaries begin to release eggs at puberty. Also, at this time most girls grow taller, hair begins to grow on the body, the breasts grow larger, and the hips widen.

A major change in females at puberty is the start of the menstrual (MEHN stru uhl) cycle. The *menstrual cycle* is a repeating set of changes that include the release of an egg from an ovary. Approximately every 28 days this cycle is repeated.

The release of an egg from an ovary is called **ovulation** (oh vyuh LAY shuhn). Ovulation often occurs at the middle of a typical menstrual cycle. During the cycle, changes occur in the body to prepare for the possible fertilization of a released egg. One change is the thickening of the lining of the uterus. More blood vessels grow in the lining. If the egg is fertilized, the lining will support the growth of the baby in the uterus.

If the egg is not fertilized, the lining of the uterus breaks down. Blood and tissue are released from the uterus and flow out of the vagina. This passage of blood and tissue from the uterus is called *menstruation* (mehn STRAY shuhn). Figure 23·4 shows the events of the menstrual cycle.

Notice in the figure that the day on which menstruation starts is the first day of the cycle. Menstruation may last from 3 to 7 days. A week to 10 days after menstruation is complete, an egg is released. If the egg is not fertilized, menstruation starts again about 14 days later.

If the egg is fertilized, the menstrual cycle stops. Neither menstruation nor ovulation will occur. Why is it important that these events stop during the growth of a baby?

The menstrual cycle continues until menopause. *Menopause* is the time at which ovulation ends and a woman can no longer reproduce. Menopause usually occurs at some time between ages 45 and 55.

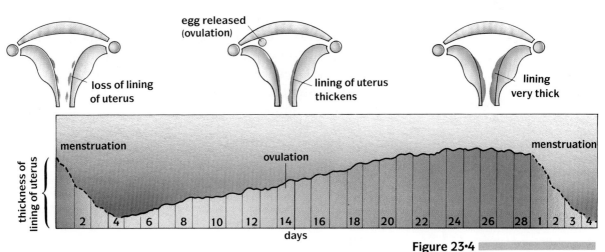

Figure 23·4
The menstrual cycle. Notice that one complete cycle and the beginning of the next cycle are shown.

REVIEW

1. What are the two products of the testes?

2. Describe the changes that occur in the body of a male at the time of puberty. Describe the changes in a female at this time.

3. Name the structures of the female reproductive system and give the function of each.

4. Describe the events that occur during the menstrual cycle.

CHALLENGE To form properly, human sperm must be kept cooler than the normal body temperature of 37°C. Explain how the structure of the male reproductive system keeps sperm cooler than body temperature.

23·2 Producing Sex Cells

MEIOSIS

As your body grows, new cells form. Body cells form new cells by a kind of division called *mitosis*. A cell that divides by mitosis produces two new, identical cells that each have a full set of chromosomes.

The sex cells — sperm and eggs — are made by a different kind of cell division. **Meiosis** is the form of cell division by which sperm or eggs are made. Unlike mitosis, meiosis produces four new daughter cells. Each of these new cells has half the number of chromosomes of a body cell. For this reason, meiosis is sometimes called *reduction division.*

Recall that body cells have pairs of chromosomes and sex cells have single chromosomes. Notice in Figure 23·5 that a cell before meiosis has pairs of chromosomes. For simplicity, only two pairs are shown. Refer to the corresponding step in the figure as you read about each stage of meiosis.

1. Each chromosome is doubled at the start of meiosis.
2. The doubled chromosomes line up in pairs along the center of the cell.

Figure 23·5

A cell before it undergoes meiosis has pairs of chromosomes *(left)*. During meiosis the doubled pairs of chromosomes *(step 1)* separate, forming sex cells having single copies of unpaired chromosomes *(step 7)*.

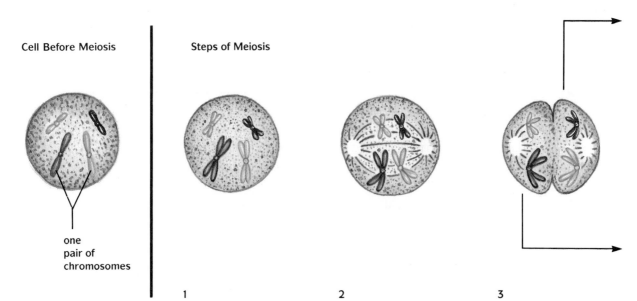

Cell Before Meiosis

one pair of chromosomes

Steps of Meiosis

1   2   3

3. The pairs of doubled chromosomes separate. Half of each pair moves to one side of the cell; the remaining doubled chromosome of each pair moves to the opposite side.
4. Two new cells, each with doubled chromosomes, form.
5. The doubled chromosomes line up along the center of each of the two new cells.
6. The doubled chromosomes separate; the single chromosomes move to opposite sides of the two cells.
7. The two cells formed earlier now divide to form four new cells. Each new cell contains single chromosomes. Notice that there are half as many chromosomes in each new cell as there were in the original cell before meiosis.

SPERM AND EGGS

The reduction of chromosome number by meiosis is important in the formation of sperm and eggs. Human sex cells each have 23 chromosomes. Sperm and egg join to form a fertilized egg having 46 chromosomes, the normal chromosome number for human body cells. Without meiosis, sperm and eggs would each have 46 chromosomes. If such sex cells

sex cells

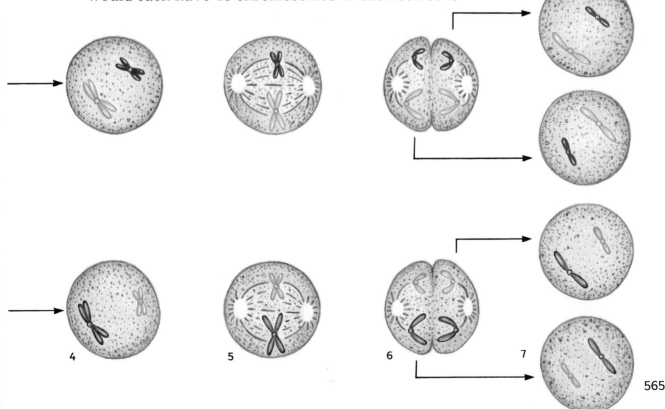

4   5   6   7

were to join, the fertilized egg would have too many chromosomes.

A mature sperm is one of the smallest cells in the body. Its total length is only about 0.05 mm. As shown in Figure 23·6, a sperm has a head, a middle region, and a tail. The head contains the chromosomes. In the middle region, sugar is broken down to release energy. This energy is used to move the whiplike tail as the sperm swims.

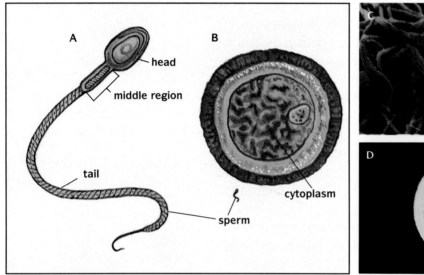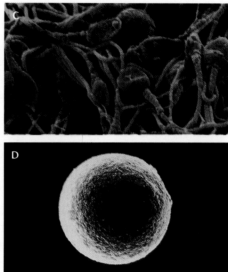

Figure 23·6

Drawings of a human sperm cell *(A)* and a human egg cell with sperm to show size difference *(B)*. Photographs of human sperm cells *(top)* and a human egg cell *(bottom)*.

Recall that four cells are formed from each cell that undergoes meiosis. When sperm are formed, all four cells can become mature sperm. But when eggs are produced, only one of the four cells becomes a mature egg. The other three cells are tiny and soon die.

An egg is about 10,000 times larger than a sperm. An egg contains a great deal of food substances that are used as the egg grows.

Sperm production starts at puberty and continues throughout a male's lifetime. But at birth a female's ovaries contain all of the eggs she will ever have. The eggs mature and are released, one at a time, about once a month. This process starts at puberty and continues until menopause. In total, only about 400 eggs will ever be released from the ovaries.

ACTIVITY   What Are the Events in Meiosis?

OBJECTIVE
Demonstrate the movement of chromosomes in meiosis.

MATERIALS
colored pencils

PROCEDURE
A. Look at the drawing of the cell.
1. How many doubled chromosomes does it have?
2. How many pairs of chromosomes does it have?

B. At the top of a piece of paper, copy the drawing of the cell. Use a different color for each pair of chromosomes. Label this drawing *1*. You will add six drawings below this one.
C. In drawing *2*, show one cell with the doubled chromosomes in pairs along a line in the middle of the cell. The pairs should be drawn close together.
D. In drawing *3*, show one cell with one doubled chromosome from each pair at one side of the cell, and the other doubled chromosome from each pair at the other side of the cell.
E. In drawing *4*, show two cells, each smaller than the ones above them. Each of these cells should have one doubled chromosome from each pair.
3. How are these cells similar to the cell in drawing *1*? How are they different from the cell in drawing *1*?
F. In drawing *5*, show two cells. Each cell should show the doubled chromosomes along a line in the middle of the cell.
G. In drawing *6*, show two cells. Show that each of the doubled chromosomes has separated into two single chromosomes that are at opposite sides of the cell.
H. In drawing *7*, show four cells, each smaller than the ones above them. Show each cell with a single chromosome from each pair.
I. Now add arrows to connect your drawings from top to bottom. The drawings now show the order of the events in meiosis.

RESULTS AND CONCLUSIONS
1. In which drawing, *4* or *7*, do the cells show single, not doubled, chromosomes?
2. In meiosis, how many cells are produced from one cell?

REVIEW
1. Describe the process of meiosis.
2. Explain why the reduction of chromosome number in meiosis is important.
3. Identify two differences between sperm production and egg production.

CHALLENGE In females, only one mature egg cell is produced from each cell that undergoes meiosis. But in males, each cell that undergoes meiosis produces four mature sperm cells. Relate this difference to the size of the male and female sex cells.

23·3 Fertilization and Development

FERTILIZATION

A new individual begins to grow when a sperm and an egg join in the process of fertilization. In humans this event is also called conception. The time between conception and birth is called *pregnancy*. Human pregnancy lasts about 280 days, or 9 months. During that time the fertilized egg grows into a complex living thing made up of billions of cells.

In human fertilization, large numbers of sperm travel through the vagina and uterus and into the oviducts. An egg is usually fertilized in one of the oviducts. Notice in Figure 23·7 that a single sperm penetrates and fertilizes the egg. A membrane then forms around the egg. When this happens other sperm are prevented from entering the egg. The fertilized egg is now called a **zygote**.

After completing this section, you will be able to

- **explain** the functions of the amnion, placenta, and umbilical cord.
- **describe** the growth of the human embryo and fetus.
- **describe** the human birth process.

The key terms in this section are
embryo	umbilical cord
fetus	zygote
placenta	

Figure 23·7

Notice the small size of the sperm fertilizing the egg.

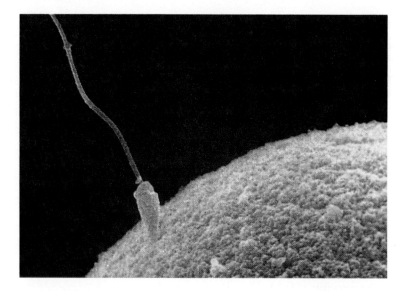

As it moves from the oviduct to the uterus, the zygote divides by mitosis. Soon the zygote forms a hollow ball of cells. About 7 to 10 days after conception, this ball of cells attaches to the lining of the uterus where it continues to grow.

DEVELOPMENT

From about the third week of growth until the end of the second month, the developing organism is called an **embryo**. The embryo is attached to the uterus by the placenta. The **placenta** is the structure through which materials pass between the embryo and the mother. Look at Figure 23·8, which shows a 6-week-old embryo and placenta.

Figure 23·8

A 6-week-old embryo is attached to a fully developed placenta *(left)*. Enlargement of a section of placenta *(right)*.

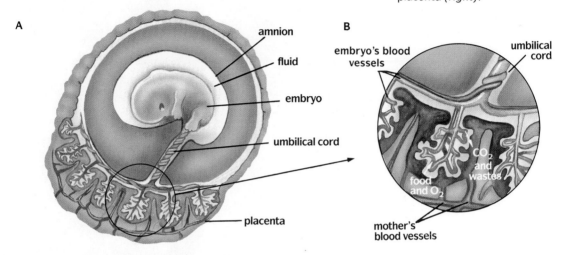

The placenta contains many blood vessels from both the embryo and the mother. The mother's blood vessels come very close to the blood vessels of the embryo. The blood of the mother and the blood of the embryo do not mix. However, nutrients and oxygen pass from the mother's blood into the blood of the embryo. In the same way, carbon dioxide and other wastes pass from the embryo's blood into the mother's blood.

The **umbilical** (uhm BIHL uh kuhl) **cord** is a ropelike structure that contains blood vessels and that connects the embryo to the placenta. Find this structure in Figure 23·8. Notice that the embryo is surrounded by a clear membrane called the *amnion* (AM nee uhn). The amnion is a sac filled with a fluid that cushions the embryo. During the embryo stage, all of the major body systems begin to form. Table 23·1 lists some of the changes that occur as an embryo grows. What happens during the fifth week of growth?

Table 23·1
Development of an Embryo

WEEK	DEVELOPMENT
4	The embryo is 0.6 cm long. The circulatory system develops.
5	The embryo is about 1.3 cm long. The heart beats, and the stomach is developing.
6	The embryo is about 2.0 cm long. The digestive, nervous, and excretory systems are developing. The skeleton contains only cartilage.
8	Bone begins to replace cartilage.

From the beginning of the third month until birth, the growing baby is called a **fetus**. Figure 23·9 shows a fetus at 11 weeks and at 16 weeks of growth. Note that at 11 weeks, the arms and legs are fairly well formed. Facial features, such as the eyes, have also formed. The fetus is about 7 cm long at this time.

Figure 23·9

A fetus at 11 weeks of development *(left)* and at 16 weeks of development *(right)*.

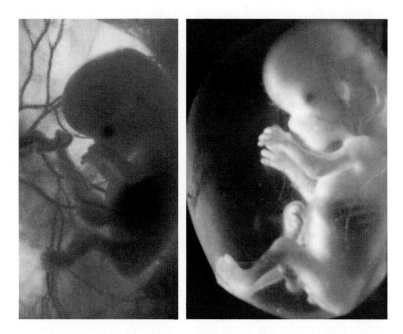

By 16 weeks of age, the fetus is about 20 cm long and most major development is complete. The fetus starts to move about, and the movements can be felt by the mother. The heartbeat can be heard with a stethoscope. During the last 3 months of pregnancy, the main change in the fetus is a rapid increase in size.

BIRTH

Near the time of birth, the fetus usually turns within the uterus. Its head points down toward the bottom of the uterus. At birth, fetuses average about 50 cm in length and weigh about 3 kg. Birth begins when muscles in the uterus start to contract. These contractions of the uterus force the baby out of the body and are called *labor*.

The period of labor can be divided into three stages. The *first stage of labor* often lasts from 10 to

12 hours. During this stage, contractions push the baby toward the bottom of the uterus. During the *second stage of labor*, the baby emerges. At this time the contractions of the uterus become stronger and last longer. The baby is usually born head first. Figure 23·10 *right* shows this stage.

Figure 23·10
The first stage *(left)* and the second stage of labor *(right)*.

When the baby is born, the umbilical cord is still attached to the placenta inside the uterus. The cord is cut at birth. The short piece of cord attached to the baby falls off within a few days. The navel, or belly button, is the scar that shows where the umbilical cord was attached.

The *third stage of labor* occurs after the baby is born. More contractions of the uterus force the amnion and placenta out of the mother's body. This mass of tissue is called the *afterbirth*. Release of the afterbirth is the last part of labor.

Changes in the mother's body continue after the birth of a baby. Hormones cause milk to form in the breasts. By nursing, the baby can feed on this milk.

REVIEW

1. Describe the amnion, placenta, and umbilical cord.
2. Describe the changes that occur in the growth from a zygote to a 2-month-old embryo.
3. Briefly describe the three stages of labor.

CHALLENGE Explain how harmful substances could reach an embryo or fetus if the mother smoked, drank alcohol, or took drugs while pregnant.

23·4 Human Heredity

INHERITANCE OF TRAITS

People who are expecting a baby often wonder what the baby will look like. They may try to predict such traits as eye color and hair color. Think of how many human traits there are — freckles, dimples, curly hair, and so on. Think how these traits vary among your friends. Notice the variety of human traits shown in Figure 23·11.

Some human traits, such as dimples, are controlled by a dominant gene. Recall from Chapter 5 that a *dominant trait* is one that prevents another trait from showing. A *recessive trait* is one that is hidden in the presence of a dominant trait. A person will have dimples if a dominant gene for dimples is present.

Remember that genes are inherited in pairs. Let *D* represent the gene for dimples. Let *d* stand for the recessive gene of the pair. Recall that *genotype* is the term that refers to the genes an organism carries. The genotype of a person with two dominant genes for dimples would be shown as *DD*. The genotype of an individual with two recessive genes would be *dd*. A hybrid would be shown as *Dd*.

Figure 23·11
The traits of humans vary greatly.

Emperor Maximilian I and his family (*below*) lived during the fifteenth century. Holy Roman Emperor Charles V (*far left*) lived during the sixteenth century. Charles was a descendant of Maximilian. Because several family portraits still exist, scientists can study the family's features.

Both Maximilian and Charles had a condition called the *Hapsburg lip*. Note that each had a lower lip that jutted out and had a slightly opened mouth. These features are believed to be caused by a dominant gene.

Recall that a Punnett square is a chart that shows the possible gene combinations resulting from a cross between two individuals. The Punnett square shown in Figure 23·12 *top* shows the possible genotypes for the children of a man with two recessive genes for dimples and a woman with two dominant genes for dimples. Each sperm carries a recessive gene, and each egg carries a dominant gene. All of the couple's children, therefore, will be hybrid for this trait. What will their genotypes be? The inherited appearance of an organism is its *phenotype*. The children each will have the dimple phenotype, because the gene for dimples is dominant. What gene combinations would be possible in children of parents hybrid (*Dd*) for the dimple trait?

The inheritance of most human traits is more complex than that of dimples. Traits such as height, skin color, and eye color are controlled by more than one pair of genes. Many shades of skin color occur in humans. Skin color is controlled by several different pairs of genes. These genes affect the amount of coloring matter, or pigment, in the skin. Several genes also control the amount of pigment in the iris of the eye. Because many different combinations of traits are possible, there is great variety among humans.

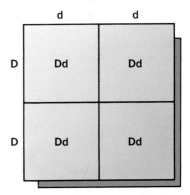

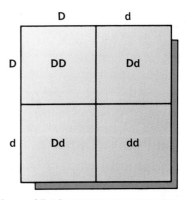

Figure 23·12

A Punnett square of parents recessive (*dd*) and dominant (*DD*) for the dimple trait (*top*). A cross of parents hybrid for the trait (*bottom*).

TWINS

No one has your exact combination of traits unless you have an identical twin. **Identical twins** are twins formed from a single fertilized egg. Because identical twins come from the same zygote, they have the same genes. These twins are the same sex and are alike in appearance.

Compare the development of identical twins with that of fraternal twins in Figure 23·13 *top*. **Fraternal twins** are twins formed from two separate fertilized eggs. Because fraternal twins are formed from different sperm and eggs, they do not have identical sets of genes. Fraternal twins are no more alike than are other brothers and sisters. They may differ in sex and appearance. Compare the two sets of twins shown in Figure 23·13.

Environment can affect how traits appear. For example, a person may have inherited genes for a given height. But if that person has poor nutrition or is very ill during childhood, he or she may not grow to that height.

Figure 23·13

The development of identical and fraternal twins *(top)*. Identical twins *(left)* and fraternal twins *(right)*.

Are Human Traits Related?

Determine if the presence of one trait can be related to the presence of another.
Construct a graph to show the frequency with which certain traits occur.

MATERIALS
colored pencils, graph paper

PROCEDURE
A. Make a data table with headings like those shown. Under *Student*, write a number for each student in your class.

Student	Male or Female	Tongue Roller?	Attached Earlobes?

B. Determine if you are able to roll your tongue upward at the sides.
C. Determine if your earlobes are attached to the side of your head. This trait is called attached earlobes. If the earlobes are not attached, the trait is called free earlobes.
D. Record your results in your data table. Write the words *yes* or *no* in the columns for the two traits. Indicate whether you are male or female. Your teacher will list the results for the class on the chalkboard. Record all the data.

RESULTS AND CONCLUSIONS
1. For the two traits listed, there are four different possible combinations. List these four combinations.
2. How many males show each of the combinations?
3. How many females show each of the combinations?
4. Prepare a bar graph to display your data. Your graph should show the eight numbers from questions **2** and **3**.
5. Do your results indicate any relationship between the traits you studied? Explain.

Scientists do not agree on the extent to which environment affects traits. Identical twins who have been raised apart have been studied to find out about the effects of environment. Because such twins have the same genes, any differences between the twins are thought to be the result of their surroundings. The studies have shown that twins raised apart still look alike. However, they may show some differences. What differences might you expect in twins raised separately?

REVIEW

1. Use a Punnett square to show the possible genotypes of children whose father has black hair (*Bb*) and whose mother has red hair (*bb*).
2. How do identical twins differ from fraternal twins?
3. Name some environmental factors that might affect how traits appear.

CHALLENGE Even when identical twins are raised in the same home, one twin may be much shorter than the other. Explain.

23·5 Genetic Disorders

After completing this section, you will be able to

- **describe** several genetic disorders and **state** their causes.
- **describe** the procedure of amniocentesis.

The key term in this section is **genetic disorders**

Disorders caused by inherited traits are called **genetic disorders**. A genetic disorder may be inherited from one parent or both parents. It can be caused by the wrong number of chromosomes or by chromosomes or genes that are abnormal.

TYPES OF GENETIC DISORDERS

Recall that the normal number of chromosomes for humans is 46, in 23 pairs. Several genetic disorders occur in people who have too few or too many chromosomes. *Down's syndrome* is a genetic disorder caused by the presence of an extra chromosome. The chromosomes of a person with Down's syndrome are shown in Figure 23·14. Which chromosome has three copies instead of the normal pair?

Down's syndrome is one of the most common genetic disorders. People with Down's syndrome often are mentally retarded. They may also have defects of the heart or other organs. However, many people with this disorder are able to lead normal and active lives.

Figure 23·14
Children with Down's syndrome competing in a race *(left)*. Down's syndrome is caused by an extra chromosome *(right)*.

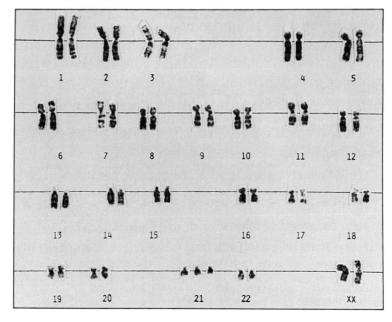

Phenylketonuria (fen uhl kee tuh NYUR ee uh), or *PKU*, is a genetic disorder caused by the presence of two abnormal recessive genes. A person with PKU lacks the enzyme needed to break down one of the amino acids that is found in many proteins. In people with PKU, this amino acid is only partly broken down. Waste products of this partial breakdown collect in the blood, causing improper development of the brain and severe mental retardation.

Today there are ways to prevent mental retardation due to PKU. The disorder can be detected by taking a sample of a newborn baby's blood. By putting a baby with PKU on a special diet, the effects of PKU are lessened.

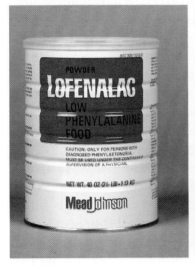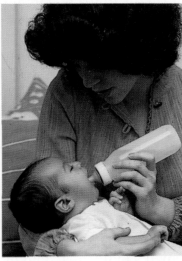

Figure 23·15
A special formula is used for babies who have PKU. This formula contains little of the amino acid that cannot be broken down.

Tay-Sachs disease is another genetic disorder caused by the presence of two abnormal recessive genes. It occurs most often among Jewish people of Eastern European descent. Babies with Tay-Sachs disease cannot make an enzyme that breaks down fatty material. A few months after birth, fatty materials begin to collect around brain cells, causing blindness, mental retardation, and loss of muscle control. Because there is no known cure for this disorder, children with Tay-Sachs disease usually die before age 4.

Cystic fibrosis is a genetic disorder that affects glands that produce mucus. With this disorder, large amounts of sticky mucus produced in the

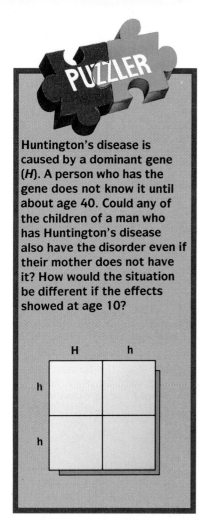

PUZZLER

Huntington's disease is caused by a dominant gene (*H*). A person who has the gene does not know it until about age 40. Could any of the children of a man who has Huntington's disease also have the disorder even if their mother does not have it? How would the situation be different if the effects showed at age 10?

	H	h
h		
h		

lungs and digestive system lead to pneumonia and other infections. People with cystic fibrosis receive treatments for digestive disorders and to clear their respiratory system. People with cystic fibrosis rarely live beyond early adulthood. Like Tay-Sachs disease and PKU, cystic fibrosis is caused by the presence of two abnormal recessive genes.

TESTING FOR GENETIC DISORDERS

As you have just learned, many genetic disorders result from the inheritance of two abnormal recessive genes. A person who inherits only one such recessive gene is called a *carrier*. Carriers do not show the genetic disorder but they can pass it on to their children. Thus, children with genetic disorders can be born to parents who appear to be normal.

Scientists are finding ways to detect genetic disorders before birth. One procedure allows study of the cells of a fetus. This procedure is called amniocentesis (am nee oh sehn TEE sihs). In this test, a long needle is passed through the wall of the mother's abdomen into the uterus. Notice in Figure 23·16 that the needle does not touch the fetus. A sample of the fluid that surrounds the fetus is removed. Cells from the fetus are present in this fluid. These cells can then be grown in a laboratory and can be tested. Some genetic disorders, such as Down's syndrome, can be detected by studying the chromosomes of the cells. Other disorders can be

Figure 23·16

In amniocentesis, some of the fluid surrounding the fetus is removed.

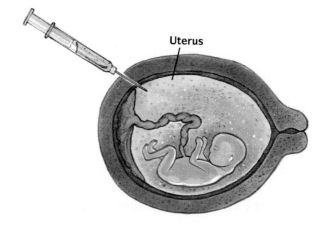

Uterus

found by chemical tests. Some genetic disorders can be treated before the baby is born. Doctors can now give a fetus medicines or even operate to correct some types of problems.

REVIEW

1. What is a genetic disorder? Give at least three examples.
2. What is the cause of Down's syndrome? What are the effects of this disorder?
3. Describe amniocentesis, and explain why it is a useful procedure.

CHALLENGE Suppose both parents are carriers of PKU. What are the chances that they will have a child with PKU? What are the chances if one parent is a carrier and one is normal?

CHAPTER SUMMARY

The main ideas in this chapter are listed below. Read these statements before you answer the Chapter Review questions.

- In human sexual reproduction, sex cells join to form a new individual. Sex cells form within the male and female reproductive systems. (23•1)
- Puberty is the time when the body becomes sexually mature. In females the menstrual cycle begins. The menstrual cycle includes menstruation, the build-up of the uterus lining, and ovulation. (23•1)
- Sperm and eggs are produced by meiosis. Meiosis results in the formation of cells that have half the number of chromosomes that body cells have. (23•2)

- When an egg is fertilized, the embryo— later called a fetus—grows inside the uterus. After about 9 months, contractions of the uterus force the baby out of the mother's body. (23•3)
- Some human traits are controlled by one gene pair; other traits are controlled by more than one gene pair. Identical twins have identical sets of genes. Fraternal twins do not have identical sets of genes. (23•4)
- Genetic disorders may result from the wrong number of chromosomes or from abnormal chromosomes or genes. (23•5)

The key terms in this chapter are listed below. Use each term in a sentence that shows the meaning of the term.

embryo	identical twins	penis	vagina
fertilization	meiosis	placenta	zygote
fetus	ovary	testes	
fraternal twins	oviducts	umbilical cord	
genetic disorders	ovulation	uterus	

Chapter Review

VOCABULARY

Write the letter of the term that best matches the definition. Not all the terms will be used.

1. The reproductive organ in which eggs are produced
2. A type of cell division that reduces the number of chromosomes
3. The pear-shaped organ in which an embryo develops
4. The process in which sperm and egg join
5. Tubes through which eggs pass from the ovaries to the uterus
6. The structure through which sperm leave the body
7. A ropelike structure containing blood vessels and that connects an embryo to the placenta
8. A fertilized egg
9. Reproductive organs in which sperm are produced
10. The passage from the uterus to the outside of the body

a. embryo
b. fertilization
c. fetus
d. genetic disorders
e. meiosis
f. ovary
g. oviducts
h. penis
i. placenta
j. testes
k. umbilical cord
l. uterus
m. vagina
n. zygote

CONCEPTS

Write the correct term for each numbered structure in the diagram.

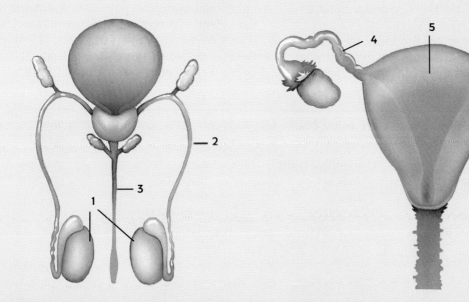

580

Identify each statement as True or False. If a statement is false, replace the underlined term or phrase with a term or phrase that makes the statement true.

6. <u>Menopause</u> is the time at which the reproductive system begins to function.
7. Meiosis produces cells that have <u>the same</u> number of chromosomes that the original cell had.
8. A growing embryo is surrounded by a fluid-filled membrane called a <u>placenta</u>.
9. Fraternal twins are <u>no more</u> alike than are other brothers and sisters.
10. Amniocentesis allows genetic disorders to be identified <u>soon after</u> a baby is born.

Answer the following in complete sentences.

11. Compare the functions of the ovaries and testes.
12. What changes occur at puberty in males? In females?
13. Describe the process of meiosis.
14. Explain why the placenta is important to the development of the fetus during pregnancy.
15. Give an example of how environment can affect an inherited trait.

---

1. Is fertilization likely to occur on the first day of the menstrual cycle? Explain your answer.
2. Your friend Tom tells you that he has an identical twin sister named Toni. How do you know that his story is not accurate?
3. One parent in a couple is normal, and the other parent is a carrier of Tay-Sachs disease. Explain why none of their children can have Tay-Sachs disease.

APPLICATION/ CRITICAL THINKING

---

1. Investigate the types of fertility drugs. Why do they sometimes cause multiple births?
2. Write a report on ultrasonography. Include information on the kinds of problems that can be detected by this procedure.
3. One of every ten couples is infertile, or unable to have children. There are many different causes. Investigate some of the causes of and treatments for infertility, and report to the class.

EXTENSION

Science in Careers

Have you read about the artificial heart? It was designed and built by biomedical engineers. Biomedical engineers combine their knowledge of engineering, biology, and medicine in their work.

Biomedical engineers have designed and built the pacemaker, artificial heart valves, artificial skin, kidney machines, and artificial arteries. They have also developed several kinds of bone and joint replacement parts, among other medical devices.

Biomedical engineers usually have a four-year college degree in engineering and additional training in biology. Some have an advanced degree in biology and training in engineering. If you are interested in a career as a biomedical engineer, you should take courses in biology, chemistry, physics, and mathematics in high school.

BIOMEDICAL ENGINEER

Did you know that yeasts are important fungi to bakers? Of course, bakers must know about cooking and baking. But they must also understand the biology and chemistry of some of the materials they use.

When yeasts carry on respiration, they break down sugar and give off carbon dioxide gas. The carbon dioxide gas that is released makes bread rise. A baker must know how much sugar to add and how warm to keep yeast to make sure that bread rises properly.

Bakers receive on-the-job training and often learn skills from more experienced bakers. If you are interested in this career, you will benefit from courses in biology and home economics in high school.

BAKER

People in Science

Dr. Hattie E. Alexander
MEDICAL DOCTOR

Dr. Hattie E. Alexander was a medical doctor and microbiologist. A microbiologist is a scientist who studies bacteria and other types of microscopic organisms.

Dr. Alexander was interested in influenzal meningitis, a disease caused by a bacterium. This kind of bacterium was found to affect tissues around the nervous system. The disease usually is fatal in infants. Dr. Alexander developed a medicine that was given to infants who were critically ill with the disease. The complete cure of these infants resulted. This work, and work that Dr. Alexander did with antibiotics, has greatly reduced the number of deaths from influenzal meningitis.

Dr. Alexander managed her time well. She was a pediatrician in a hospital, a researcher, and a teacher, all at the same time. Dr. Alexander wrote, organized and detailed research reports about the meningitis bacterium. She also studied other disease-causing bacteria and viruses.

Issues and Technology

What Are the Effects of Hospital-Acquired Infections?

People go to a hospital to get well. But for about 5 percent of the people who go to American hospitals each year, the trip means becoming ill with something they did not have when they arrived there. Each year 2 million people get infections that originate in hospitals.

Nosocomial (nahs uh KOH mee uhl) infections are infections that patients develop while they are in the hospital. Usually a nosocomial infection is more of a nuisance than a danger. However, for about 3 percent of the patients who get nosocomial infections, the result is death.

In 1970 the National Nosocomial Infection Study (NNIS) was started. Hospitals that take part in the study collect information about these infections. This information includes the number of infections as well as the kind and source of each infection. The purpose of the NNIS is to find out why nosocomial infections occur.

One reason that these infections are so common in hospitals is that people who are ill tend to be more susceptible to infection. Bacteria that can cause infection are everywhere. Healthy people can resist many infections, but sick people are weakened and are less able to resist infection.

Nosocomial infections are spread in many ways in hospitals. Some infections are transmitted through air, food, or water. Others are transmitted through objects, such as sheets and towels, or through contact with other people.

Infections also can be spread through medical procedures. For example, some patients need transfusions of blood or injections of medications. In surgery and in some kinds of tests, openings are made in the skin. This breaks the body's first barrier to infection.

Some scientists say that part of the problem is in the way hospitals are designed. In hospital nurseries and intensive care units, patients are usually cared for in large open areas. It is easy for bacteria to be spread from one person to another under these conditions. Figure 1 shows some related data from the NNIS.

APPLYING CRITICAL THINKING SKILLS

1. How did the rate of nosocomial infection change over the 5 years?
2. In what year did the lowest rate of infection occur? What was this rate?
3. How does the rate of infection in the study com-

Figure 1

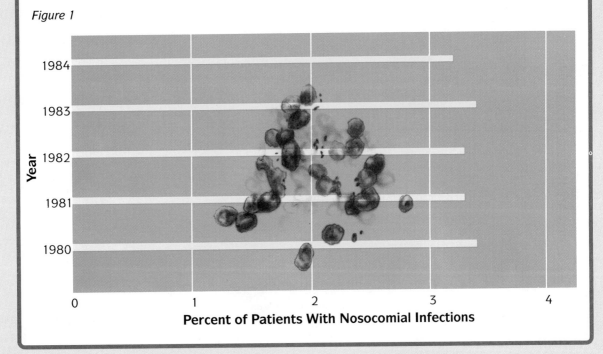

Percent of Patients With Nosocomial Infections

pare with the national average of 5 percent? What does this difference suggest about the hospitals taking part in the NNIS?

4. Of the factors involved in nosocomial infections, which do you think would be the easiest to control? How would you control this factor?

5. Of these factors, which do you think would be the most difficult to control? Why?

There are several ways to control bacterial infections. Patients can be treated with antibiotics. Hospitals also use antiseptics and disinfectants to keep things clean.

These practices kill most ordinary kinds of bacteria. But these practices do not kill all bacteria. The bacteria that survive are those that are especially strong and resistant. They live and multiply in hospitals. In fact, hospitals may be helping the resistant bacteria by killing competing bacteria. As a result, new resistant strains of bacteria are developing all the time.

Another part of the problem may be caused by doctors. Some doctors prescribe antibiotics very often. The doctors prescribe antibiotics for viral infections, such as colds, even though antibiotics do not kill viruses. As a result of antibiotics, resistant strains of bacteria develop. The resistant strains of

bacteria can live in the patient and be spread to other patients, as well.

There are about 80 different antibiotics in use today. They are used to treat infections such as pneumonia, dysentery, typhoid, cholera, and tuberculosis. These drugs are valuable and save many lives. However, many scientists believe that antibiotics should not be prescribed too freely. Controlling the use of antibiotics could help to reduce the number of resistant strains of bacteria.

The infections that people get from the resistant bacteria often are difficult to treat. The usual antibiotics are not effective. It takes strong and sometimes dangerous drugs to stop these infections.

Staphylococcus aureus (S. aureus) is a type of bacteria that is often involved in nosocomial infections. This species of bacteria has many resistant strains. Figure 2 shows the cases of nosocomial infection caused by resistant strains of *S. aureus*.

APPLYING CRITICAL THINKING SKILLS

1. What percentage of infections were resistant in 1980? In 1984?

2. What year showed a decrease in resistant infections? Suggest a reason for this decrease.

3. The use of antibiotics for viral infections does not

Figure 2

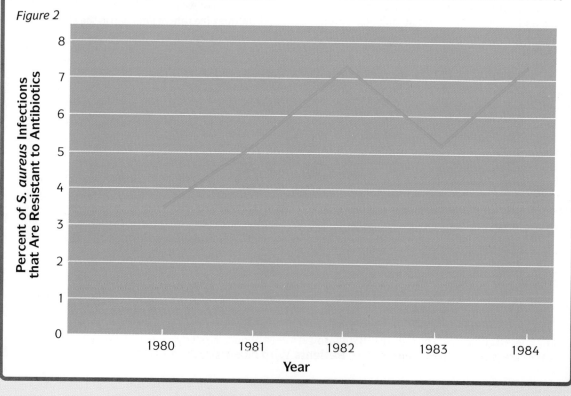

584

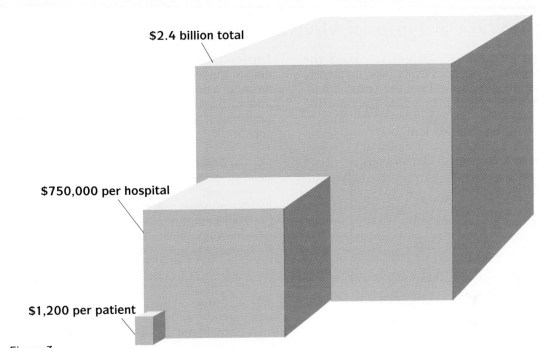

$2.4 billion total

$750,000 per hospital

$1,200 per patient

Figure 3

affect the viruses. What might be a benefit of using an antibiotic in such a case?

4. Some people say that doctors prescribe antibiotics in cases when the patient's own defenses could fight the infection. What is the advantage of using antibiotics in such a case? What might be a disadvantage?

In addition to being a health problem, nosocomial infections can be an economic problem. Often, patients have medical insurance plans. Under many plans the insurance company will pay a preset fee for the treatment of a certain illness. This fee is based, in part, on the number of days the patient is expected to stay in the hospital. If the patient stays longer because of a nosocomial infection, the insurance may not pay the extra cost. The patient or the hospital then has to pay the extra amount. Figure 3 shows the cost of nosocomial infections.

Not all hospitals have infection control programs. Some doctors are worried about close monitoring of patients for nosocomial infections. These doctors fear that the collection of data about infections will give patients information to use in lawsuits against doctors or hospitals.

Other doctors think that an infection control program is a good idea. They say that the improved health care is an important benefit. Also, the extra concern about infection makes patients more secure.

It will cost money to continue to study nosocomial infections. It will also cost money to make changes in hospital procedures. Some people think that the expense is too great for a problem that affects only 5 percent of all hospital patients. Other people say that the expense is worth it. They believe that any expense is justified if it saves a life.

APPLYING CRITICAL THINKING SKILLS

1. What is the cost of a nosocomial infection per patient? What expenses does this money pay for?

2. Suppose a patient develops a nosocomial infection and the insurance company will not pay the extra expense. Should the patient pay? Should the hospital pay? Should patients take out extra insurance to cover such a problem? Explain your answers.

3. Do you think infection control programs are a good idea? Who should pay for these programs?

4. Studies like the NNIS cost money. Many such studies are funded by the government. If the government were to stop paying for the NNIS, should the study continue? if so, who should pay for the study?

APPENDIX 1 Units of Measurement

The modern metric system is called the International System of Units, abbreviated SI in all languages. In SI there are seven fundamental units called base units. They are the meter (m), kilogram (kg), second (s), ampere (A), Kelvin (K), candela (cd), and mole (mol).

The meter is a unit of length; the kilogram, a unit of mass; the second, a unit of time; the ampere, a unit of electric current; the Kelvin, a unit of temperature; the candela, a unit of brightness; and the mole, a unit of amount of substance.

Metric to English Conversions

1 cm = 0.394 in.
1 m = 39.372 in.
1 m = 3.281 ft
1 km = 0.621 mi
1 g = .0353 oz
1 kg = 2.205 lb
1 L = 1.057 qt

English to Metric Conversions

1 in. = 2.540 cm
1 yd = 91.440 cm
1 mi = 1.609 km
1 lb = .454 kg
1 oz = 28.350 g
1 qt = .943 L

Approximate Equivalents

1 km	ten football fields
1 cm	width of a fingernail
1 mm	thickness of a dime
1 g	mass of a dollar bill
1 mg	mass of a human hair
1 L	volume of a quart of milk
20°C	room temperature

Commonly Used Metric Units

Length

Unit	Symbol	Equal to
meter	m	—
kilometer	km	1000 m
centimeter	cm	1/100 m
millimeter	mm	1/1000 m

Mass

Unit	Symbol	Equal to
gram	g	—
kilogram	kg	1000 g
milligram	mg	1/1000 g
tonne	t	1000 kg

Volume

Unit	Symbol	Equal to
liter	L	—
milliliter	mL	1/1000 L

Temperature

$$°F = 9/5 \, °C + 32$$
$$°C = 5/9 \, (°F - 32)$$
$$K = °C + 273$$

APPENDIX 2 *Safety*

An important part of your study of science will be working on activities. Most of the activity work you will do is quite safe. Yet some equipment and chemicals can cause you or a classmate injury if you do not handle them properly.

For certain activities, safety symbols are included next to the heading PROCEDURE. These safety symbols alert you to specific hazards in the procedure and to safety measures. Read the following guidelines and safety symbol explanations.

Safety Guidelines

- Prepare for every activity by reading through the entire activity before starting.
- Follow all written directions exactly unless your teacher gives you other directions.
- Make sure your working area is dry and clutter-free.
- Read all labels before using chemicals.
- Work in a careful, organized manner. Do not play or fool around.
- Report all spills, broken glassware, faulty electrical equipment, accidents, or injuries to your teacher immediately.
- Use only tongs, test-tube holders, or hot pads to hold or move hot glassware.
- Do not allow cords from hot plates or electrical equipment to dangle from work tables.
- Do not use any electrical equipment with frayed cords, loose connections, or exposed wires. Do not handle electrical equipment with wet hands.
- Never try to cut a specimen while holding it in your hand.
- Never place unknown plants, berries, seeds, or fruits into your mouth.
- At the end of every activity, clean up your work area, put everything away, and wash your hands.
- Check with your teacher for any additional safety guidelines to follow.

Safety Symbols

 Danger of cuts caused by glassware, scissors, or other possibly sharp laboratory tools.

 A lab apron should be worn to prevent damage to clothes by chemicals, acids, or stains.

 Safety goggles should be worn when there is a possibility of danger to eyes.

 Chemicals can possibly cause noxious fumes; preservatives used on specimens can be an irritant, so proper ventilation is necessary.

 Plants that are studied may have sharp edges or thorns; outdoor work may expose you to plants that can cause an allergic reaction.

 Exhibit care in handling electrical equipment.

 Be careful and gentle when handling any live animal.

 Exhibit caution when working with the Bunsen burner and when handling hot equipment.

 Be careful when using the Bunsen burner and check that the gas outlet is turned off when not in use.

 Substances in an investigation could be poisonous if ingested.

 Radioactive materials are present.

APPENDIX 3 *Taxonomy Tree*

gymnosperms
horsetails
brown algae
vascular plants
dicots
angiosperms
ferns
club mosses
mosses and liverworts
monocots
arthropods
mollusks
segmented worms
roundworms
vertebrates
chordates
lancelets
tunicates
echinoderms
flatworms

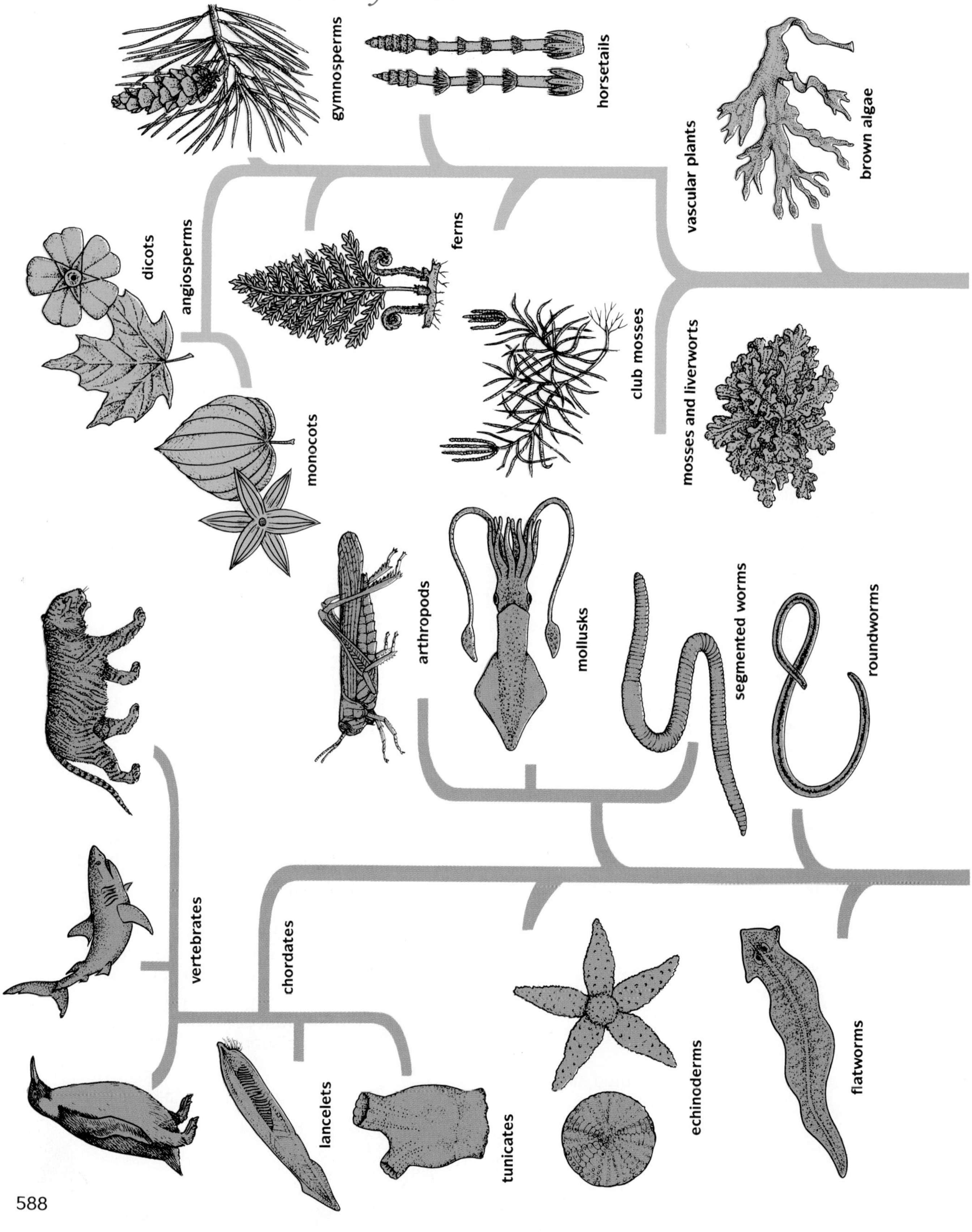

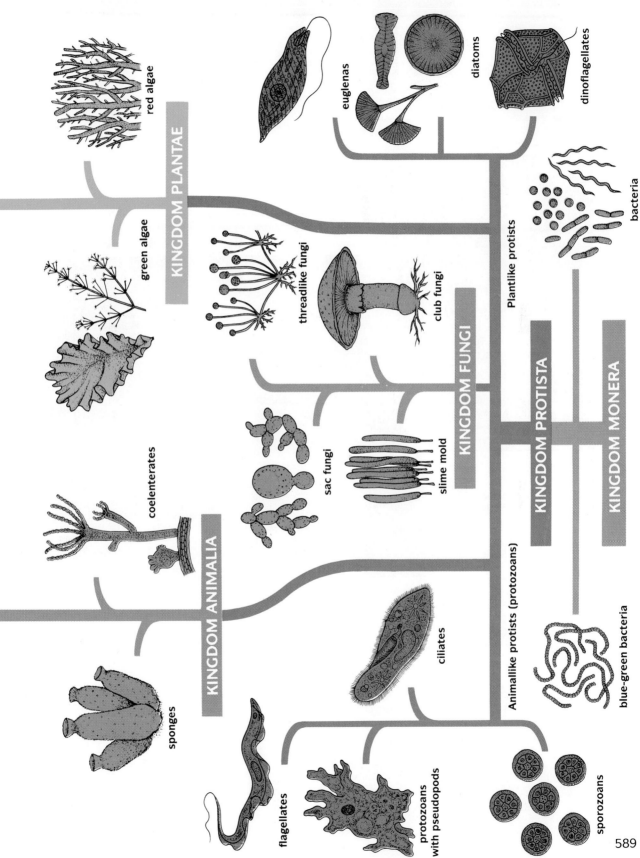

red algae

KINGDOM PLANTAE

green algae

euglenas

diatoms

dinoflagellates

Plantlike protists

bacteria

threadlike fungi

club fungi

KINGDOM FUNGI

coelenterates

sac fungi

slime mold

KINGDOM ANIMALIA

KINGDOM PROTISTA

KINGDOM MONERA

ciliates

Animallike protists (protozoans)

blue-green bacteria

sponges

flagellates

protozoans with pseudopods

sporozoans

589

APPENDIX 4 *Periodic Table of Elements*

Transition Elements

Group 1	Group 2	3	4	5	6	7	8	9
1 1.0 **H** Hydrogen								
3 6.9 **Li** Lithium	**4** 9.0 **Be** Beryllium							
11 22.9 **Na** Sodium	**12** 24.3 **Mg** Magnesium							
19 39.1 **K** Potassium	**20** 40.0 **Ca** Calcium	**21** 44.9 **Sc** Scandium	**22** 47.9 **Ti** Titanium	**23** 50.9 **V** Vanadium	**24** 51.9 **Cr** Chromium	**25** 54.9 **Mn** Manganese	**26** 55.8 **Fe** Iron	**27** 58.9 **Co** Cobalt
37 85.4 **Rb** Rubidium	**38** 87.6 **Sr** Strontium	**39** 88.9 **Y** Yttrium	**40** 91.2 **Zr** Zirconium	**41** 92.9 **Nb** Niobium	**42** 95.9 **Mo** Molybdenum	**43** (99)* **Tc** Technetium	**44** 101.0 **Ru** Ruthenium	**45** 102.9 **Rh** Rhodium
55 132.9 **Cs** Cesium	**56** 137.3 **Ba** Barium	Lanthanide Series†	**72** 178.4 **Hf** Hafnium	**73** 180.9 **Ta** Tantalum	**74** 183.8 **W** Tungsten	**75** 186.2 **Re** Rhenium	**76** 190.2 **Os** Osmium	**77** 192.2 **Ir** Iridium
87 (223)* **Fr** Francium	**88** (226)* **Ra** Radium	Actinide Series‡	**104** (259)* **Unq** Unnilquadium	**105** **Unp** Unnilpentium	**106** **Unh** Unnilhexium	**107** * *	**108** * *	**109** * *

† **Lanthanide Series**	**57** 138.9 **La** Lanthanum	**58** 140.1 **Ce** Cerium	**59** 140.9 **Pr** Praseodymium	**60** 144.2 **Nd** Neodymium	**61** (147)* **Pm** Promethium	**62** 150.3 **Sm** Samarium	**63** 151.9 **Eu** Europium
‡ **Actinide Series**	**89** (227)* **Ac** Actinium	**90** 232.0 **Th** Thorium	**91** (231)* **Pa** Protactinium	**92** 238.0 **U** Uranium	**93** (237)* **Np** Neptunium	**94** (242)* **Pu** Plutonium	**95** (243)* **Am** Americium

*Atomic masses appearing in parentheses are those of the most stable known isotopes.

■ These elements occur in nature, and are solids at room temperature (20°C).

□ These elements occur in nature, and are liquids at room temperature (20°C).

□ These elements occur in nature, and are gases at room temperature (20°C).

■ These elements do not occur in nature, and have been produced in laboratories.

18

13	14	15	16	17	18

2 4.0
He
Helium

5 10.8	6 12.0	7 14.0	8 15.9	9 18.9	10 20.1
B	**C**	**N**	**O**	**F**	**Ne**
Boron	Carbon	Nitrogen	Oxygen	Fluorine	Neon

10	11	12

13 26.9	14 28.0	15 30.9	16 32.0	17 35.4	18 39.9
Al	**Si**	**P**	**S**	**Cl**	**Ar**
Aluminum	Silicon	Phosphorus	Sulfur	Chlorine	Argon

28 58.7	29 63.5	30 65.3	31 69.7	32 72.5	33 74.9	34 78.9	35 79.9	36 83.8
Ni	**Cu**	**Zn**	**Ga**	**Ge**	**As**	**Se**	**Br**	**Kr**
Nickel	Copper	Zinc	Gallium	Germanium	Arsenic	Selenium	Bromine	Krypton

46 106.4	47 107.8	48 112.4	49 114.8	50 118.6	51 121.7	52 127.6	53 126.9	54 131.3
Pd	**Ag**	**Cd**	**In**	**Sn**	**Sb**	**Te**	**I**	**Xe**
Palladium	Silver	Cadmium	Indium	Tin	Antimony	Tellurium	Iodine	Xenon

78 195.0	79 196.9	80 200.5	81 204.3	82 207.1	83 208.9	84 (210)*	85 (210)*	86 (222)*
Pt	**Au**	**Hg**	**Tl**	**Pb**	**Bi**	**Po**	**At**	**Rn**
Platinum	Gold	Mercury	Thallium	Lead	Bismuth	Polonium	Astatine	Radon

64 157.2	65 158.9	66 162.5	67 164.9	68 167.2	69 168.9	70 173.0	71 174.9
Gd	**Tb**	**Dy**	**Ho**	**Er**	**Tm**	**Yb**	**Lu**
Gadolinium	Terbium	Dysprosium	Holmium	Erbium	Thulium	Ytterbium	Lutetium

96 (247)*	97 (247)*	98 (251)*	99 (254)*	100 (257)*	101 (258)*	102 (255)*	103 (256)*
Cm	**Bk**	**Cf**	**Es**	**Fm**	**Md**	**No**	**Lr**
Curium	Berkelium	Californium	Einsteinium	Fermium	Mendelevium	Nobelium	Lawrencium

* *No names have been given and no mass data is available.

Atomic masses based on C-12 = 12.0000

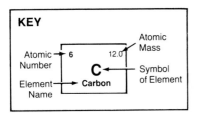

KEY

Atomic Number → 6   12.0 ← Atomic Mass

C ← Symbol of Element

Element Name → **Carbon**

APPENDIX 5 Weather Map Symbols

Symbol	Wind Speed km/hr
◎	Calm
——	0-4
⌐	5-13
\\	14-22
\\	23-32
\\	33-41
\\\	42-50
\\\	51-59
\\\\	60-69
\\\\	70-78
\\\\\	79-87
A	88-96
A\	97-100
A\\	101-105

Location of Weather Station

Type of high clouds
Type of middle clouds
Temperature (°F) — 55
Type of precipitation — **
Wind speed and direction — 54°
Dew point temperature

Barometric pressure (abbr. for 1025.7 mb) — 257
Change in barometric pressure in last 3 hours — +28
Total percent of sky covered by clouds
Type of low clouds

Fronts and Pressure Systems

- ⒽⒸ Center of high or low pressure system
- ▲▲▲▲ Cold front
- ⌒⌒⌒ Warm front
- ▲⌒▲⌒ Occluded front
- ⌒▼⌒▼ Stationary front

Symbols Showing Percentage of Cloudiness

0	$\frac{1}{10}$	$\frac{2}{10}$	$\frac{3}{10}$	$\frac{4}{10}$	$\frac{5}{10}$	$\frac{6}{10}$	$\frac{7}{10}$	$\frac{8}{10}$	$\frac{9}{10}$	$\frac{10}{10}$
○	⍉	◔	◔	◑	◑	◕	◕	●	◉	●

Symbols Showing Precipitation

drizzle	rain	shower	snow	sleet	fog	hail	thunderstorm
,	●	▽	*	△	≡	⊖	⍑

Clouds

High Clouds
- → Scattered cirrus
- ⌐ Dense cirrus
- Veil of cirrus covering entire sky
- Cirrus not covering entire sky

Middle Clouds
- ∠ Thin altostratus
- ⫽ Thick altostratus
- Thin altostratus in patches
- Thin altostratus in bands

Low Clouds
- ⌒ Cumulus fair weather
- ∪ Stratocumulus
- - - - Fractocumulus bad weather
- —— Stratus fair weather

Glossary

abdomen The last part of an arthropod's body. *p. 55*

acceleration (ak sehl uh RAY shuhn) A change in velocity over a period of time. *p. 252*

acid A substance that releases hydrogen ions, H^+, when it dissociates in a solution. *p. 215*

activation energy The amount of energy needed to start a chemical reaction. *p. 211*

adaptation (ad ap TAY shuhn) An inherited trait that makes an organism better able to live in its environment. *p. 126*

addiction A condition in which the body requires a drug. *p. 551*

adult An animal that has grown and developed enough to reproduce. *p. 60*

alkali (AL kuh lī) **metals** The elements in Group 1 of the Periodic Table. *p. 232*

alkaline (AL kuh līn) **earth metals** The elements in Group 2 of the Periodic Table. *p. 233*

alpha (AL fuh) **particle** Radiation that contains two protons and two neutrons. *p. 325*

alternating current (ac) A type of electric current that changes direction at regular intervals. *p. 291*

ampere (A) (AM pihr) A measure of the number of electric charges that flow past a point in one second. *p. 278*

anus An opening at the end of the digestive tract through which undigested food leaves the body. *p. 40*

arachnid (uh RAK nihd) An arthropod that has four pairs of jointed legs. *p. 68*

arthropod An animal that has a body made up of segments, a hard outer covering, and jointed legs. *p. 54*

atoll (AT ohl) A ring-shaped reef that surrounds a body of water. *p. 511*

atom The smallest particle of an element that has the properties of that element. *p. 183*

base A substance that releases hydroxide ions, OH^-, when it dissociates in a solution. *p. 217*

beach A collection of rock material along a shore. *p. 517*

beta (BAY tuh) **particle** An electron given off by a radioactive atomic nucleus. *p. 325*

big bang theory   The most widely accepted idea about the origin of the universe, stating that it began with a tremendous explosion of all the energy and matter concentrated together. *p. 376*

biome   A large region with a distinct combination of climate, plants, and animals. *p. 157*

birth rate   The ratio of the number of births in a year to the number of individuals in a population. *p. 149*

bivalve (BĪ valv)   A mollusk having two shells that are hinged together. *p. 46*

black hole   An object that is so dense that its gravity keeps light from escaping. *p. 372*

blade   The wide, flat part of a leaf. *p. 84*

brain   The main control center of the nervous system. *p. 537*

breaker   A breaking wave. *p. 513*

budding   A type of asexual reproduction in which an organism forms a bud that later develops into an adult organism. *p. 33*

cambium (KAM bee uhm)   A layer of dividing cells that produce new xylem and phloem cells. *p. 83*

carbon-oxygen cycle   The movement of carbon and oxygen through an ecosystem. *p. 147*

cast fossil   A fossil that has the same outer shape as the animal or plant part that formed it. *p. 131*

centipede   An arthropod that has one pair of legs attached to most of its body segments. *p. 70*

central cavity   Hollow center of a sponge or a coelenterate. *p. 32*

centripetal (sehn TRIHP uh tuhl) **acceleration**   The acceleration of an object moving in a curved path or circle at a constant speed. *p. 265*

centripetal force   The force that causes an object moving at constant speed to move in a curved path or circle. *p. 266*

cerebellum   The part of the brain that controls muscle coordination and body balance. *p. 538*

cerebrum   The part of the brain that functions in learning, memory, and reasoning. *p. 537*

chain reaction   A nuclear reaction in which a product of a reaction causes the reaction to continue. *p. 337*

chemical equation   A shorthand way to show the changes that take place in a reaction. *p. 200*

chemical formula   A group of chemical symbols that shows the makeup of a compound. *p. 188*

chemical property   A property that describes how particles of matter react and change with other kinds of matter. *p. 180*

chemical reaction   A process in which one or more substances are changed into one or more different substances. *p. 200*

chemical symbol   A notation of one or two letters that represents an atom or element. *p. 185*

chemical weathering   A process that changes the minerals in rocks into new substances. *p. 408*

chromosomes (KROH muh sohmz)   Threadlike cell structures that contain DNA and that control heredity. *p. 113*

cirrus (SIHR uhs) **clouds**   Thin, feathery clouds that form at high altitudes. *p. 470*

clastic rocks   Sedimentary rocks that form from pieces of other rocks. *p. 400*

climate   The average weather conditions in a region over a long period of time. *pp. 157, 490*

climax community   The final community in succession. *p. 154*

cloud   A collection of water droplets or ice particles floating in the atmosphere. *p. 468*

cloud seeding   A process by which dry crystals are added to a cloud to bring rain to areas that need it. *p. 496*

cochlea (KAHK lee uh)   A coiled, fluid-filled tube that contains sound receptors. *p. 545*

coelenterate (sih LEHN tuh rayt)   An invertebrate that has a central body cavity with a single opening. *p. 34*

colloid (KAHL oid)   A mixture whose properties are between those of a solution and those of a suspension. *p. 195*

colony   A group of animals that live together and that share work and food. *p. 64*

compound   Matter formed from the chemical combination of two or more elements. *p. 186*

concave lens   A lens that is thinner in its center than at its edges. *p. 313*

concave mirror   A mirror whose reflecting surface curves inward. *p. 308*

condensation (kahn den SAY shuhn)   The process by which water vapor changes into liquid water. *p. 459*

conductor A substance that allows electric charges to flow through easily. *p. 273*

cones Receptors that allow color vision. *p. 543*

coniferous (kuh NIHF uhr uhs) **forest** A biome made up mainly of cone-bearing trees or conifers, such as pines and spruces. *p. 159*

constellation A group of stars that forms a pattern or picture in the sky. *p. 356*

continental drift (theory of) A theory stating that the continents of the earth were once joined but had broken apart and moved to their present positions. *p. 432*

continental margin The underwater area that borders a continent. *p. 506*

continental shelf The gently sloping part of the continental margin which begins at the shoreline. *p. 506*

contour interval The difference in height between two adjacent contour lines. *p. 388*

contour line A line that connects points of the same elevation on a topographic map. *p. 388*

controlled experiment A method for testing hypotheses. *p. 20*

convex lens A lens that is thicker in its center than at its edges. *p. 313*

convex mirror A mirror whose reflecting surface curves outward. *p. 308*

coral reefs Rocklike structures formed in warm, shallow water by colonies of tiny sea animals called corals. *p. 512*

cornea (KAWR nee uh) The clear area at the front of the eye. *p. 542*

covalent bond The force of attraction that results when two atoms share electrons. *p. 190*

crop In earthworms a chamber that stores food. *p. 43*

crust The outermost layer of the earth. *p. 384*

crustacean (kruhs TAY shuhn) An arthropod that has five pairs of jointed legs. *p. 66*

cumulus (KYOO myuh luhs) **clouds** Fluffy clouds, often with flat bases. *p. 469*

death rate The ratio of the number of deaths in a year to the number of individuals in a population. *p. 149*

deciduous (dih SIHJ yoo uhs) **forest** A biome in which the main plants are broad-leaved trees that lose their leaves in the fall. *p. 160*

decomposition reaction A chemical reaction in which a compound breaks down into two or more substances. *p. 205*

degassing (dee GAS ihng) The process in which gases are released by volcanic activity. *p. 504*

degree Celsius (°C) A unit used in measuring temperature. *p. 20*

density The amount of mass in a given volume. *p. 179*

deposition The settling of materials carried by the agents of erosion—water, wind, and ice. *p. 418*

desert A biome that receives less than 25 cm of rain per year. *p. 163*

dew Water vapor that condenses on cold surfaces on cool mornings. *p. 466*

dew point The temperature to which air must be cooled to become saturated. *p. 465*

direct current (dc) A type of electric current that travels in one direction in a circuit. *p. 292*

dome mountains Mountains that form when magma within the earth pushes the surface upward. *p. 452*

dominant trait A trait that prevents the showing of another trait. *p. 108*

double replacement reaction A chemical reaction that occurs when the compounds in a reaction exchange ions. *p. 208*

drug A chemical that causes physical, emotional, or behavioral changes in the body. *p. 551*

dune A large hill of sand. *p. 424*

eardrum A round membrane that vibrates when sound waves strike it. *p. 544*

earthquake The shaking or trembling of the earth, caused by the sudden movement of the earth's crust. *p. 445*

echinoderm (ih KĪ nuh derm) A spiny-skinned invertebrate that lives in the ocean. *p. 71*

ecosystem (EE kuh sihs tuhm) An area in which living and nonliving things interact, exchanging energy and materials. *p. 146*

ectoderm The outer tissue layer that forms tissues and organs in some developing animals. *p. 29*

electric cell   A device that changes chemical energy into electrical energy. *p. 277*

electric circuit (SER kiht)   A path through which an electric current can travel. *p. 279*

electric current   The flow of electrons or flow of charges. *p. 277*

electric motor   A device that changes electrical energy into mechanical energy. *p. 289*

electric power   The amount of electrical energy used each second. *p. 281*

electromagnet   A current-carrying coil of wire wound around an iron core. *p. 287*

electromagnetic spectrum   The different forms of radiant energy. *p. 299*

electron   The negatively charged particle in an atom. *p. 184*

embryo (EHM bree oh)   A many-celled organism in the early stages of its development; in humans the developing organism from about the third week of development until the end of the second month. *pp. 95, 569*

endocrine (EHN doh krihn) **system**   A control system made up of glands. *p. 547*

endoderm   The inner tissue layer that forms tissues and organs in some developing animals. *p. 29*

endothermic (ehn doh THER mihk) **reaction**   A chemical reaction that takes in, or absorbs, energy. *p. 213*

epidermis (ehp uh DER mihs)   The protective outer tissue layer of a leaf. *p. 85*

erosion   The wearing away and moving of rock materials by natural forces. *p. 417*

evaporation (ih vap uh RAY shuhn)   The process by which liquid water changes to water vapor. *p. 458*

evolution   Change that occurs in living things over time. *p. 135*

exoskeleton (ehk soh SKEHL uh tuhn)   A skeleton that covers the outside of an animal's body. *p. 55*

exothermic (ehk soh THER mihk) **reaction**   A chemical reaction that gives off energy. *p. 213*

extinct (ehk STIHNGKT)   Species of the past that no longer exist. *p. 133*

extrusive (ek STROO sihv) **rocks**   Igneous rocks that form from lava. *p. 394*

fault   A place where rocks have moved on one or both sides of a crack in the earth. *p. 445*

fault-block mountains   Mountains formed by the movement of large blocks of crust along faults. *p. 451*

fertilization   The process in which egg and sperm join. *p. 560*

fetus   The growing baby from about the beginning of the third month until birth. *p. 570*

filter   A transparent or translucent substance that allows only certain colors of light to pass through. *p. 316*

flatworm   An invertebrate with a flattened body. *p. 37*

flower   A reproductive organ in which a flowering plant forms seeds. *p. 92*

folded mountains   Mountains that form when sedimentary rock layers fold or bend. *p. 451*

foliated (FOH lee ay tihd) **rocks**   Metamorphic rocks that have minerals arranged in bands or layers. *p. 402*

foot   In mollusks a muscular structure that is used in movement. *p. 46*

forecast   A prediction about future weather. *p. 480*

fossil   The preserved remains of or a trace left by an organism that lived in the past. *p. 130*

fraternal twins   Twins formed from two separate fertilized eggs. *p. 574*

frost   Ice that forms on objects when water vapor sublimates. *p. 467*

fruit   A ripened flower ovary that contains one or more mature seeds. *p. 95*

fuel   Any substance that is used to produce energy. *p. 338*

galaxy   A large system of stars. *p. 373*

gamma (GAM uh) **rays**   Waves of electromagnetic energy. *p. 326*

gene   A section of a chromosome that carries the information for a single trait. *p. 113*

generator (JEHN uh ray tuhr)   A device that changes mechanical energy into electrical energy. *p. 290*

genetic disorders   Disorders caused by inherited traits. *p. 576*

genetic engineering The technology of transferring genes from one organism to another. *p. 120*

genetics (juh NEHT ihks) The scientific study of heredity. *p. 105*

genotype (JEEN uh tīp) The genetic makeup of an organism; the traits that it carries. *p. 111*

gizzard (GIHZ uhrd) A chamber in which food is ground into small particles by the action of muscles. *p. 43*

glacier A large mass of moving snow and ice. *p. 424*

glass A supercooled liquid. *p. 239*

grassland A biome with moderate rainfall and grasses as the main plants. *p. 162*

guard cells Cells that surround and control the opening and closing of a stomate. *p. 86*

Gulf Stream An ocean surface current that begins in the Straits of Florida and flows along the Atlantic coast of the United States. *p. 514*

hail A form of precipitation made of rounded pieces of ice formed by strong updrafts in cumulonimbus clouds during thunderstorms. *p. 474*

half-life The time that it takes for one half of a sample of radioactive nuclei to decay. *p. 328*

halogens (HAL uh juhns) The elements in Group 17 of the Periodic Table. *p. 242*

head The first part of the body of an arthropod. *p. 54*

heredity (huh REHD uh tee) The passing of traits from parents to young. *p. 105*

horizons Layers that are formed as soil develops. *p. 414*

hormone A chemical that is produced in one part of an organism and controls an activity in another part of the organism; a chemical produced by an endocrine gland. *pp. 97, 547*

humidity (hyoo MIHD uh tee) Water vapor in air. *p. 461*

hybrid An organism that results from a cross of parents that have different forms of a trait. *p. 107*

identical twins Twins formed from a single fertilized egg. *p. 574*

igneous (IHG nee uhs) **rocks** Rocks that form from molten rock material. *p. 391*

impulse The electrical message that travels along a neuron. *p. 535*

induction (ihn DUHK shuhn) The process of charging an object through the presence of a nearby charged object. *p. 275*

inertia (ihn ER shuh) The tendency of an object to remain at rest or in motion. *p. 255*

inner core The innermost layer of the earth, believed to be mostly iron, nickel, and cobalt. *p. 383*

insect An arthropod that has three pairs of jointed legs. *p. 57*

insulator (IHN suh lay tuhr) A substance that does not allow electric charges to flow through easily. *p. 273*

intensity The brightness of light. *p. 301*

intrusive (ihn TROO sihv) **rocks** Igneous rocks that form from magma. *p. 394*

invertebrate (ihn VER tuh briht) An animal that does not have a backbone. *p. 28*

ionic bond The force of attraction between oppositely charged ions. *p. 189*

iris In the eye, a ring of muscle that contracts or relaxes in response to light. *p. 542*

isobars On a weather map, lines that connect places having equal air pressure. *p. 485*

isotherms On a weather map, lines that connect places having equal temperature. *p. 485*

kilogram (kg) An SI unit used to measure mass. *p. 17*

larva An insect in its wormlike phase. *p. 61*

lava Molten rock on the earth's surface. *p. 440*

Law of Conservation of Mass A law stating that in a chemical reaction, the total mass of the reactants equals the total mass of the products. *p. 201*

leaf A plant organ in which food is made by photosynthesis. *p. 84*

lens A transparent object that is used to refract light from an object to form an image; a clear, flexible structure that focuses light in the eye. *pp. 312, 543*

light-year (ly) A unit of distance equal to the distance that light travels in one year: 9,460,000,000 km. *p. 360*

limiting factor A factor that keeps a population from increasing in size. *p. 150*

liter (L) A unit of volume. *p. 18*

longshore current An ocean current that moves along the shoreline. *p. 518*

magma Molten rock in the earth. *p. 440*

magnet Any substance that can attract iron or other magnetic materials. *p. 283*

magnetic field The area around a magnet where the magnetic force acts. *p. 284*

magnetism (MAG nuh tihz uhm) The attraction that magnets have for magnetic materials; the attraction and repulsion between magnetic poles. *p. 284*

main sequence star A star that appears on the band of the H-R diagram starting in the upper left corner and continuing to the lower right of the diagram. *p. 368*

mantle A fleshy tissue that covers and protects the organs of a mollusk; the layer between the core and the crust of the earth. *pp. 46, 383*

matter Anything that has mass and takes up space. *p. 178*

medulla (mih DUL uh) The part of the brain that controls involuntary actions needed for life. *p. 538*

meiosis (mī OH sihs) A form of cell division by which sperm or eggs are made. *p. 564*

mesoderm The middle tissue layer that forms tissues and organs in some developing animals. *p. 29*

metalloids Elements that have properties of both metals and nonmetals. *p. 231*

metals Elements that have luster, are good conductors of heat and electricity, and are ductile and malleable. *p. 229*

metamorphic (meht uh MAWR fihk) **rocks** Rocks formed from existing rocks that are changed by heat or pressure. *p. 391*

metamorphosis (meht uh MAWR fuh sihs) A series of distinct changes of form through which an animal passes as it grows from egg to adult. *p. 60*

meter (m) The SI unit used when measuring length or distance. *p. 17*

microclimate The climate in a small area. *p. 497*

Milky Way galaxy A spiral galaxy that contains billions of stars and is the home of our solar system. *p. 375*

millipede An arthropod that has two pairs of jointed legs on most of its body segments. *p. 70*

mixture A combination of substances that can be separated by physical means. *p. 192*

mold fossil A hollow space in the shape of a once-living thing. *p. 131*

molecule A combination of two or more atoms held together by a covalent bond. *p. 191*

mollusk An animal that has a soft body usually covered by a hard shell. *p. 46*

momentum A quantity equal to an object's mass multiplied by its velocity. *p. 257*

moraine A layer of rock materials deposited by a glacier. *p. 427*

motion The change in position of an object as compared with a reference point. *p. 250*

mutation (myoo TAY shuhn) A change in the genes of a cell. *p. 128*

natural selection The survival and reproduction of those organisms best suited to their environment. *p. 137*

neap tides Tides that are caused when the earth, moon, and sun form a right angle. *p. 522*

nervous system A control system made up of the brain, spinal cord, and nerves. *p. 534*

neurons Nerve cells that carry messages throughout the body. *p. 534*

neutralization (noo truh luh ZAY shuhn) The chemical reaction between an acid and a base. *p. 219*

neutron A particle with no charge found in the nucleus of an atom. *p. 183*

Newton's First Law of Motion A law stating that an object at rest remains at rest until an unbalanced force acts on it. *p. 254*

Newton's Second Law of Motion A law stating that an unbalanced force on an object causes the object to accelerate in the direction of the force. *p. 259*

Newton's Third Law of Motion A law stating that for every action by a force there is an equal and opposite reaction by another force. *p. 261*

nitrogen cycle The movement of nitrogen through an ecosystem. *p. 148*

noble gases The elements in Group 18 of the Periodic Table. *p. 243*

nonclastic rocks   Sedimentary rocks that form from dissolved minerals in water or from the remains of once-living things. *p. 400*

nonfoliated rocks   Metamorphic rocks that do not have bands or layers of minerals. *p. 402*

nonmetals   Elements that lack luster, that generally do not conduct electricity or heat, and that are not ductile or malleable. *p. 231*

nuclear fission (FIHSH uhn)   The splitting of a nucleus into two smaller nuclei. *p. 336*

nuclear fusion (FYOO zhuhn)   The joining of light nuclei to form heavier nuclei. *p. 343*

nuclear reactor   A device that controls nuclear reactions that produce useful energy. *p. 338*

nucleus   The central part of an atom. *p. 183*

nymph (nihmf)   A young insect that looks like a small adult. *p. 60*

ocean basin   A deep depression that holds most of the surface water of the earth. *p. 509*

outer core   The outer of the two layers of the earth's core, probably composed mostly of iron. *p. 383*

ovary   A reproductive organ that makes eggs. *p. 561*

oviducts   The tubes through which eggs pass from the ovaries to the uterus. *p. 561*

ovulation (oh vyuh LAY shuhn)   The release of an egg from an ovary. *p. 562*

palisade (pal uh SAYD)   A layer of columnlike cells below the upper epidermis of a leaf. *p. 85*

parallax (PAR uh laks)   The apparent shift of an object when it is seen from different places. *p. 361*

penis   The male organ through which sperm pass to the outside of the body. *p. 561*

Periodic Table   A table of the elements arranged in groups and periods in order of increasing atomic number. *p. 227*

petals   Colored structures that surround and protect the reproductive parts of a flower. *p. 92*

petiole (PEHT ee ohl)   The stalk that joins the blade of a leaf to the stem. *p. 84*

pharynx (FAR ihngks)   A tube that joins the mouth with the rest of the digestive tract. *p. 38*

phenotype (FEE nuh tīp)   The appearance of an organism. *p. 110*

phloem (FLOH ehm)   A vascular tissue that carries food throughout a plant. *p. 79*

photoelectric effect   The release of electrons from a metal when light strikes it. *p. 303*

photosynthesis (foh tuh SIHN thuh sihs)   The process in which plants use light energy from the sun to make food. *p. 85*

physical property   A property of a material that can be observed without changing the material. *p. 179*

physical weathering   A process that breaks large rocks into small rocks. *p. 408*

pioneers   The first organisms to grow in an area where primary succession occurs. *p. 154*

pistil (PIHS tuhl)   The female reproductive structure of a flower. *p. 92*

placenta (pluh SEHN tuh)   The structure through which materials pass between the embryo and the mother. *p. 569*

plane mirror   A mirror that has a flat surface. *p. 307*

plankton   The many tiny organisms, both plant and animal, that float near the surface of the water. *p. 166*

plate boundaries   The areas where the earth's plates meet. *p. 438*

plate tectonics (tehk TAHN ihks) **(theory of)**   A theory stating that the earth's crust is broken into moving plates. *p. 437*

plates   Rigid blocks of the earth's outer crust that are about 50–150 km thick. *p. 437*

polar climate   A climate where the average temperature during the year stays below 10°C. *p. 493*

population   A group of organisms of one species living in a given area. *p. 149*

population density   The number of individuals per unit of space. *p. 149*

pores   Small openings in the surface of a sponge that connect with the central cavity. *p. 32*

potential difference   A measure of the energy available to move charges in a circuit. *p. 278*

precipitation (prih sihp uh TAY shuhn)   Water that returns to the earth as rain, snow, sleet, or hail. *p. 460*

products   The new substances that are formed in a chemical reaction. *p. 201*

proton   The positively charged particle found in the nucleus of an atom. *p. 183*

protostars Regions of dense matter that may contract further into spinning balls of gas and dust. *p. 369*

psychrometer (sī KRAHM uh tuhr) An instrument that measures relative humidity. *p. 462*

pulsar (PUHL sahr) A spinning neutron. *p. 372*

pupa (PYOO puh) The stage of insect development between the larva and the adult. *p. 61*

pupil In the iris the opening whose size controls the amount of light entering the eye. *p. 542*

purebred An organism that results from a cross of parents that have the same form of a trait and whose parents are also purebred for that trait. *p. 106*

radial symmetry (RAY dee uhl   SIHM uh tree) The arrangement of body parts around a central area. *p. 72*

radiant energy Energy that travels in the form of electromagnetic waves. *p. 299*

radiation (ray dee AY shuhn) The energy and particles that are released as an atom decays. *p. 324*

radioactive dating The use of radioactive elements to find the age of a fossil. *p. 132*

radioactivity (ray dee oh ak TIHV uh tee) The spontaneous release of energy and particles from the nucleus of an atom. *p. 324*

rain Liquid water that falls to the earth. *p. 472*

reactants The starting substances in a chemical reaction. *p. 201*

real image An image that can be projected on a screen. *p. 315*

recessive trait A trait that is hidden in the presence of a dominant trait. *p. 108*

red giant A cool but large red star found in the upper right of the H-R diagram. *p. 368*

reflecting telescope A telescope that uses a concave mirror to gather light rays and produce an image. *p. 358*

reflection The bouncing back of waves from a surface. *p. 302*

reflex A quick, automatic response to a stimulus. *p. 539*

refracting telescope A telescope that uses a lens to gather light and produce an image. *p. 358*

refraction The change in direction of a wave as it passes from one medium to another. *p. 302*

regeneration A type of asexual reproduction in which there is regrowth of body parts that have been lost or damaged. *p. 33*

relative humidity The amount of water vapor in the air compared with the maximum amount of water vapor that the air can hold at a given temperature. *p. 461*

resistance (rih ZIHS tuhns) The opposition to the flow of charges in a substance. *p. 279*

respiration The process by which foods are broken down and energy is released. *p. 87*

retina The layer of receptor cells located at the back of the eye. *p. 543*

Richter (RIHK tuhr) **scale** A scale of magnitudes that is used to measure the relative sizes of earthquakes. *p. 447*

river A large, flowing body of water. *p. 419*

rods Receptors that detect the presence or absence of light and that allow vision in dim light. *p. 543*

root An organ that anchors a plant in the ground and that absorbs water and minerals from the soil. *p. 79*

roundworm A smooth, cylinder-shaped worm with pointed ends and a tubelike digestive system. *p. 40*

salinity (suh LIHN uh tee) The number of grams of dissolved salt in a kilogram of seawater. *p. 504*

salt A compound formed from the positive metal ions of a base and the negative nonmetal ions of an acid. *p. 220*

science A method of obtaining knowledge about nature. *p. 2*

sea-floor spreading (theory of) A theory stating that the ocean floor spreads out from the Mid-Ocean Ridge. *p. 434*

sedimentary (sehd uh MEHN tuh ree) **rocks** Rocks that form from sediments that have been pressed together. *p. 391*

seed The product of sexual reproduction in a seed plant. *p. 92*

segmented worm A worm whose body is made up of ringlike sections, or segments. *p. 42*

selective breeding The crossing of organisms with useful traits to produce offspring that have the useful traits of both parents. *p. 119*

semicircular canals Structures in the ear that help the body keep its balance. *p. 545*

semiconductor A substance that conducts little electricity at low temperatures but conducts more electricity at higher temperatures. *p. 239*

sepal (SEE puhl) A leaflike part found at the base of a flower. *p. 92*

setae (SEE tee) Short bristles that help an earthworm move. *p. 42*

sex chromosomes The two chromosomes, X and Y, that determine sex. *p. 115*

sex-linked trait A trait that results from a gene found on the X chromosome but not on the Y chromosome. *p. 116*

shoreline The boundary between the land and the ocean. *p. 517*

single replacement reaction A chemical reaction that occurs when one element replaces another element in a compound. *p. 207*

snow The solid form of precipitation that occurs when snowflakes do not melt as they fall. *p. 474*

social insect An insect that lives in a colony. *p. 64*

soil The loose material on the earth's surface in which plants with roots can grow. *p. 413*

solution A homogeneous mixture of two or more substances. *p. 194*

spinal cord A structure that carries messages between the brain and the other parts of the body. *p. 537*

sponge The simplest invertebrate. *p. 31*

spongy layer A layer of loosely packed cells located below the palisade layer of a leaf. *p. 85*

spring tides Tides that are caused when the sun and moon are in line with the earth. *p. 522*

stamen (STAY muhn) The male reproductive structure of a flower. *p. 92*

static electricity A type of electricity produced by the separation of negative and positive charges. *p. 272*

stem An organ that supports the leaves or flowers of a plant. *p. 82*

stinging cell A cell that has pointed, threadlike parts used in getting food. *p. 34*

stomates (STOH mayts) Small openings located on the lower surface of a leaf. *p. 84*

stratus (STRA tuhs) **clouds** Clouds that spread out in a layer where a large body of air is slowly lifted into the atmosphere. *p. 470*

subduction The process by which one of the earth's plates is pushed below another. *p. 438*

subduction zone The area where one of the earth's plates is pushed below another plate. *p. 438*

subsoil The B-horizon in a soil profile, where minerals carried downward by water are deposited. *p. 414*

succession The sequence of changes that occur in a community over time. *p. 153*

supernova The violent explosion of a star near the end of its life. *p. 371*

suspension A heterogeneous mixture in which the particles are temporarily mixed in a liquid. *p. 194*

synapse A gap that impulses cross as they move from neuron to neuron. *p. 535*

synthesis reaction A chemical reaction in which two or more substances combine to form a compound. *p. 204*

technology The use of scientific knowledge to improve the quality of human life. *p. 12*

temperate climate A climate where the average summer temperature is above 18°C and the average winter temperature is below 10°C. *p. 494*

tentacles (TEHN tuh kuhlz) Armlike extensions used to catch food and bring it into the body cavity. *p. 34*

testes The reproductive organs that produce sperm, the sex cells of the male. *p. 560*

theory A hypothesis that has been tested many times and that is supported by evidence. *p. 10*

thorax The middle body part of an arthropod's body, joining the head and abdomen. *p. 55*

tides The periodic rise and fall in the level of the ocean. *p. 521*

topographic map A map that shows the shape and height of land by using lines that connect points of the same elevation. *p. 388*

topsoil The A-horizon, or top layer, in a soil profile, containing humus and weathered minerals needed by plants to grow. *p. 414*

tracer A radioactive atom or molecule that is used to study processes in living things and in nonliving things. *p. 330*

trait   An inherited feature of an organism. *p. 104*

transition elements   The elements in Groups 3 through 12 in the Periodic Table. *p. 236*

transpiration   The loss of water from plants through the stomates. *p. 90*

trench   A deep valley on the sea floor formed by subduction. *p. 439*

tributary (TRIHB yuh tehr ee)   A stream that flows into a larger stream or a river. *p. 419*

tropical cimate   A climate where the average temperature during the year stays above 18°C. *p. 493*

tropical rain forest   A warm, humid biome that has the greatest variety of life forms. *p. 161*

tropism (TROH pihz uhm)   The growth of a plant toward or away from an outside factor. *p. 98*

tube feet   Hollow tubes used in movement and having suction-cuplike ends. *p. 71*

tundra   A cold, dry land biome in which most plants are low-growing and short-lived. *p. 157*

umbilical (uhm BIHL uh kuhl) **cord**   A ropelike structure that contains blood vessels and that connects the embryo to the placenta. *p. 569*

univalve (YOO nuh valv)   A mollusk that is usually covered by a single shell. *p. 47*

upwelling   A process where wind causes deep ocean water to rise and replace warm surface water along the coast, moving the surface water out to sea. *p. 515*

uterus (YOO tuhr uhs)   The organ in which a baby develops. *p. 561*

vagina (vuh JĪ NUH)   The passage from the uterus to the outside of the body. *p. 561*

vein   A bundle of vascular tissue that carries materials to and from a leaf. *p. 84*

velocity (vuh LAHS uh tee)   Speed in a definite direction. *p. 251*

virtual image   An image that does not exist in the place it seems to be. *p. 308*

volcanic mountains   Mountains that form from lava and other volcanic materials. *p. 450*

volcano   A structure made of materials from within the earth that build up around an opening in the earth's surface. *p. 440*

water cycle   The movement of water through nature; the movement of water between the earth's land, air, and bodies of water. *pp. 146, 458*

watershed   The land area that supplies water for a river. *p. 419*

weather maps   Maps that provide an overall picture of weather activity across the earth. *p. 484*

weathering   The breakup and change of rocks and minerals. *p. 408*

white dwarf   A small, hot star found in the lower left of the H-R diagram. *p. 368*

X chromosome   A sex chromosome found in the cells of both males and females. *p. 115*

xylem (ZĪ LEHM)   A vascular tissue that carries water and minerals from the root of a plant to the stem and leaves. *p. 79*

Y chromosome   A sex chromosome found only in the cells of males. *p. 115*

zygote (ZĪ GOHT)   A fertilized egg. *p. 568*

Credits

Cover: Richard Amundsen

Maps and graphs: JAK Graphics

Activity art: Phil Jones

Puzzler art: Ernest Albanese

All art by Silver Burdett & Ginn unless otherwise indicated.

Contributing artists Michael Adams: 515. Ernest Albanese: 111, 113, 122, 184, 231, 275, 358, 573. Ames & ZAK: 32, 35, 37, 38, 40, 60, 61, 72 *t.* Ralph Brillhart: 7, 8, 357. Suzanne Clee: 537–539, 546, 547, 566, 578. Rick Cooley: 13. Mark Hannon: 382, 492. Seward Hung: 18, 19, 29, 87, 120, 140, 219, 238, 357, 361, 465, 485. Sue Johnston: 130, 146–148, 153, 160, 165, 166, 284, 306, 363, 364, 414. Phil Jones: 135, 203, 207, 210, 272, 308, 309, 311, 313–315, 476. George Kelvin: 54, 57, 62, 66, 68, 72 *b.,* 95, 189, 264, 265, 278, 287, 299, 301, 312, 316, 317, 436, 446, 450–452, 507, 509, 511, 535, 536, 542, 544, 545. Peter Krempasky: 4, 5, 16, 157, 168, 196, 277, 279, 280, 285, 342, 386, 420, 426, 447. Joseph LeMonnier: 114, 116, 117, 140, 149, 150, 152, 251–253, 288, 290, 292, 304, 307, 327, 339, 346, 424, 438, 439, 443, 462, 502, 512, 518, 563, 574. Davis Meltzer: 2, 3, 356, 358, 367, 371, 376, 383, 433, 434, 440, 445. Rebecca Merrilees: 58, 79, 80, 82, 84, 85, 89, 92, 96, 98, 107, 109, 110, 425, 458, 471, 474. Denise Mickalson: 132, 227, 298, 320, 328, 366, 404, 455. Taylor Oughton: viii, 1, 6. Alex Pietersen: 360. Tom Powers: 91, 106, 183, 325–327, 336, 337, 343, 366, 374, 393, 472, 490, 521. Richard Renbein: 263. Stacy Rogers: 461. Dolores Santoloquido: 564, 656. Sally Schaedler: 539. Catherine Twomey: 43, 50, 561, 562, 569, 580. Herman Vestal: 133.

All photographs by Silver Burdett & Ginn unless otherwise indicated.

Chapter 1   4: Walter H. Hodge/Peter Arnold, Inc. 5: *l.* Richard P. Smith/Tom Stack & Associates; *r.* E.R. Degginger. 6: California Institute of Technology and Carnegie Institution of Washington. 7: E.R. Degginger. 8: Courtesy Lawrence Berkeley Laboratory. 10: *t.* Richard Faverty; *b.* Robert Bakker; *inset* University of Colorado at Boulder. 11: Roger Ressmeyer. 12: *t.* The Granger Collection; *b.* © Mikki Rain/Science Photo Library/Photo Researchers, Inc. 13: © Hank Morgan/Science Source/Photo Researchers, Inc. 14: *t.l.* © Science Photo Library/Science Source/Photo Researchers, Inc.; *t.r.* © Science Photo Library/Science Source/Photo Researchers, Inc.; *m., b.* Courtesy of Georgia-Pacific. 15: *l.* Goddard Space Flight Center/NASA. 17: *t.* E.R. Degginger: *l., r.* NASA. 21: *b.l.* © Dr. Jeremy Burgess/Science Photo Library/Photo Researchers, Inc.; *b.m.* © D.M. Phillips/Taurus Photos; *b.r.* © Martin Rotker/Taurus Photos.

Unit One Opener   24: *t.* Dan McCoy/Rainbow; *b.l.* John Gerlach/Tom Stack & Associates; *b.r.* © Dr. Brad Amos/Science Photo Library/Photo Researchers, Inc. 25: *l.* The Bettmann Archive; *m.* Brian Parker/Tom Stack & Associates; *r.* William E. Ferguson.

Chapter 2   26: Sea Studios, Inc./Peter Arnold, Inc. 28: *t.l.* Taurus Photos; *t.m., t.r.l* Al Grotell; *t.m.l* Runk/Schoenberger/Grant Heilman Photography; *t.m.r* L.A. Rosenberg/Taurus Photos. 29: *l.* Eric Crichton/Bruce Coleman; *r.* Runk/Schoenberger/Grant Heilman Photography. 30: © Nancy Sefton/Photo Researchers, Inc. 31: *l.* Al Grotell; *m.* © Jeff Rotman; *r.* Dave Woodward/Taurus Photos. 33: *l.* Matt Bradley/Tom Stack & Associates; *r.* Jeff Rotman/Peter Arnold, Inc.; *l.* © Biophoto Associates/Science Source/Photo Researchers, Inc.; *m.* © William Curtsinger/Photo Researchers, Inc.; *r.* © Jeff Rotman. 36: © David Hall/Photo Researchers, Inc. 37: © Michael Abbey/Photo Researchers, Inc. 39: *l.* E.R. Degginger; *r.* © Biophoto Associates/Science Source/Photo Researchers, Inc. 40: © Eric Grave/Photo Researchers, Inc. 41: *l.* Arthur M. Siegelman; *r.* © Biophoto Associates/Photo Researchers, Inc. 42: *l.* E.R. Degginger; *r.* Breck P. Kent. 45: Runk/Schoenberger/Grant Heilman Photography. 46: *t.l., b.l.* Breck P. Kent; *m.* © Steinhart Aquarium/Tom McHugh/Photo Researchers, Inc.; *r.* © Robert C. Hermes/Photo Researchers, Inc. 47: *t.* Animals Animals/© Zig Leszczynski; *m.* © Gilbert Grant/Photo Researchers, Inc.; *b.* C. Allan Morgan. 48: *t.l.* © Steinhart Aquarium/Tom McHugh/Photo Researchers, Inc.; *m.* Phil Degginger; *t.r.* © Steinhart Aquarium/Tom McHugh/Photo Researchers, Inc.; *b.r.* E.R. Degginger; *b.* Z. Leszczynski/Breck P. Kent.

Chapter 3   52: David Scharf/Peter Arnold, Inc. 54: Robert & Linda Mitchell. 55: Ron Dillon/Tom Stack & Associates. 56: © Stephen Dalton/Photo Researchers, Inc. 58: G.C. Kelley/Tom Stack & Associates. 63: *l.* Robert & Linda Mitchell; *m.* © James L. Castner; *r.* Breck P. Kent. 64: *t.* Runk/Schoenberger/Grant Heilman Photography; *b.* © Treat Davidson/Photo Researchers, Inc. 65: D. Wilder/Tom Stack & Associates. 67, 69: Robert &

Linda Mitchell. 70: *l.* © Tom McHugh/The National Audubon Society Collection/Photo Researchers, Inc.; *r.* Alan Blank/Bruce Coleman; *inset* E.R. Degginger. 71: *l.* Breck P. Kent; *m.* E.R. Degginger; *r.* Carl Roessler/Tom Stack & Associates.

Chapter 4   76: Ken W. Davis/Tom Stack & Associates. 78: Tom Algire/Tom Stack & Associates; *b.l.* Wendell Metzen/Bruce Coleman; *m.* © Paolo Koch/Photo Researchers, Inc.; *r.* Jack Dermid/Bruce Coleman. 80: *l.* Dwight R. Kuhn; *inset* Dwight R. Kuhn/Bruce Coleman. 81: D. Plowers. 82: *l.* Jane Burton/Bruce Coleman; *m.* Grant Heilman Photography. 83: *l.* Jack Dermid/Bruce Coleman; *r.* Earth Scenes/© Breck P. Kent. 84: *t.* © Joseph Nettis/Photo Researchers, Inc.; *b.* Runk/Schoenberger/Grant Heilman Photography. 86: *t.l., b.l.* © Ray Simon/Science Source/Photo Researchers, Inc.; *r.* Runk/Schoenberger/Grant Heilman Photography. 90: *t.* Runk/Schoenberger/Grant Heilman Photography; *b.l., b.m., b.r.* IMAGERY. 94: *l.* © Dr. J. Burgess/Science Photo Library/Photo Researchers, Inc.; *r.* Hans Pfletschinger/Peter Arnold, Inc. 95: *l.* Hans Reinhard/Bruce Coleman; *m., t.r.* Runk/Schoenberger/Grant Heilman Photography; *b.r.* Larry Lefever/Grant Heilman Photography. 97: Runk/Schoenberger/Grant Heilman Photography. 98: Grant Heilman.

Chapter 5   102: Hans Reinhard/Bruce Coleman. 104: *l.* © Junebug Clark/Photo Researchers, Inc.; *r.* Malcolm S. Kirk/Peter Arnold, Inc. 105: Culver Pictures. 106: Lee Foster/Bruce Coleman. 108: Larry Lefever/Grant Heilman Photography. 111: Earth Scenes/© Holt Studios, Ltd. 113: TRIPOS Associates, Inc./Peter Arnold, Inc. 115: © N.Y.U. Cytogenics Laboratory/Peter Arnold, Inc. 119: *l.* © Mary M. Thatcher/Photo Researchers, Inc.; *t.m.* Earth Scenes/© Holt Studios, Ltd.; *b.m.* Breck P. Kent; *t.r.* E.R. Degginger; *b.r.* Tom & Sue Hacking/Earth Images. 120: Sygma.

Chapter 6   124: Rosemary Chasthey/Ocean Images, Inc. 126: *l.* Lou Jacobs, Jr./Grant Heilman Photography; *r.* © Tom Bean/The Stock Market of N.Y. 127: *l.* C. Allan Morgan/Peter Arnold, Inc.; *r.* Grant Heilman Photography. 128: *l.* Stephen J. Krasemann/DRK Photos; *r.* Heather Angel/Biofotos. 129: *l.* John Shaw/Tom Stack & Associates; *r.* Runk/Schoenberger/Grant Heilman Photography. 130: E.R. Degginger. 131: *l.* E.R. Degginger; *r.* Runk/Schoenberger/Grant Heilman Photography; *b.* E.R. Degginger. 134: James Collison. 136: The Granger Collection. 138: Breck P. Kent. 139: Animals Animals/© Oxford Scientific Films.

Chapter 7   144: © Kent & Donna Dennen/Photo Researchers, Inc. 150: E.R. Degginger. 152: *t.* Stephen J. Krasemann/DRK Photos; *b.* Breck P. Kent. 154: *l.* © John Eastcott/The National Audubon Society Collection/Photo Researchers, Inc.; *r.* Phil Degginger. 155: *l., m.,* Breck P. Kent. 156: Leonard Lee Rue, III/Click, Chicago. 158: *l.* Budd Titlow/Tom Stack & Associates; *b.* Bruce Richardson/IMAGERY; *r.* Jean Kepler/Rainbow. 159: *t.* Breck P. Kent; *l., inset,* E.R. Degginger. 160: *l.* Breck P. Kent; *m.* IMAGERY. *r.* E.R. Degginger. 161: *l., r.* E.R. Degginger; *inset* Breck P. Kent. 162: *t.* Dale Jorgensen/Tom Stack & Associates; *b.* IMAGERY; *l. inset* Breck P. Kent; *r. inset* Luke Wade/Taurus Photos. 163: *b., l. inset* IMAGERY. *r. inset* © Pat & Tom Leeson/Photo Researchers, Inc. 164: Earth Scenes/© L.L.T. Rhodes. 170: *l.* © Linda K. Moore/Rainbow; © Liane Enkells/Stock, Boston.

Unit Two Opener   174: *l.* Christopher Springman/The Stock Market of N.Y.; *r.* © Chemical Design, Ltd., Oxford/Science Photo Library/Photo Researchers, Inc. 174–175: © Globus Brothers/The Stock Market of N.Y. 175: *l.* Chuck O'Rear/West Light; *r.* © Brookhaven National Laboratory/Photo Researchers, Inc.

Chapter 8   176: Courtesy IBM Zurich Research Laboratory. 178: *l.* Denver Museum of Natural History/© Tom McHugh/Photo Researchers, Inc.; *m.* © John Zoiner/Peter Arnold, Inc. 182: *t.* Earth Scenes/© Breck P. Kent; *b.* © Kerry T. Givens/Tom Stack & Associates. 184: Courtesy Westinghouse Electric Corp. 185: *t.* E.R. Degginger; *m.* Barry L. Runk/Grant Heilman Photography. 187: © Bob McKeever/Tom Stack & Associates. 188: E.R. Degginger. 189: Tino Hammid. 191: Courtesy International Business Machines Corp. 194: *r.* Mark E. Gibson/The Stock Market of N.Y.

Chapter 9   198· © Wesley Bocxe/Photo Researchers, Inc. 200: Bill Evans/Artistic Photography. 201: Yoav/Phototake. 202: E.R. Degginger. 204, 205: Yoav/Phototake. 211: John Kelly/The Image Bank. 213: *l.* Tom Stack & Associates; *r.* P. Saloutos/The Stock Market of N.Y.; *inset* James H. Carmichael/Bruce Coleman. 214: *l., r.* Leonard Lessin/Peter Arnold, Inc. 215: *l.* © 1989 Roger Worth/Woodfin Camp & Associates; *m.* Alan Pitcairn/Grant Heilman Photography; *r.* Barry L. Runk/Grant Heilman Photography. 216: Yoav/Phototake. 217: *l.* Courtesy Autex Fibers; *r.* Courtesy E.I. duPont de Nemours. 218: *t.* Earth Scenes/© Patty Murray. 220: *l.* © Dr. Jeremy Burgess/Science Photo Library/Photo Researchers, Inc.; *r.* © Eric Grave/Science Source/Photo Researchers, Inc.

21·1 Composition of Seawater

After completing this section, you will be able to

- **list** the main substances in seawater.
- **identify** factors that affect the composition of seawater.

The key terms in this section are
degassing
salinity

ORIGIN OF THE OCEANS

Early in its history, the earth was a much hotter place. Liquid water could not collect on the earth's surface beause the surface was too hot. Volcanic activity constantly released gases. The process in which gases are released by volcanic activity is called **degassing** (dee GAS ihng). Only when the earth cooled could gases condense to form clouds and then rain water. This rain water formed the first oceans.

COMPOSITION OF THE OCEANS

salis (salt)

Thousands of samples of seawater from around the earth have been studied. Scientists have found that seawater is a complex solution. It contains most of the elements found on the earth. If a kilogram of seawater is left to evaporate, an average of 35 g of salt remains. The **salinity** (suh LIHN uh tee), or saltiness, of seawater is defined as the number of grams of dissolved salt in a kilogram of seawater. Thus the average salinity of seawater is 35 g/kg. In addition to salt, seawater contains smaller amounts of other compounds and elements. Figure 21·1 lists the most common elements in seawater. What two elements make up most of the dissolved minerals? What substance do these two materials form?

Figure 21·1

What percent of seawater is dissolved minerals?

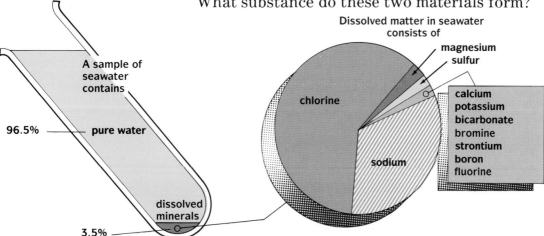

A sample of seawater contains

96.5% — pure water

dissolved minerals

3.5% —

Dissolved matter in seawater consists of

chlorine

sodium

magnesium
sulfur

calcium
potassium
bicarbonate
bromine
strontium
boron
fluorine

CHAPTER 21

THE EARTH'S OCEANS

*O*n many maps and globes, oceans are shown as smooth, blue surfaces. Yet beneath the ocean surface are a mountain taller than Mount Everest and a valley many times deeper than the Grand Canyon. The ocean floor is as rugged and varied as any place on the earth's continents. The ocean separates the land masses of the earth, affects the weather and climate, and supplies the atmosphere with water. Where the ocean meets the land, waves pound the shore and remove sand and rock. The photograph shows the effects of waves over time. The rocks shown were once part of a huge cliff.

- *What is the shape of the land under the ocean?*
- *What causes waves in the ocean?*
- *How can wave erosion be prevented?*

Index

Reading a Seismic Profile of the Ocean Floor

OBJECTIVE
Interpret information from a seismic profile of the ocean floor.

MATERIALS
none required

PROCEDURE
Echo sounding is a method by which sound waves are used to measure the depth of the ocean. Sound waves are sent toward the ocean bottom by a ship. When the sound waves strike the bottom, the waves are reflected back to instruments on the ship. By measuring the amount of time it takes for the waves to return to the ship, the depth of the ocean can be calculated. When enough measurements are made, a picture called a

seismic profile can be drawn of the ocean floor. Study the seismic profile of the ocean floor shown. Answer these questions.

1. What is the length of the profile shown?
2. What is the depth of the ocean here?
3. What is the highest elevation of the underwater mountain?
4. How deep is the deepest valley of the underwater mountain?
5. How can you tell that the underwater mountain is made of sediments?

RESULTS AND CONCLUSIONS
1. Describe the profile of the ocean floor shown.
2. What information can be read from a seismic profile of the ocean floor?

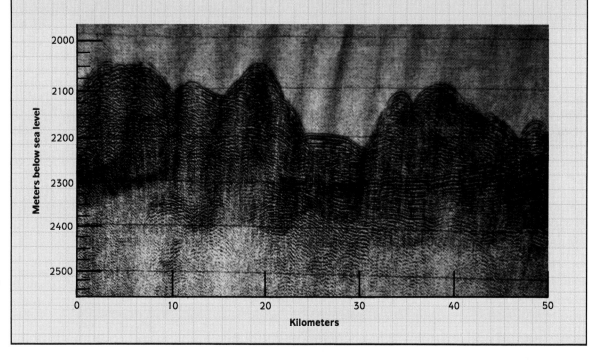

At the end of the continental slope, the continental rise begins. Sediments that settle at the foot of the slope build the continental rise. The *continental rise* is a thick layer of sediment on the ocean floor that begins at the continental slope.

CONTINENTAL MARGINS

The **continental margin** is the underwater area that borders a continent. Each continental margin has three main parts: the continental shelf, the continental slope, and the continental rise.

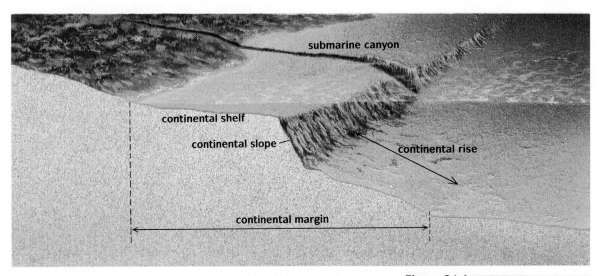

Figure 21·4

The continental margin borders the continents. Which part of the continental margin is the steepest?

The **continental shelf** is the gently sloping part of the continental margin that begins at the shoreline. It varies in width from almost nothing to about 1600 km, averaging about 65 km. The width of the continental shelf of North America is much less than that of the continental shelf of South America. The continental shelves contain deposits of oil and natural gas. The water above the shelves supports large quantities of sea life, making it the world's richest fishing grounds.

Notice in Figure 21·4 that as a continental shelf extends into the ocean, it gives way to a much steeper slope. The steep part of the continental margin is called the *continental slope*. Among the main features of a continental slope are deep canyons cut into the slope's surface called *submarine canyons*. These canyons are similar to river valleys. One submarine canyon, the Monterey Canyon off central California, is as large as the Grand Canyon. Submarine canyons are believed to be formed by currents caused by underwater landslides.

21·2 The Oceans

OCEANS AND SEAS

Oceans cover more of the earth's surface than do the continents—about 71 percent. Many people think of oceans as separate bodies of water, but they are connected. They form one great body of water in which the continents lie like huge islands.

Scientists divide the earth's great body of water into four major oceans: the Pacific Ocean, the Atlantic Ocean, the Indian Ocean, and the Arctic Ocean. The Pacific Ocean is the largest and deepest of all oceans. It is equal in area to the Atlantic and Indian oceans combined. The Pacific Ocean contains half of the water in the earth's oceans.

The Atlantic Ocean is next in size. It extends as far north and south as does the Pacific Ocean, but the Atlantic is much narrower. The Indian Ocean is the third largest ocean. It is slightly smaller in area but deeper than the Atlantic Ocean. The smallest ocean is the Arctic Ocean. Much of the Arctic Ocean is covered by ice year-round.

The earth also has bodies of water called seas, which are smaller than oceans. A sea may be part of an ocean or may be separate. Notice in Figure 21·3 that the Caribbean Sea is part of the Atlantic Ocean. The Mediterranean Sea, however, is separate from the Atlantic Ocean.

Figure 21·3

Oceans of the earth form one great body of water. A sea may be part of an ocean or may be separate from it.

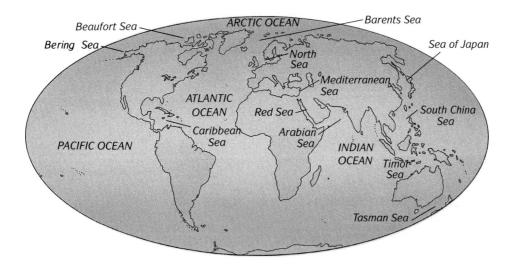

There is a constant cycling of salts to and from the ocean. Salts are added by volcanoes at the Mid-Ocean Ridge. Water and salts are added by rivers that empty into the ocean. At the same time, salts settle to the bottom of the ocean and living things use salts from the water. Also, salts become buried in the ocean floor. Since the ocean's salt content does not seem to be changing, these processes balance each other.

salts added from rivers, volcanic activity, and mid-ocean ridges

salts removed by living things and sediment formation

gases added from atmosphere (nitrogen, oxygen, carbon dioxide) and from plants (oxygen)

gases removed by living things (oxygen, carbon dioxide) and a rise in ocean temperature

Figure 21·2
Gases and salts are constantly being added to and removed from the ocean.

Although the salt content of seawater is stable, the amounts of gases in seawater vary. There are more gases in surface water because this water interacts with air. Carbon dioxide, nitrogen, and oxygen are added to seawater from the air. These are the most abundant gases in seawater. How would living things affect the amounts of these gases?

REVIEW

1. What are the main substances in seawater?
2. What are the factors that affect the composition of seawater?

CHALLENGE What effect would the formation of a new volcanic island in the Hawaiian Islands have on the composition of the ocean around Hawaii? Would any change be permanent? Explain your answers.